Eggshells
&
Broken Dreams

A MEMOIR

Eggshells
&
Broken Dreams

A Memoir

J. P. Rodgers

MacRuairi Art

Published by MacRuairi Art,
Main Street, Williamstown,
Co Galway, Republic of Ireland.

It is an account of events based on my own recollection. The names of
people and places therein, have been changed to protect the innocent.

A catalogue record for this book is available from the British Library

13 Digit ISBN 978-0-9550239-1-0
10 Digit ISBN 0-9550239-1-2

Cover origination by Capt Nisio.
Artwork and Illustration by Charlie McIntyre.
Typeset by Gough Typesetting Services, Dublin.
Printed in Ireland by Colourbooks Ltd, Dublin.

I would like to dedicate this book to the memory of all the wonderful characters I knew in Williamstown. Their likes will not be seen again for a thousand years.

Acknowledgements

I've yet to see a book where the author thanks the readers for their support. Writers are a bit like musicians I think, if there were no listeners or readers to appreciate out efforts then we would cease to exist. So for that reason I would like to thank the many people who went out bought my first book and went to the trouble to write to me. It filled my heart with gratitude.

I would like to thank my Agent Diane Banks in London for having helped spread the gospel. I look forward to working with you again.

I'd like to thank the following people who helped me put my second book together. Therese Carrick, my editor, Helen Lilley, my good friend, and Katie Shackleton, my publicist, who read the manuscript and showed me where I was going wrong. Many thanks, to my son Óisín who somehow kept my computer alive when so called experts said it was dead. Also, my daughters Síle and Róisin who encouraged me to keep writing when I thought it might be a lost cause. A special word of thanks to, Chris and Maureen, who gave me their whole hearted support when it might have been a lot easier to have said no. And where would I be without the Queen herself, Julie, who ensured my files were always kept up to date. Thanks also to my typesetter Shane Gough of Gough Typesetting Services, Dublin; and all the staff at Colourbooks for their expertise and advice. And last but not least, a special word of thanks to my good friend Charlie McIntyre who designed the cover over a few free pints. Charlie, will you have another?

Introduction

I had no intention of telling anyone what it was like to grow up as an outcast – a so-called bastard child – but events in my life dictated otherwise. You see, I wrote a book called *For the Love of My Mother* in which I described my mother's heroic efforts to track me down and to survive in an Ireland that was dominated by religion and self-righteousness. That book had a profound effect on a great many people and touched their hearts in so many ways, they came up to me in the street – some even wrote from England, America and Australia – and asked, "When are you going to write and tell us what happened to you." In truth, I would rather have sat down and written about somebody else; their lives always seem more interesting. But if people want to read the other half of what was a truly gripping story - about an incredibly brave woman, who was to spend thirty years in various institutions, then who am I to say no?

Chapter One

June 1953

The fact that I ever grew up half-normal, and didn't end up an outcast is more than a miracle. You see, few people in this world were as alone as I was. I was alone from the day I was born; with no living relative to my name, or so I thought, until one day I found there was somebody out there.

I was born in a Home for unmarried mothers, and shortly afterwards my mother was taken away and I was put into a Children's Home.

All memories of my time in the Children's Home have been washed away with the mists of time. But there was a time when I had a vague recollection of playing with a lot of infants in some sort of monastic settlement. But that was it; until one day, two of the nuns who looked after me, took me by the hand and put me into the back of a white van and brought me out into the country. Finally, the van slowed down, turned down a narrow by-road by a picturesque lake and into a small village where it pulled up outside a thatched house.

Further up the street were four more thatched houses; all of them on the right-hand side. Each had a chimney and gable end bordering the road. The house furthest away showed serious signs of decay. The back of it was streaked with a green slimy scum that seemed to have leaked from the thatched roof during the winter. Nurtured by the warm summer sun, the decaying roof was now growing swards of green grass that seemed to match the walls. The house itself sat hunched and drawn beneath a line of huge sycamore trees. The sagging roof, clinging to the scrawny neck of the chimney, was like a desperate child clinging to a father, who'd no shirt collar.

On the left hand side of the narrow road, opposite each house, were dilapidated old sheds and stables with assorted galvanized roofs, anchored with stones, old axles and cart wheels; beside them, were smaller cabins that seemed to house hens, ducks and geese. Alongside them were rickety old lean-tos crammed full of bicycles, donkey carts, tooth harrows, ploughs and swingles. Beside each of the stables adjoining the road, were stinking manure heaps; home to more than a million and one flies. The midges formed swirling dark clouds as they hovered around the fermenting manure heaps that give off a pungent smell that invaded my nostrils. The flies continued to hover in a never ending swirl despite the fact that high overhead, swifts and swallows flew regular sorties beneath the scorching midday sun as they swooped, swallowed and feasted on the tiny insects without making any appreciable difference.

All around the houses were scores of hens, ducks and geese sunning themselves. But the minute the two nuns and I stepped out of the van, the geese stood to attention. They stretched their long white necks and began to make a loud hissing noise as they watched our every move and I moved closer to the nuns for protection.

The two nuns, Sister Concepta, and Sister Greta, carried a small brown suitcase with them as they escorted me across the rough cobble stoned road strewn with horse manure and other animal waste. Holding me by the hand, they led me gingerly, towards what was to become my new home. The front of the house was snow white and the roof was crowned with a neat coat of thatch. The door – made up of two half doors – and the three windows were painted bright red. The windows had tied-back lace curtains, each highlighting a large flowering plant a facing the sun; and the long black T hinges across the closed half door matched the black painted window sills on either side.

A few of the hens came running towards us as the nuns tentatively knocked on the door. An elderly man and woman appeared, and opened the half door in response. The man looked bright and cheerful. He wore an old trilby hat and plaid shirt with the sleeves rolled up; a v-neck sleeveless jumper with holes in it: a pair of brown trousers with irregular patches and a pair of wellingtons with the tops turned down. The woman too looked bright, though less cheerful. She wore a three quarter length grey skirt, a grey short sleeved blouse and a pair of green bootees. Her face was pale and wrinkled with a noticeable dimple on her chin, while her dark greying hair was plaited and coiled up beneath a brown hairnet.

'Hello Mrs O'Brien,' said Sr Concepta, holding out her hand.

'How are you?'

'Oh, hello sisters, ye're very welcome. And how is my little boy?'

'He's great. Say hello to Mrs O'Brien,' urged Sr Concepta turning to me and shaking me by the shoulder. But I kept my mouth shut.

'Good day sir,' she added, as herself and Sr Greta bowed their heads and shook hands with Mr O'Brien.

'This is my husband Edward, or Ned as everyone around here calls him,' said Mrs O'Brien.

'And this is your little boy, John Paschal. I hope that you'll both be happy with him. Shake hands with the man,' said Sr Concepta as she pushed me forward, but I turned away because I was frightened and clung to Sr Concepta.

Despite my unwillingness Mrs O'Brien led me inside and began talking to me but I wasn't listening. After a few minutes, she made a pot of tea and they all sat down at the table where they had tea and biscuits. But I refused to sit down and kicked up a fuss when they tried to put me sitting at the table.

When they'd finished their tea, the woman brought the two nuns down into a room and showed them what was to become my bedroom. They went out into the back kitchen and stayed talking there for a few minutes. Suddenly, I realised I was on my own and that the man sitting in the corner was looking at me and I didn't like that at all. He took off his well-worn hat and hung it on the knob of a press door beside him. I could see for the first time he was bald except for a light band of grey hair running round the back of his head with a few straggled wisps running over the top. Realising I was on my own I ran under the table and started crying. I could hear the sound of the van in the street, it was very loud at first but then it seemed to fade. I was terrified of my new surroundings as I watched the man of the house going to the dresser where he took down a cracked mug and dipped it into a large bucket of water that was in a corner beside the entrance to the back kitchen. He raised the mug to his lips and drank it all before he left the mug back up on the dresser without washing or drying it.

The place was awfully quiet. A beautiful clock sat in the middle of the dresser. Inside the clock was a lovely red hen surrounded by a clutch of yellow chickens. The hen was pecking the ground all the time and making a strange *clocking* noise as she slowly rocked back and forward; going *tuck-tuck, tuck-tuck, tuck-tuck, tuck-tuck, tuck-tuck,* all the time. She was constantly pecking at the ground trying to get her baby chicks to eat but they wouldn't. No amount of pecking ever got them to eat. The woman came into the house and tried talking to me as she hung a blue apron with white dots over her head and tied it round her waist. She reached in under the table and pulled me out. I began to cry in earnest as she lifted me up on her knee and tried to get me to eat some currant bread but I wouldn't. I kept struggling on her lap until she let me down. Then I ducked under the table again where I could see everything. I could hardly stand the awful silence around the place and kept looking at the clock. If the little chicks weren't going to eat, then I wasn't going to eat, I decided. Besides I wasn't hungry. I kept wondering where all my friends were. Were they still in the playground or were they coming to this strange house as well? I started to get afraid and began to cry again because the place was so strange and because the woman didn't look like any of the nuns. The man went outside for a while and when he came back in he had a crooked stemmed pipe in his mouth. He tried to light it with a tiny bit of paper but when that burnt out he lifted one of the burning sods with his bare hand and tried to light his pipe with it. One end of the sod was glowing red while the other was as black as soot. As he inhaled vigorously, part of the glowing sod exploded, showering hot embers all over the floor. I screamed when I saw the hot embers on the floor but the man just looked at me as he drew fierce blasts of smoke on his pipe while the woman got the sweeping brush and swept all the red bits into

3

the grate.

I hated the house because the man and woman wouldn't stop looking at me. I was so lost I didn't know what to do with myself or where to go. They kept asking me my name and how old I was.

Then I thought I heard a commotion at the front door. A man in a navy uniform pushed open the red half door and said,

'God save all here.'

'Musha, Tommy you're welcome. I thought you had nothing for us today,' said the woman as she picked up the letter that the man had thrown on the table. I knew straight away he was a postman because a postman used to come into the Children's Home every day and hand a bundle of letters to one of the nuns.

'Dollars, Mrs O'Brien: dollars. You can't beat the dollars,' said the postman

The man with the pipe stood up to let the postman sit down while he sat on the other side.

'Ned, you should have stayed where you were. Aren't you far more entitled to that chair than I am?'

'Ah well, for the short time you'll be here…' Ned had started to say.

'Ah! Dollars how are you! The devil-a-dollar ever comes into this house,' said the woman, as she reached for the large brown teapot that was sitting on the front of the dresser.

The postman removed his mail bag and slung it across the back of the chair. Then he took off his hat and sat down beside the fire. He removed the black bicycle clips from the bottom of his trousers and put them in his pocket. He stretched out his black hob nailed boots – the soles of which were elaborately lined with steel studs – and took out a small packet of woodbines. He was a thin wiry looking man with a weather beaten face. He had thinning grey hair, with the track of his hat clearly visible right round his head. As the postman withdrew a cigarette from a green and orange packet, he spotted me hiding under the table and said,

'Well be the cripps almighty, is that a young lad I see under the table?' Is he the lad'een ye were telling me about?'

'It is then. That's him. We're only just after getting him…' said Ned as he took out his penknife and began to cut his tobacco.

'The nuns are just after leaving. Sure you must have met them going down the road. They were driving a white van,' said Mrs O'Brien, informatively.

'I did then. I did then…be damn but I did! And said I to myself, they must be out collecting for the foreign missions or something; and we barely able to feed ourselves. So that's who *they* were? Isn't this a great little country all the same, when they can bring down the likes of a little lad like that and drop him off at the house? There's service for ye! How old is he or what's his name?'

'That's John Paschal. He's six,' said Mrs O'Brien proudly, as she began to settle the teapot on a bed of glowing cinders on the hearth so that it could brew for a minute or two.

'Look at the lovely blue eyes and fair hair he has. I'd say that fella came from good stock. Do you see the way he's looking at me? Well John Paschal, are you going to shake hands with me?' asked the postman.

When I didn't say anything, Mrs O'Brien started to reach under the table to drag me out but I screamed to high heaven and the postman put up his hand and pleaded, 'Shush! Shush now a grá. Leave him where he is Mrs O'Brien. Leave him where he is in the honour of God. What harm is he doing on you? Let him settle, can't you! Let him settle! Don't disturb him on my account. That fella will come out himself when he's good and ready. I've often seen our Sylvester at home and he'd be the same bloody way. He'd create *Mila murder* if we didn't leave him alone. They say it's a sign of intelligence. That's how a child learns to defend itself.'

'I know! But I hate to see him stuck under the table like that,' said Mrs O'Brien, having let go of me.

'Troth he'd better not start that auld carry on here, screaming like that, or I'll soon knock the screaming out of him,' she added.

'Shush now can't you; leave him and let him settle. That fella will come round in his own good time. Ye behaved bloody well to get him.'

'Well…we did, I suppose. I'm glad we decided to go for a young fella, anyway. At least we'll have someone to look after us in our old age... we hope. It's all very fine having girls in the family but then they go off and get married and you're left on your own. And I wouldn't like that,' said Mrs O'Brien.

'Well, I hope in God that he'll be lucky for ye. You can't bate a bit of help around the house. There's yeer daughter Colleen now and she has to cope with two young ones, the poor creature while Snowy or Máirtín – should I say – is gone to England. I'm telling you, it's not easy.'

'Maybe she's as well off without him. He might find something over there that'll suit him. I've never seen anyone that's as afraid of the land as that fella,' said Mrs O'Brien.

'It isn't afraid of the land he is; it's afraid of hard work! Sure he's not cut out for the land. I don't know what that lady of ours ever saw in him,' said Ned, as he again tried to light his pipe with a glowing ember, which this time he held with the tongs.

'Well… whatever she saw in him, she married him,' replied Mrs O'Brien. 'Maybe in God, he'll find something over there.'

'Believe me, he will. There's plenty of work over in John Bull's country. It's not like here. And there's no such thing as a slate behind the counter.' said Ned.

'I couldn't agree more, Ned. That's what has this country ruined. Too many hand outs and not enough work being done,' added the postman, as he reached forward to accept a large mug of tea and a slice of bread and jam from

Mrs O'Brien.

'And Harry Ryan is on the batter again, I see,' added the postman as he leant back in his chair.

'Oh…I don't believe it!' gasped Mrs O'Brien.

'Sure it's not three months since he was on it before?'

'Well… just about. It was what… after the last child was born? That's three months ago… if it is.'

'Well Glory-be-to-God Almighty… but…I think you're right.

'Twas after the last child, sure enough: about three months ago. And you'd think now that with fourteen of them under the one roof he'd try and pull himself together. Twelve children's no joke.

'Arrah but he won't, he can't help it. It runs in the family. As Jim Leonard, says when he has a few drinks on him; *what's bred in the mare, comes out in the foal.'*

* 'So they say. And Doctor Roland is gone to hell I believe?'

'Well gone to Hell. It's shocking! Shocking altogether! Sure he'll kill himself with drink,' said Tommy, as he wedged the last bit of bread into his mouth and sat back contentedly while he chewed it thoughtfully.

'I don't know why he does it, because he's the best bloody doctor that ever came around here. He'd know what was ailing you, just by looking at you.'

'Oh he would! He would… he'd know alright,' laughed Ned as he removed the pipe from his mouth and spat into the fire.

'Didn't he cure Mrs Mitchell without examining her at all? "There's nothing in the world of God I can do for you Missus, because you're always moaning. Go home now like a good woman and consult Doctor Diet, Doctor Quiet and Doctor Merryman. And if they can't cure you, no one in the world of God, can."'

'Begod yes,' acknowledged the postman, joyously, 'She went home and never went near him again. Seemingly she took his advice; she's lost a power of weight… and… the signs are on her, she looks a hell of a lot better.'

After discussing a number of people, the postman looked at his watch, stood up and reached for his hat and mail bag. He slung the mail bag round his shoulder and headed off out the door, saying, 'Well, the blessing of God on ye. I'll see ye tomorrow; with the help of God.'

'And you too Tommy,' said Mr and Mrs O'Brien in unison, as I tentatively crawled out from under the table and watched the three of them as they stood at the door. I ducked under the table again as Mrs O'Brien turned round and reached for the letter that still lay unopened on the table. Going towards the fire, she tore open the blue and white stripped envelope and took out a folded letter. When she unfolded the letter, she discovered four five dollar bills.

'Ah well; will you look at what uncle Paddy is after sending. It's a bloody good job I didn't open it while Tommy was here. You know, that fella would know what was in a letter before he'd hand it to you. The dollars will come in handy now and help pay Harry Ryan what we owe him,' she smiled as she showed the dollars to Ned as he came in from the back kitchen.

But Ned didn't say anything. Instead he reached for his battered grey hat and went off out, pulling the red half door after him.

Mrs O'Brien dragged me out from under the table; put me sitting on her lap and tried to make me eat something. But I wouldn't. I was only interested in the clock on the dresser. Inside the clock, behind the red hen and the yellow chickens was a picture of a thatched cottage with a haggard in the background. It had started raining heavily outside but the top half of the red door was still wide open. I wanted to go out and look for my friends as I thought they might be playing outside, somewhere. I only had a short pair of trousers on me, a short sleeveless shirt and a pair of buckled sandals. The woman noticed me shivering and put a new jumper on me and put me sitting on a stool beside the fire and tried talking to me. She offered me a piece of an apple but I shook my head. When it stopped raining she took me by the hand and brought me out into the back garden to show me the hens, ducks and geese. And when the hens started following us, I started crying because I was terrified. The woman picked me up and carried me, explaining what everything was.

In the garden was a huge cock of hay with a wooden pole sticking straight up out of it. Next to it was a reek of straw and beside that again – near the ditch – was a reek of turf. And beside the reek of turf was an old rusty barrel that had a brown and white dog in it. As soon as the woman spoke, the dog stood up and wagged its bushy tail. It could not come near us because it was on a short chain. The woman petted the dog and tried to make me pet it too but I wriggled and tried to get away when he looked at me and barked.

'That's Bonzo,' she said.

'There's no need to be afraid of him. He won't touch you because he's too old.'

Back inside the house, the woman began cooking the tea. She went out to the back kitchen and brought in two herrings. I thought they looked horrid, with their small button shaped eyes looking straight at me. She spread the glowing coals on the fire and placed the fire tongs over the fire from one hob to the other. She placed the two herring on the tongs while I stood watching and listening. Soon the fish began to sizzle and tiny drops of fish oil spilled onto the red hot coals causing little spurts of flame to ignite every now and again.

When the tea was ready, Mrs O'Brien went out and called in Ned. They finished their tea by pushing the fish skeleton round and round the plate while they mopped up the gravy with brown bread.

Again the woman tried to make me eat something and put a mug of milk to my mouth but I pushed it away.

'Lord, I never saw such a puss on anyone in all me life. What will we do if he doesn't come round and talk to us?'

Ned said nothing. He looked at me and made a funny face and I started crying again. After that they knelt down, one each side of the fire, and said the rosary while I watched them from under the table.

When it was time to go to bed, she brought me down to the room that she had shown Sister Concepta, and took off my clothes. She made me pee into a pot and pushed the pot under the bed and dressed me in a long plaid shirt. She tucked me into bed, took my hand and made me do the sign of the cross, saying, *In the name of the Father and of the Son and of the Holy Ghost, Amen.* Then she smiled at me; said good night and closed the door after her.

I lay in bed surveying every inch of the room. The walls were painted yellow, and had a lovely two inch paper border with lots of birds and nests and butterflies and trees. On the top right hand corner, high up over the foot of my bed was a large grey patch where the paper was coming away from the wall. The ceiling had narrow mahogany boards the same as the kitchen. The back of the bedroom door was brown, and hanging on it were several coats and jackets. In the corner was a large double wardrobe with one of the doors half open. On top of the wardrobe was a trilby hat like the one Ned wore. Opposite the wardrobe was a small brown table with a matching chair. On the window sill was a small metal bucket with a red flowering geranium in it. Outside the window, a little black and white cat jumped up on the window sill, curled its tail under its bottom and looked in at me.

In the Children's Home, I had often heard the cows mooing in the fields and the horses going clippedy-clop, clippedy- clop along the road. But here the cows were mooing all the time and the horses were going clip-clop, clip-clop as they went lazily through the village. They sounded so close I thought they were going to come into the house and I was frightened. Later, I heard some men shouting and when I sat up and looked out the window I could see two men driving a herd of cattle past our house. They were shouting and running after them with sticks. The cat jumped down off the window and ran away.

I lay down once more and was almost asleep when I thought I heard a commotion outside. I sat up, a sudden fear gripping my heart. I didn't know where I was. And when I looked out the window, I saw two donkeys twisting and turning in the street. A man with a peeked cap was running after them. The donkeys were running wild. One of them had a long black thing hanging out of his belly and was going, *Aw- he-haw, he-haw, he-haw, he-haw.* He was trying to get up on the other donkey but she wouldn't let him, because every time he tried, she kicked him with her hind legs and ran off up the street but the other donkey kept after her. Then all was quiet. After a while, the black and white cat jumped back up on the window; stood on its hind legs and started scratching the glass. I was so happy to see it; I jumped out of bed and went over to have a look. But when it saw me, it jumped down and ran away. I could see the thatched roof of the house next door. It was brown with one or two patches of grass growing out of it. There was smoke rising from the chimney. It rose higher and higher until it reached the sky. Then two men in white overalls cycled right by the house, and up to the house next door. They were carrying a long ladder on their shoulders. It was so long, one man had to go in front, the ladder hooked on his shoulder while the other cycled behind him with the other end on his shoulder. When they went to stop, they both gave a loud, 'hup,' and threw the ladder away from them. They hopped off their bicycles and disappeared around the other side of the house but came back out again a few seconds later, picked up the ladder and pushed it on to the flat roof of a little shed across the road. They were tall and skinny, about twenty, with short fair hair. They went into the house and I didn't see them anymore.

I tried to get up on the window sill to see where the cat was but I couldn't. I stood at the window watching the birds flying everywhere but then I thought I heard something on the floor behind me and when I turned round I caught a glimpse of something with a long tail disappearing beneath my bed. I was terrified and started screaming. The woman came rushing into the room and asked me what I was doing out of bed. She took me by the hand and brought me down beside the fire and sat me on her lap. She had lots of funny looking things in her hair. She tried to make me eat a piece of sweet cake but I shook my head and sighed. I was so lonely, all I wanted was to lay my head down and cry.

Chapter Two

I woke the next morning and thought I felt somebody in the bed beside me. I looked at the sleeping head and saw it was the man of the house. I couldn't think of his name or if he had a name at all but then I remembered the postman had called him Ned. I stayed very quiet because I was afraid. I wondered why he was sleeping beside me. I wanted to wee so badly, but I couldn't get out because my side of the bed was pushed up against the wall and there was a high iron railing at the bottom and top of the bed. The only way I could get out was to climb over the man with the bald head. I thought if I wet the bed the man might beat me. Then I began to wonder, where were the nuns? Was the woman with the things in her hair a nun? And if she wasn't, why was she wearing things in her hair?

Ned began to groan and yawn as he turned over on his side. He reached under the bed and picked up the pot that I had used before going to bed. He covered the pot with the blanket and yawned again. When he opened his mouth I saw he only had three teeth. How did he manage to eat, I wondered? He had very bushy eyebrows and hair growing out of his ears and nose.

He reached under the blanket and put the pot under the bed again. I closed my eyes in case he turned over and caught me looking. By now I was really desperate for a pee so I squeezed my legs together and tried to stop it. Then I heard the man whispering something and I recognized the *Morning Offering* that the nuns always said in the morning before the breakfast.

'Oh my God, I offer you all my thoughts, words, actions and sufferings of this day for thy greater honour and glory, through Christ Our Lord, Amen.'

But why was he whispering the prayer, I wondered? Why didn't he say it out loud like Sr Concepta? Maybe the man didn't want to wake me. And if he didn't want to wake me, that must mean he was good. So, I opened my eyes and looked at him and saw that he was staring straight back at me. He asked did I sleep well. I nodded my head. I could feel the wee coming now because it was stinging my legs. I was afraid what might happen if anyone found out. I tried to stop it, but it was no good, it kept coming. I wondered would the nuns ring the bell and bring me to the toilet and make me wash my face and hands and give me my breakfast like they always did. I could hear someone moving in the next room. Then the room door opened and the woman, Mrs O'Brien who'd put me to bed, spoke to Ned.

'Well, how is he?'

'He's alright. And if he doesn't turn out to be a footballer then I'm a poor judge of mutton. He never stopped kicking all night.'

'Well, you better get used to it. Your breakfast is on the table if you'd care to get up and have it now; or you can milk the cows first if you like? I better dress that fellow now and see will he eat anything.' Mrs O'Brien lifted me out, dressed me and brought me out to the back kitchen and washed my face and hands in a basin of warm water while the man dressed himself and went outside. I could see him through the back kitchen window. He too was washing his face and hands, in a barrel of rain water. Mrs O'Brien put me sitting at the table and tried to make me eat a boiled egg and some bread and butter, but I wouldn't eat anything. Instead, I sat at the table looking out the window. I thought I might see Sr Concepta coming down the street. Where were all of my friends? I wondered. Why weren't they here?

After a while, the man came into the back kitchen with two buckets of milk. He poured some of the milk into two smaller buckets and brought them out. He spilt some of the milk on the floor but the woman said nothing. She cleaned it all up and poured the rest of the milk into a big round crock that sat on a corner of the table in the back kitchen. The man came back and washed his hands, and then he sat down with Mrs O'Brien and had his breakfast.

Getting up from the table she said to Ned.

'You might keep an eye on him, while I let out the hens.'

As soon as she came in, she began washing and cleaning. She swept the floor and dusted the chairs while Ned put on his hat and went out, closing the half door after him. I sat at the table looking out the window. I saw him going off up the street, on a big chestnut horse. He went past the house where the men with the white coats had thrown down the ladder. I sat there waiting for the white van to come back with my friends, but they never came. In the end, I laid my head down and cried.

I must have fallen asleep because the next thing I remember was sitting on Mrs O'Brien's knee and she trying to talk to me.

'What's your name? A little bird told me your name was John Paschal. I think we'll leave out the Paschal bit and call you John. Why won't you talk to me, a grá? You're not afraid of me are you? Sure I won't do a thing to you. Say something to me and see what I'll give you?'

I didn't answer, because I was heartbroken that none of my friends had come with me. I could picture them running around the playground playing with each other while I was on my own. Mrs O'Brien put me down, cut some raisin bread and tried to make me eat it, but I wouldn't.

'Oh, John'een, I dunno what I'll do with you at all,' she gasped.

'You won't eat and you won't talk! I never saw the like. And there's me thinking that at six years of age you'd be half-reared: that there'd be no stopping you.'

Going out to the back of the house, she brought in a wooden drum that was sitting on the garden wall. She washed and scalded the drum and put it sitting on a chair in the middle of the floor. She went out to the back kitchen and brought in a big crock of cream and poured it into the drum. She got another chair and sat beside the drum and started winding a handle which she'd slotted into the side of the churn, earlier. She was winding the handle for a long, long time during which she switched hands several times. Suddenly she stopped, lifted the lid, looked in and said,

'Well blast it to hell, it should be coming on by now.'

She filled a large mug with cold water and poured it into the drum. This time she started winding the handle faster and faster. After two or three minutes, she seemed to slow down. Then she stopped altogether, looked in again and said,

'Well not before bloody time.'

Pulling a handkerchief out of her sleeve she mopped her furrowed brow, drew a deep breath, saying 'Well thanks-be-to-God! That's another job out of the way.'

She went into the back kitchen and brought in a wooden bowl and three pieces of wood that looked like sticks but weren't sticks. She dipped one of the sticks into the drum and lifted out huge blobs of milky butter which she put into a wooden bowl.

'Well, John Paschal, have you ever seen anything like this before?' she asked, as she continued to push and squeeze the butter all around the dish.

I didn't answer her. But I kept wondering why she was beating the butter with a flat stick. She held up the stick and said,

'This is a butter spade for squeezing the milk out of the butter. When I've the milk drained off, I'll add some salt and we'll have some nice fresh butter for the tea. When you're bigger, with God's help, you'll be able to do all the churning for me and I won't be killed doing it every week.'

I didn't understand what she meant as I sat beside the fire trying to take it all in.

'Here! Would you like to taste it?'

She dipped her finger into the bowl and turned round to me with a small blob of butter on the end of her finger. But I got off the chair and ran under the table. I knew what butter was like but it didn't look like the butter in the Home. In the Home, the butter was almost white, but the butter the woman was after making was the same colour as an egg yolk. And because I wouldn't taste it, she said,

'Ah, blast you! You don't know what's good for you,' and stuck the blob straight into her mouth.

While she was putting everything away, I looked out over the half door. It was a glorious summer's day. I could see birds with forked tails ducking and diving everywhere. The cat was sitting on the roof of a cabin the other side of the road, beside the manure heap. It was watching the birds as they flew right by. It sat crouched, following their every move with its swivelling green eyes. Suddenly, the cat sprang into the air and fell to the ground. For a second, I thought it was dead. But then it scooted away under the hedge with a bird in its mouth.

Mrs O'Brien took me by the hand and brought me into the garden where she began gathering the clothes that were spread on the bushes. As she did that, a woman with red curly hair, came out of the house next door. She too was wearing a blue apron with white dots and was carrying a basket of clothes which she started spreading on the bushes, on her side of the garden.

'Well if it isn't Mrs O'Brien herself. I've not seen you for a day or two. You must have been at the hay or in the bog?' she said, spreading the wet clothes.

'Hello Margaret: yes we were down in *Johnston's*. We had a field of hay down, but thank God we managed to save it. We have two more to cut but *himself,* thinks, they're not fit yet. And we were in the bog a while yesterday. I didn't see *you* either, though I was at the *well* a few times.'

'Ah sure, we had two fields of hay down ourselves. I thought we'd never get it, it was so heavy. It should have been cut a fortnight ago: if I could have got anyone to do it. The only one we could get was Jim Ward,' said Margaret, as she leaned across the hedge and looked at me.

'I see you've a little helper today. Who is he or what's his name?'

'That's John Paschal. Remember I was telling you about him...?'

'Arrah is that him? Well look it...'

'That's him now... for better or worse...'

'You mentioned him a few times, right enough. Isn't he a lovely little fella? And look at the lovely rosy cheeks he has. How old is he?'

'He's six. But so far I haven't been able to knock a word out of him.'

'Ah, what hurry is on you? Give the poor lad a chance. They say some of them boarded out ones can be very strange: they can take a while to settle. But he looks a grand little fella.'

'Hello John Paschal! How are you a grá?' said Margaret, as she smiled and waved at me.

I said nothing but looked at Mrs O'Brien for a reaction. Instead, she caught me by the hand, shook me and said,

'Won't you say hello to Margaret? That's Margaret Collins, my next door neighbour.'

When I didn't respond in any way, she turned to Margaret and said, 'I'm sure he'll be in and out to you when he settles.'

'Well, he'll be very welcome. And Frank can show him the bird cage he's making. I hope in God, Missus, that he'll be lucky for you. Where did you get him, was it in Tuam or Galway?'

'I went for Tuam at the latter end; it was that bit nearer. I must say the nuns were very nice and brought him down to me yesterday. I've missed Colleen so much since she got married, I made up me mind I'd go for a boy. I thought it might be nice to have someone to look after me as I get older. Colleen came with me because she was thinking of getting one herself, to help her look after the children. I had planned on getting someone a bit older, but when I saw this fellow, I took pity on him.

'Well I think you made a great choice…And did Colleen get a boy as well?'

'No, she didn't! She decided in the heel of the hunt to wait a while to see how I'd get on. I don't even know why she'd bother: she has her hands full as it is.'

'Were there many children there?

'Children! Sure the place was full of them. I thought it looked more like a school. But in fairness, the nuns were very nice to us and left the choice up to ourselves. They gave us tea and cake and everything. They told me this fella was very quiet and that his mother was a very refined lady; but of course a bit head-strong: so they packed her off somewhere, to try and knock a bit of sense into her. I hope to the Lord that they keep her; that she doesn't come here looking for him.'

'Aaaah no! I don't think they'd let her do that! And who's the father or what's his surname?'

'This fella's name is Rodgers. But I don't know anything about the father. They didn't seem to know either. Then again that might be his mother's name. Maybe the nuns know who the father is: but they didn't tell me anyway.' said Mrs O'Brien.

'Well, I'm not surprised. They say an awful lot of them children are put into the Home to hide the sins of the Lord and Lady mucks: because if word ever got out that his Lordship had fathered a child with a maid or servant girl, their name would be ruined for ever.'

While they were talking, Mrs O'Brien tried again to make me say *Hello* to Margaret but I wouldn't. And when they both started laughing at me, I turned around so that they couldn't see my face and that made them laugh even more and I didn't like that at all.

'Did you ever see such a puss in all your life?' said, Mrs O'Brien as she tried to mollycoddle me.

Back in the house, Mrs O'Brien began washing and drying a small basket of eggs. Then she looked at me and said,

'Stay here now like a good lad until I see are there any more eggs.'

I stood looking at her – as she pulled the half door after her – wondering how she could see any more eggs. While she was gone I noticed a pot of jam on the table. There was a picture of a Golliwog on the side of the jar. I reached across the table and pulled it towards me so I could look at the picture and as I did so Mrs O'Brien came back in, the corners of her apron in her fist.

The minute I saw her, I let go of the jar and it crashed to the ground with a deafening thud. There were bits of glass and jam all over the floor. I started crying and ran under the table in case she beat me, like the nuns whenever I broke anything.

She looked at me and said, 'Ah for God's sake stop crying,' as she began cleaning up the mess. She kept telling me to come out from under the table but I was afraid. The dimple on her chin began twitching and made her cross looking and I didn't like that. When I wouldn't come out, she reached under the table and dragged me out by the collar and I started screaming

'Aaah stop your crying!' she said, as she picked me up and put me sitting on her lap and tried cuddling me but I was too afraid of her. Eventually she left me down and began cleaning the few eggs she had brought in out of the garden. She transferred all the eggs into a big basket and left them up on the table. Then she washed her hands and tidied her clothes and combed her hair.

'Now I think we'll go as far as the town. Come here until I wipe that dirty puss of yours.'

She went up to her room and brought down a lovely scarf that had a picture of a horse on it. She folded it neatly and laid it over her head, around her face and tied it under her chin. She picked up the basket of eggs, led me outside and locked the two half doors behind us. Holding my hand, we walked down the road together and around by the lake.

At the end of the by-road, we crossed over the main road and into the first shop on the right hand side. It had the name Harry Ryan over the door in big red letters. On our way in, we saw two men with their sleeves rolled up fixing bicycles in a shed beside the shop. Their hands were black with oil and grease. Two other men were taking bags of flour off a lorry and carrying them into a yard at the back of the shop.

Inside the shop, Mrs O'Brien put the basket on the floor with a sigh of relief.

'Bad cess to you Harry, if you were any good, you'd send someone up to collect my eggs and not have me kilt carrying them.'

'Well I would then, with a heart and a half. But when I suggested that to you, you didn't want to hear of it. You wanted to get top dollar for your eggs by bringing them in yourself. Anyway, isn't Lakeland only a stone's throw away: won't the bit-a-fresh air do you the world-a-good? What is it but a five minute walk?' said the man behind the counter, with a mischievous grin.

'Troth then, you should try it yourself sometime. Anyway, how much a score are you paying this week?'

'I'm afraid eggs are back in price, Missus,' he said with a glint in his eye.

'Clean fresh eggs four and sixpence a score. And you'll be lucky if they're not down more next week,' he added with a smile.

'Ye housewives never had it so good; I paying ye seven and sixpence a score all year.'

'Aaah, stop it will you,' said Mrs O'Brien,

Then, in a more business like tone, Harry added, as he made his way out from behind the counter, 'There's a glut of eggs on the market at the moment. And as always, Missus, quantity dictates the price.'

The shopkeeper was a big powerful man. He was dressed in a navy pinstriped suit, white shirt and navy tie. He wore thick brown framed glasses and had a mop of oily red hair swept to the back of his head. He picked up the basket and counted the eggs as he was putting them into the egg cartons. He filled each carton and placed them one on top of the other until the basket was empty.

'Six score, exactly.' And turning to face Mrs O'Brien, he asked, 'And who's this young man you have with you today?'

Mrs O'Brien told him the same story she had told the woman next door. Then he came out from behind the counter and put his hand into an open box of biscuits, and said, 'Here you are á Mach!* Look after your mammy now when you go home, and be a good boy.' It was a nice looking biscuit with raisins in it, but I wouldn't take it. He tried to put it into my hand but I pulled away. When that failed, he tried stuffing the biscuit into the pocket of my short trousers, but I screamed and hid behind Mrs O'Brien because the man was coming too close and I didn't like that. He said nothing but turned round and went back behind the counter and began putting things into the basket. When he had finished, he made out a list, pressed a button on a silver box that was on the counter. The box opened like magic and he took out some money and gave it to Mrs O'Brien.

'Musha, Harry is that all I'm getting?'

'That's the best I can do for you today Missus. It's been a pleasure and thanks a million. And don't forget to call soon again,' the shopkeeper said as he handed the basket of groceries to Mrs O'Brien and opened the door for us.

Back home, Mrs O'Brien took all of the things out of the basket and put them on the table: a packet of tea, a pot of jam, a Swiss roll, a bag of sugar, a box of salt, a bag of tomatoes, a box of cheese, a bag of apples, three oranges and a half a quarter of *Walnut* plug tobacco and the biscuit the shopkeeper had tried to give me. She left the jam on the table and put the rest of the things away in the bottom half of the dresser. But I couldn't take my eyes off the pot of jam. It looked different to the jam I used to get in the Home. It had a lovely picture of a Golliwog that was different again to the one I let fall on the floor. The new Golliwog looked as if he could walk away from the jar. He had a lovely black face. He smiled a lot and seemed happy. And when Mrs O'Brien saw me looking at the jam she said, 'Would you like some bread and jam?'

I said nothing as I watched her cut a slice of soda bread for me. Then she spread some butter on it and tried to screw the lid off the jar but she couldn't. She reached across the table to the pin cushion that was hanging on the side of the

* á Mach (son).

window and took down a sewing needle and stuck it into the lid. When she did that it made a hissing noise. And when she tried to open the lid again it came off easily. She spread some jam on the bread and tried to make me eat it but I wouldn't. She sighed and said,

'Well Glory be-to-God Almighty, but what do you want?' and stood there looking at me.

'What are we going to do with you, a grá? You'll have to eat something or you'll fade away and maybe get sick on me. The nuns said you'd eat bread and jam until it came out your ears. And here you are and you won't eat a thing for me. Is it that you don't like blackcurrants? Maybe it's marmalade you'd like?'

When she said that, I thought she sounded nice, so I inched my hand across the table.

'Is it the jar you want? I can't give you the jar a grá because you'll break it.'
And when I left my hand where is was, she said,

'Do you want to look at the picture?' And when she pushed the jar tentatively towards me and I touched the picture with my little finger she smiled and said, 'Well that's a good one.' She peeled the Golliwog off the side of the jar and handed it to me. I felt like a new man.

At long last I had a friend. I sat there at the table and I played with Golly for hours and hours. He was better than any of my friends in the Home, because he never cried. No matter what I did with him, he smiled at me all the time. Even when I put him standing on his head, he still smiled at me. Then I put him lying on his back; and on his side and he still managed to smile at me. I tried covering his face with my hand and then I peeped in at him and he was still smiling and I liked that. And then I thought there must be some reason why he was so happy. Maybe it was the jam. He must like jam otherwise he wouldn't be on the jar. I thought maybe I should just taste the jam that was still on the bread on the table. I could hear Mrs O'Brien working away out in the back kitchen so I reached across the table and dipped my finger into the jam. It tasted delicious. It was the nicest jam I had ever tasted. I dipped my finger in again and took another dollop. By now I was ravenous with the hunger so I scooped off all the jam and ate every bit of it and picked up the crumbs in case Mrs O'Brien noticed them. But I could still see the track of the jam on the bread so I picked it up to lick off the jam. As I was doing this a bit of bread fell on the floor and when I picked it up there was Mrs O'Brien standing, looking at me. I dropped the rest of the bread and started crying. I felt terrible because I'd been caught stealing.

But Mrs O'Brien said I was a great lad altogether; that I must be starving with the hunger: that I could eat as much bread and jam as I wanted. She cut another thick slice and covered it with jam and handed it to me. I picked off all the lovely currants and ate them before devouring the bread. It was my first bite in two days and I was very happy.

That night I brought Golly to bed with me but when I woke up the next morning I couldn't find him anywhere; no matter how hard I tried. Mrs O'Brien asked me what I was looking for under the bed, but I didn't say. I was afraid she might get cross with me because I broke the jar and stole the bread and she had to clean up the mess.

After that, I decided to eat all the bread and jam I could so that Mrs O'Brien would have to go into the town to buy more jam and I'd get another Golly. That night as I lay awake in bed waiting for the cat to appear at my window, I heard Ned and Mrs O'Brien talking below in the kitchen. Ned sounded angry, as he said, '...If he was going to talk at all, he'd have said something by now, I'm thinking. There must be something wrong with him? It's a wonder you didn't try and knock a word out of him when you picked him out? It wouldn't have killed you!'

'Arrah blast you to hell! You wouldn't even come with me when I asked you. I only asked because I thought you'd like to have a say in picking out someone. But no! You leave everything to me: like you always do! But first thing tomorrow morning I'll get in touch with Sr Concepta. And I'll let you deal with her. Then we'll see if you can do any better,' said Mrs O'Brien

'Look! It has nothing at all to do with me! It was your idea.' Ned shouted.

'You can deal with it what ever way you like. Send him back if you want: that's if they'll take him back: but I doubt it, once you've signed the papers.'

'Well, I only signed the bloody things because Colleen said he was a nice looking lad; and because Sister Concepta said he was very quiet. I didn't want to go fostering out some young ruffian that would break our hearts. How was I to know that he'd never open his mouth? The first time I saw him, he was running around playing with the other children. And when Sr Concepta introduced him to me and he didn't say anything, I thought maybe it was because he was shy. God forgive me; it's wan thing to be landed with a ruffian but it's another to be landed with someone that's not able to talk. I'm not able for that sort a thing any more. It would be alright if I was a bit younger, maybe. Besides, I thought it would be nice if you had someone to help you around the place: if it was only to throw a bit-a-hay to the cattle now and again.'

'Ah...I dunno,' sighed Ned wearily.

'I think I'll go rambling. We'll just have to wait; and see what happens.'

When I heard them giving out, I was frightened. I began to wonder, were they talking about me? I could hear someone open the front door and slam it after them. When I looked out the window I saw Ned walking off up the street with a jacket thrown over his shoulder. For a while I sat looking out, watching him as he walked up past all the houses and then he was gone. I could hear footsteps coming towards my bedroom door so I lay down and pretended to be asleep. Mrs O'Brien opened the bedroom door and came into my room. She sat on the edge of my bed and placed her hand on my forehead.

'In the honour of God, will you say something to us? Surely to God you can say something? I don't want to send you back if I can help it a grá.'

She left the room and pulled the door behind her. Then I heard my bedroom door being opened again. I could hear the woman shuffling about the room. I got such a fright when I though it was raining, I sat up in the bed. But it was only the woman shaking holy water on my head. She was saying, 'In the name of the father and of the son and of the Holy Ghost, Amen.'

Then she tucked me in again, left the room and closed the door quietly behind her and at that moment I saw the cat jump up on the window. But I wasn't interested in the cat any more. I could sense something was wrong. I began to think about what Ned had said.

'Send him back if you want. 'Did that mean they were going to send me back to the Home? And if they did, would I see my friends again? If I did, it would be great I thought. But why were they going to send me back? It must be because I broke the jar and stole the bread. But didn't Mrs O'Brien say I was a great boy altogether; that I could eat as much bread and jam as I wanted? That must mean she liked me. Maybe I should say something, I thought; and then I fell asleep.

The next morning, Mrs O'Brien dressed me and put me sitting at the table and tried talking to me. But I still didn't say anything. After all the breakfast things had been cleared, I sat at the table looking round the kitchen. Strewn on the window were lots of old letters and a biscuit tin with bits of wool and some knitting needles. Hanging on the side of the window beside the lace curtain was a small decorative pin cushion with lots of pins and needles. Also in front of me were two large photographs hanging on the wall; one each side of the window looking down on the table. They were pictures of very old people wearing strange clothes. The bottom of the walls were painted green and reached up to the back of the chairs. From there up, the walls were covered with cream coloured wallpaper that had rambling roses, with a narrow decorative border.. There were seven chairs in the kitchen altogether; three at the table where I was sitting and one each side of my bedroom door. There were two wooden armchairs, one each side of the fire. All the chairs were painted mahogany the same as the dresser and ceiling, except for the two armchairs which were not painted at all but had cushions tied to them There was a door each side of the fire place, a big one and a small one. The door on the left was to a room that had a table, a bed and a big wardrobe in it. But the door on the right wasn't a room at all. It was a narrow press with two bags of flour in it. Underneath it was a smaller press with several pairs of shoes. Over the fire place was an arch with huge stones that were painted green. Above the arch, the wall was papered the same as the rest of the kitchen. Each side of the fire grate was a hob. Sitting on one of the hobs was a dusty old flash lamp and a goose quill that Mrs O'Brien used to sweep the hearth every now and again. On the other hob were two pairs of socks with holes in them and a pea tin. The pea tin was used to boil the eggs for the breakfast. Hanging over the fire was a soot-stained steel frame with three crooks hanging out of it. The crook in the middle was the longest. It had five holes in it and could be moved up or down. When Mrs O'Brien wanted to boil the kettle she let the crook down until it was almost sitting on the fire. When it was boiled, she moved the crook up and left the kettle hanging on it. Hanging on the wall, high up over the fireplace was an old picture with three big words with smaller words underneath. The three words I would later learn, read, *Bless this House*. On the other wall opposite the kitchen window were two more pictures, one each side of the dresser. One was of Our Lord with his heart on fire; the other was of Our Lady, wearing a blue and white robe. There were no pictures on the wall leading to my bedroom because there were two boards one each side of the door with nails for hanging coats and hats and umbrellas.

Again I noticed Ned's old hat was missing off the wall and I remembered how he'd been very cross after I went to bed and I thought it might be a good time to say something to Mrs O'Brien. I didn't know what to say. I thought I might say *Hello* because that was what she wanted me to say. I sat there trying to pick up the courage to say *Hello* but I couldn't. I thought about it for a while and then I started to admire all the things on the dresser. There were two old biscuit tins on top, along with two wooden boxes. There were three huge plates on the top shelf. The one in the middle was speckled brown and the other two were dark blue. But all of them had the exact same picture; two cows and a baby calf in a garden with a fence all around. Underneath that shelf were two rows of cups and saucers. The first one had fancy plates and cups and saucers that were decorated with roses. The second one had nicer cups and saucers decorated with shamrocks. The other shelves had lots of mugs and plates and saucers with four large jugs on the right hand side. Some were cracked and had little chips on them. And sitting in middle of the dresser was the clock that I liked.

The bottom half of the dresser was a press with two doors. When Mrs O'Brien opened the doors I could see a packet of tea, a bag of sugar, a packet of jelly, a bag of oatmeal, a pot of jam and lots of other things. Hanging on a nail, high up on the front of the dresser beside the three big plates was a gold watch and chain. Hanging on the same nail over the watch was a pair of scissors and over the scissors was pair of crystal rosary beads. It was then I recalled how Ned and Mrs O'Brien had knelt down and said the rosary, before I went to bed.

It was at that point I decided to say *Hello* to Mrs O'Brien but when I went to say it something different came out,

'I can bless myself.'

Mrs O'Brien who was about to take another slug of tea, stopped and looked at me, her mouth half open.

'Glory-be-to-God Almighty, I don't believe it! You're able to bless yourself! Show me how you do it!'

I smiled to myself for a moment because the woman seemed so happy. While she was looking I made a fleeting sign of the cross. Her crinkled face broke into a smile as she reached across to hug me, saying,

'Well, do you know something John Paschal, you're the best boy in

Williamstown? Where in the name of God, did you learn to do that?'

'I just learnt it,' I replied, cheerfully.

And that morning, we both went on to have our first full blown conversation. It was the first of many discussions we had over breakfast each morning. She taught me lots of new words and what they meant. She encouraged me to address herself and Ned as my mother and father, which led to an air of confusion for a while.

Then one morning shortly after my breakfast, Mrs O'Brien gave me a large penny biscuit for myself as Ned lifted me up and put me sitting in the horse cart and brought me for a spin. First, we went up to a big field that Ned called *Górt Mór*, which was a long way from the house. On our way home, he drove up across some boggy fields, to a big two storey house that stood on its own. The woman of the house brought me in and gave me a mug of tea along with some bread and jam. I was surprised to see it was Colleen. She was the same woman who visited Mrs O'Brien and who had tried talking to me when I was in the Home. She had two girls, Una and Sadie, aged one and two

When I'd finished my tea, Ned brought me with him while he put a roll of barbed wire and some stakes into the cart. When we were ready to leave, he lifted me up on the cart as Una, Sadie and Colleen waved goodbye. Just as we were leaving, a tall man in a white short sleeved shirt came cycling down a narrow by road. Una and Sadie went running to meet him. He picked them up and gave them a spin on his bicycle. The man had a very distinctive appearance. He'd a mop of dark wavy hair that had a patch of pure white hair on the forehead. He spoke briefly to Ned and then we drove down across the bog again, on past our house and down through the town to another big field called Johnston's. I stayed in the cart while Ned threw the wire and stakes out beside the ditch. As he turned the cart round, I asked him, who the man with the white spot in his hair was.

Ned looked at me perplexed for a moment as he took his pipe out of his pocket and began to light it.

'Is it Snowy you talking about, the man in Colleen's house?

'The man with the bicycle,' I replied.

'That's Snowy... Colleen's husband! Snowy is some character, I'll tell you!' he added thoughtfully after a long pause, as he tugged at the horse reins, 'Giddy up, Giddy up there!'

We drove out along the rough cobble stoned road towards Williamstown. Soon we were back home, where Mrs O'Brien gave us our dinner;

And that was the end of my first week, in my new home in Lakeland, Williamstown.

Chapter Three

Every day, Ned would tackle-up the horse and cart to go working somewhere on the farm. And if the weather was fine, he'd lift me up and put me sitting in the front with my feet hanging out over the shaft. Sometimes he too sat down, his legs dangling the other side of the cart. But more often than not he preferred to stand: that way he could see everything that was going on, he said.

People with horse drawn mowers were busy cutting hay for farmers all over the country. Farmers who couldn't afford a horse drawn mower cut the meadow themselves, with a scythe. Everywhere men women and children in straw hats, were tirelessly working to save the hay, while the weather was still fine.

The O'Briens spent long hot days down in Johnston's. From early morning, Ned twisted and turned and shook out the hay around the headlands with a fork while I roamed all around the field. Around midday, Mrs O'Brien would join us by cycling down when she had all the jobs done. I couldn't wait to see her coming across the field in her straw hat with fresh tea and sandwiches. When she'd arrive, all three of us would take a well earned rest from the sweltering heat by sitting in the shade of the ditch while she divided out the sandwiches. There, she'd pour out enamel mugs of warm tea out of a *Lucozade* bottle which Ned said was great for the thirst. When the two of them had finishing eating and taken a well earned rest, they'd start turning the hay again. Walking briskly side by side they'd go up and down the big field turning the hay with their long wooden rakes as they turned row after row after row in the stifling heat. Sometimes I followed them lazily around the field until I grew weary. Often I'd lay down to rest only to fall asleep in a corner of the field. Sometimes my mother or father – as I now referred to the O'Briens would suddenly disappear around one end of the field where there was an old quarry.

'Why has Daddy gone over to that big hole in the ground?'

'He's gone to *loosen a button*. It means he's gone to do a wee-wee or a poo-poo. That's what we say when we want to do a poo-poo out in the field.'

I soon learned that the quarry in Johnston's was a great place to *loosen a button* as there was plenty of long grass to clean our backsides, not like at home where we'd have a job to find enough grass to do the job at the end of our back garden. Besides there was no knowing who might be watching us at home, through the garden hedge.

Other days, I'd spend hours in the shade of the headland, watching crows, jackdaws and seagulls as they circled the skies, scouring the newly exposed ground for slugs and worms. Wandering aimlessly round the summer field, I couldn't help but absorb the smell of the newly mown hay as milk white butterflies danced hither and thither around the headlands where they'd be joined by blue and red and brown butterflies as they alighted daintily on buttercups, dandelions and daisies. Then I'd lie in the long grass and watch honey bees gather nectar from purple clover blossoms, as close by I could hear the lovely rhythmic sounds of grasshoppers as they clicked their wings incessantly. In my eagerness to hunt them down, they'd sense my presence and stop clicking altogether making it almost impossible for me to find them. But I'd lie patiently in the long scented grasses waiting for them to start up again. And when they did, it was magical: to see them clicking their back legs with such speed it was almost beyond my imagining. I'd watch spellbound as they made gigantic leaps from one plant stem to another, their body colour blending in perfectly with their new surroundings. Some grasshoppers had red legs and olive green backs with dainty black spots. Others were dark green with yellow under bellies as they clung quietly to the tall grass stems, watching my every move. But once or twice I was stung on the leg by an unsuspecting bee which made me flee across the field to my mother who soon made it better as she rubbed the sting with a dock leaf.

After working hard in the field all day, there would still be an awful lot of work to do when we got home. My job was to run out and throw a bucket of mashed up potatoes and oats to the hens, ducks and geese. But when the last of the oats was gone, we had to boil more potatoes for them; and mix it all up with a scoop of Indian meal to help the hens keep laying. Mrs O'Briens job was to feed the pigs and bring down two buckets of water from the well and then get the tea ready while Ned cleaned out the stables, brought in the cows, milked them and fed the suck calves. And when he'd finished milking, he'd drive the cows out into the field again for the night.

If the weather was still fine, Mrs O'Brien would get up early the next morning. She'd go to the well, bake the bread, make the churn and do a whole lot of other jobs – like washing and ironing – before cycling down to *Johnston's* to join Ned. Together they'd turn the hay once more so that it would be fit for tramping after the dinner.

They'd begin by pushing every six rows together until they had one big row the entire length of the field. Out of that they'd build a row of dome shapes cocks of hay, making sure to taper each cock evenly so that it would not absorb the rain. And as each cock was being headed, Ned would kneel down beside it and make a long hay rope by pulling out a thin wisp of hay which he swivelled round and round in his hand until he had a ball of hay rope long enough to tie down the cock. It was my job to stand beside the cock with my back to whatever wind there was and hold the rope while Ned lifted the centre of the rope across the top of the cock with his hay fork where he balanced it carefully and tapped it down into place before kneeling down beside the cock. With one end of the rope in his mouth, he'd spin a tight band of hay from the butt of the cock on which to tie the rope. Then he'd come around to where I was standing and repeat the exercise. While all this was happening Mrs O'Brien would have laid the foundation of another cock and together we'd start heading a cock all over again.

About two weeks later, when other more important jobs such as saving the turf or spraying the potatoes were out of the way, the O'Briens would bring in the hay with the help of Tom Farrell or one of the neighbours. Tom and my father would load half a dozen cocks onto the horse cart and draw it into the haggard where they'd build two giant hay stacks in the back garden beneath the tall sycamore trees. And Ned in turn would help Tom to bring in *his* hay.

Sometimes in the mornings, I'd have to help Mrs O'Brien drive the geese and ducks down to the lake, which was very close to our house. That meant they'd be away from the house all day and not be quacking for food every time Mrs O'Brien stuck her head out of the door. She was forever chasing the hens and ducks away, because they were forever scuttering around the front and back of the house. Not only that, but if the front or back doors were left open for a second, some of them would saunter into the house to eat the breadcrumbs beneath the table. And before anyone could shoo them out, they'd lower their tails and squirt inky jets of black goo across the floor and Mrs O'Brien would have to clean it up by sprinkling a shovelful of turf mould on it, before sweeping it all up to throw out on the manure heap across the street.

Late in the evenings as the sun was disappearing behind the lake, the geese would make their way home marching one behind the other in single file. There was always a touch of elegance to their homecoming. They'd step it out, all the way up from the lake, in slow graceful motion, the goose leading the way followed by her goslings with the gander bringing up the rear. But the ducks were the complete opposite. They'd not come home until it was very late. And sometimes they wouldn't come home at all. If that happened, Ned and I would have to go looking for them. He'd bring a bucket with a fistful of oats in it to try and coax them out. And because there were other ducks on the lake, it was almost impossible to distinguish which were domestic and which were wild. It was only when the wild ones took to the air that our ducks could be enticed home. Ned knew how to coax them out. He'd rattle the bucket, calling out; *tuck-tuck, tuck-tuck, tuck-tuck, tuck-tuck*. But it didn't always work. Occasionally they were too contented. They'd stay on the lake despite our best efforts and not come home until the following day, when they were hungry. When that happened, we'd lock them up for a few days to teach them a lesson and not let them near the lake again for a while.

On his way home in the evenings, Ned would give a gentle tug on the horse reins saying 'Giddy up' and lead the horse in off the road so she could have a drink in the lake. I could never get over the amount of water the horse was capable of consuming. She was a huge animal – eighteen hands, my father said – chestnut brown with a white forehead.

'Daddy, is she ever going to stop?' I asked, as the horse kept her head down, siphoning up great mouthfuls as the collar and hames slid down around her ears.

'She will, when she has enough drank.'

'Would she drink a kettleful of water, if you gave it to her?'

Ned laughed, as he relaxed his hold on the reins.

'She would then. What's more she'd drink a bucket of water… and maybe two or three. A horse can drink two buckets of water in one go. I'll bet you didn't know that?' he said, as he took advantage of the break in the journey to light his pipe.

Suddenly there was a strange cooing sound that frightened me.

'What was that?' I asked fearfully.

'Ah that's only a water hen,' replied Ned as the horse suddenly lifted her head, snorted loudly and threw the collar back from around her neck as she too looked to where she heard the cooing, before lowering her head again to drink yet more water.

'Have you ever seen a water hen?

I shook my head, 'No. What is it?'

Ned stepped down cautiously from the cart and stood in his wellingtons in the shallow water before turning to me,

'Come here, and I'll show you.'

He lifted me out of the cart and carried me on his shoulder over to where the sound had come from. As we were closing in on the mass of reeds, standing like long green pencils, a water hen with a sleek black coat and red beak flew out of the reeds and alighted a short distance away. As we ventured closer still, Ned showed me the nest the water hen had built on a pile of withered reeds. In the nest were four speckled eggs with a hint of blue that Ned said would produce four baby chicks

As we neared the house, Bonzo would give a loud bark and slowly wag his tail to welcome us home. First thing, Ned would pull up outside the horses' stable and take the horse out from under the cart. Next he'd remove the breechen, the straddle, the hames and the horse's collar. The horse always seemed naked standing there, having had the tacklings on her all day. And while I'd nervously hold the horse's reins, Ned would push the cart into the cart-house – which was an open tumble down shack, beside the cows' stable. After that, he'd tie the horse in the stable, take down her nosebag and put a few fistfuls of oats into it. As he began to pull the nose bag up over the horse's mouth to hang it over her ears' the horse would try to muzzle her way impatiently into the nose bag and he'd be forced to shout. *Easy girl! Easy! Easy!*

When she'd finished eating, he'd lead the horse into the high garden, remove the bridle and let her off; giving her a playful slap across the backside, saying, 'Off with you now Miss.'

Straight away the horse would throw her hind legs into the air and start galloping around the garden, farting and whinnying excitedly. All of a sudden, she'd stop galloping, lie down on the lush grass and roll over several times. Then just as quickly she'd jump up again; shake her body vigorously and start whinnying again. And having given the two of us one last look she'd settle down to graze, contentedly for the night.

When I went into the house, I told Mrs O'Brien how I'd seen a water hen's nest. She was delighted to hear my story. That evening, before it was time for me to go to bed, she asked me to go out with her to the hens' cabin; to hold the candle while she checked the eggs. There were three laying boxes in the hens' cabin. They were left up on the roosts inside the door. When the hens were ready to start laying, they'd fly up and go into one of the boxes. Each laying box had two compartments, so that several hens could lay at the same time. In one of the boxes there was a black hen nesting. Mrs O'Brien handed the lighted candle to me while she put her hand under the hen. As she did so, the hen made a strange noise and tried to stop her by pecking at her. But Mrs O'Brien took no notice. To stop the hen from pecking, she put her other hand over the hen's eyes, took out an egg from under her and said,

'You know when a hen is ready to start hatching, she makes a different sound to the one she normally makes and that means she's clocking.'

'What's clocking?'

'Clocking is when she goes gluck, gluck, gluck around the garden; which means she has laid enough eggs and is ready to start hatching. She becomes sort of very quiet and angry at the same time. If you go near her while she's hatching, she will ruffle her feathers as if about to attack you; to warn you to keep away. Once she starts doing that, she's called a clocker because she's ready to hatch. Then when the chickens are reared she'll stop clocking.'

'What's hatching?' I asked, as I watched Mrs O'Brien carefully removing the eggs one at a time from under the clocker, before holding them up to the lighted candle. As she examined each egg. She marked them with a biro by placing an x on them before carefully putting them back under the clocker again and removing another egg for inspection.

'Lord, but you're a great one for questions,' sighed Mrs O'Brien.

'Hatching a grá is when the clocker is sitting on the eggs. This is a big hen and can easily cover twelve eggs. So I've put an extra one in for good measure. There are thirteen eggs under her now and with any bit-a-luck she'll hatch out eleven or twelve. She'll sit on the eggs for twenty one days and then the birds will hatch out. After the twelfth day, you can always check the eggs to see how many birds you are going to have.'

Mrs O'Brien made me hold the candle for her so she could get a better view. After a few minutes she got cross with me, saying,

'Look, will you hold the bloody candle up there, like that, until I see how many birds I'll have.'

I'd never been in the hens' cabin before, when it was dark. I could feel the breeze blowing in under the rafters. The galvanized roof began to creek and rattle under the force of the draft and I shivered uncontrollably. I didn't like being in the cabin and the strange eerie sound coming from the rafters made the hairs stand on my neck. I held the candle up and moved a bit closer to Mrs O'Brien as she raised yet another egg up in front of the candle. She must have known I was feeling cold because she grabbed me by the shoulder and turned me around so that I stood with my back next to her warm body. She made me hold the candle out in front of me so that I too could see what she was looking at. Holding the egg up to the candle, she placed her right hand across the top of the egg and I could clearly see the egg was black three quarters of the way up, with the top of the egg crystal clear. It was like looking at a pot of blackcurrant jam that was three quarters full.

'When there's a space at the top of the egg like that it means there's a bird in it. I'm checking to see if I've any gluggers.'

'What's gluggers?'

'If you wait a minute, I might be able to show you.'

Holding up one of two eggs she had left aside earlier, I could see they glowed from top to bottom when she held them up to the candle.

'As you can see, that's a glugger: there's nothing in it.'

Taking the biro she sketched a firm naught on the egg and having examined the second one she did the same thing.

'I'll still leave them under the clocker, in case they're late developers, but I doubt it. That's eleven birds I'll have now. And with any bit-a-luck I'll have a few more laying pullets before the year is out. God knows I need all the eggs I can get.'

'Why do you need so many eggs?'

'Ah musha God help you a grá. How do you think we live? I have over a hundred hens but a lot of them are getting old, I'm afraid. I'll need to rear more chickens this year. The more laying hens I have, the more eggs I can sell which means I should I be able to buy a few things in the town.'

The day before the chickens were due to hatch out, Mrs O'Brien took one of the eggs from under the clocker and held it to my ear, saying if I listened I could hear the chick inside. But I couldn't hear anything except feel the tingling sensation as the egg touched my ear and I started laughing. But when Mrs O'Brien told me to shut up and stop laughing I could clearly hear the little chick tapping away inside.

'That means the chickens are ready to hatch out. They're trying to get out. That's why they're tapping. They're due out tomorrow.'

'And what happens if they can't get out?' I asked, worryingly.

'Don't worry! They'll get out alright, when they're good and ready: although some of them can be slow enough. But once the clocker hears them she'll help them to break the shell,' she said, as she put the egg back under the clocker again.

A few days later when all the chickens were hatched out, I thought it was the most wonderful sight I had ever seen. They were so cute and so full of devilment I spent all my time watching them. Some were black, some were white, some were brown and some were black and white.

'Why have some of the chickens got black and white dots?' I asked.

'Because they're a mixed breed, that's why. Most of them – like the white ones – are White Leghorns; the brown ones are Rhode Island Reds; and the black ones are Black Minorcas. The rest are a cross somewhere between the three. The black, the white and the brown are the most popular hens for laying. When they get too old for laying, I kill them for the Sunday dinner, although I'd prefer a rooster or a duck any day: they're easier to cook.'

'What's a rooster?' I asked as Mrs O'Brien closed in the hens and chickens for the night by winding the piece of string round a nail.

'Roosters are cocks that run with the hens. You can ask me about them again, because I think it's time for you to go to bed now. Go into the kitchen and wash your hands first,' she said as we went back into the house.

Next morning when she was feeding the hens, I asked her about the roosters?

'They're the big fellas with the long tails and red combs. Some of them have coloured stripes,' she said, as one of the roosters did a fancy dance and tried to jump up on a hen. That cock there was trying to thread a hen. If they didn't thread the hens, we wouldn't have any chickens.'

By now I was a little confused, so I asked, 'What's a cock?'

'Cocks and roosters are the same thing. There're the male chickens that help the hens to lay eggs. Now have you got it?'

I nodded, I had. But I was still a little confused.

'And where do babies come from?' I suddenly asked,

'Babies!' laughed Mrs O'Brien. It would take someone like you to ask. Babies are found under a bush or a head of cabbage.'

'Can we have a baby?'

'Well the Lord Almighty may save us; you're not asking for much. We can't a grá because we haven't room in the house. And what would I want a baby for? Haven't I got you? Isn't that enough?'

From that day onwards, hens and chickens were part of my everyday life.

From early morning, the roosters could be heard crowing and the hens cackling as they went about laying their eggs. And it was my job to keep an eye on the chickens. Every day, I watched over them like a hawk. I followed them everywhere as they roamed all over the front and back gardens. Mrs O'Brien had warned me to watch out for stray cats, rats, weasels and in particular magpies as they could attack the chickens any time. I could see the magpies perched high up on the blackthorn bushes watching the chickens as the clocker brought them on an endless tour of the gardens. The clocker spent most of her time in the back garden where she could spend hours rooting around in the butts of the old stacks, seeking grain, black jacks, maggots, and worms. When she found something she'd call excitedly, tuck-tuck, tuck-tuck, tuck-tuck, and the little ones would come fluttering to her side, to devour whatever tasty morsel she had unearthed for them.

But every day I feared for their lives. I knew that one lapse in security and a stray cat or magpie could pounce. In the evenings, I'd help Mrs O'Brien round up the chickens and together we'd drive them into a small wooden box in the hens' cabin and close them in by propping a board in front of it with a stone, so no rat or weasel could get in, while leaving enough room for the air to get in.

'When will the chickens be able to fly up and sleep with the other hens?' I asked as we closed them in again for the night.

'When they're old enough, they'll learn to fly up and roost for themselves.'

Most Saturdays, Mrs O'Brien would kill and pluck one of the older hens for Sunday dinner. Boiled chicken was her favourite, though now and again we might have roast duck but they were not near as plentiful as the hens. After First Mass on Sunday, she'd go into the field a facing the lake and pull a few carrots, parsnips and onions and dig half a bucket of new potatoes. She'd boil the chicken and vegetables together to make a stew, while the potatoes were boiled in another skillet. And while we were waiting, we'd sit around the fire and have a mug of soup.

In the evenings, as the sun was going down and dark grey clouds were beginning to close in on the night sky, the hens would make their way into the cabin, in ones and twos and threes to roost for the night. When it was time to close the cabin door, Mrs O'Brien would know whether they were all in or not, because there was just about enough room for all of them. If she saw a vacant spot on any of the roosts she'd know there were still one or two hens out somewhere. And if they failed to come home, I'd be sent on an urgent scouting mission the next day to see if they were hatching out. It was my job to try and find a nest amongst the weeds and nettles. Though I was constantly being stung, nine times out of ten I'd find a nest. After being stung, it was a wonderful feeling to discover a nest out in the nettles after all the searching. Often I'd find a nest with as many as thirty eggs where two or more hens had been laying out for maybe two weeks. Sometimes the eggs were so old they had to be thrown out. Mrs O'Brien was an expert and would know by the colour of the eggs whether they were old or not. One day I found a black hen nesting on top of the ditch near the bottom of the garden. I ran into the house and told Mrs O'Brien and she came out to have a look. She reached into the nest and grabbed the hen as she was about to fly away. After a quick look, she threw the hen down where it ran off, cackling loudly.

'Thanks-be-to-God, it's one of my own. I was afraid it might be Margaret's,' she said as she gathered her apron to form a pouch for the newly discovered eggs.

'How would you know it was ours?'

'Did you not see the ring on her foot?'

'No.'

'Well, that's because you weren't looking. All my hens have red rings and all Margaret's have green. Whenever I have a new batch of laying pullets, I put a blue ring on along with the red ones so that I'll know which are young and which are old,' she said, as she continued to put the eggs into her apron.

'Margaret does the same thing, except hers are yellow.'

Most evenings, I'd hang around the street watching the last few hens trying to find a perch for the night. Very often they'd fly up to a roost only to find that they couldn't squeeze in and they'd fall down again. Other times when a powerful young rooster sought a perch for the night, he'd fly up and make such a determined effort to squeeze in amidst his flock, he'd knock down two or three hens and the whole process of trying to find a perch for the night would start all over again.

Sometimes Mrs O'Brien would be sitting by the fire, sewing a patch on an old pair of trousers or darning a jumper when she'd try to get Ned to do some odd job about the place.

'… and I was thinking – if you had time – you might stick another roost or two in the hens' cabin. It's shocking to see them trying to squeeze in every night, because there just isn't room for them any more.'

But Ned never seemed to take any notice as he'd continue reading *The Connaught Tribune*, which was the only newspaper to come into our house. A week or two later when it looked like nothing was going to be done about it; Mrs O'Brien would suggest I remind Daddy.

'He might listen to you a grá, because God knows he never listens to me.'

Straight away I'd run down to one of the fields opposite the lake where my father was working, to convey the message.

'Mammy wants to know, when you're going to fix the hens' cabin. She wants you to put up another roost, so the hens can go to sleep.'

Straightening his back from thinning turnips Ned would sigh wearily and say, 'Oh dear, oh dear! I don't think I'll ever stick it. If I did it yesterday, á Mach* it wouldn't be half soon enough for some people. And besides… where am I going to get money for roosts. Timber costs money and I've hardly the price of a bit of tobacco.'

Taking a brief respite from work, he'd take out his pipe and start filling it while contemplating his predicament.

'It's an awful thing to be scrimping and saving all your life. I hope you never have to go through what I have to go through. Make sure when you grow up you've a few bob in your pocket and enough to eat: that's all the advice I'll give you,' he said with a dewy glint in his eye.

'If only I could go to England, it would be something. I might manage to save a few bob. But sure I can't be everywhere.'

'Could I go with you?' I asked.

'Aaah…I'm afraid you couldn't, a grá. You're too young yet. Would you like to go to England?' he asked eagerly, looking me up and down as he hunched his back and turned it against the gentle breeze in order to light his pipe.

I nodded. I would. 'Is England a town?'

'Ah no, England's a country. You'd have to cross the Irish Sea to get to England. It would be like going on a boat and crossing to the other side of the lake there,' he nodded; 'only England's a hundred times further. Maybe when you're older, you'll go on your own. I know one thing… if I had my life over again, that's where I'd go.'

'Were you in England before?' I asked, as he drew vigorously on his pipe in an effort to keep it going. When he was satisfied he'd get a decent smoke, he'd put the lid back on his pipe -which he'd fashioned from the lid of an old jam jar – and begin blasting away contentedly, sending plumes of blue smoke into the atmosphere.

'I was then…but it was a long time ago.'

'Were you thinning turnips?'

My father began to chuckle and cough at the same time.

'Ah musha… I was not,' he sighed, as he took the crooked stemmed pipe from his mouth and spat across the ridge, clearing his throat.

'The devil-a-much-money I'd get for thinning turnips. I was working in a coal mine. And I worked bloody hard I can tell you. But at least I was able to save a few bob. Maybe one of these days I'll go again,' he added after a momentary pause. 'And if I did… I might be able to buy you a watch, for the Christmas, he added thoughtfully. Would you like that?'

Again I nodded, contentedly. I would.

My father had a beautiful gold watch which hung on a chain on the side of the dresser. Every now and again he'd take it down and wear it to Mass or when

---

* á Mach (Son).

he was going some place special. But before he'd put it back up on the dresser again, he'd let me look at the watch, the back of which showed a fowler shooting a pheasant. Occasionally he'd screw open the back of the watch where I could see the ruby coloured jewels glistening with the fine delicate hair spring swinging back and forth. The very idea that someday I'd own a gold watch like his, was mind boggling to me.

I told Mrs O'Brien what my father had said, but she wasn't impressed.

'A nice looking article he'd be going to England at his age. He must think he's still in his prime. Will you go out to the back kitchen like a good lad and get me the hammer and nails until I see if I can do anything with the hens' cabin.'

Because there was no money for timber to make proper roosts, it was left to Mrs O'Brien to nail a few branches together to add to the roosts. Most of the time, however, the new roosts would fall down and I'd have to try and help her to put them back up again. When we'd finished, she showed me how to clean out the hens' cabin properly. After that, I always had to help clean out from under the hens, ducks and geese and put in a new bed of straw every other day. But every once in a while she'd sprinkle a bucket of lime on the floor of the cabin

'Why are you putting that white stuff on the ground?'

'Lord God Almighty, but I never heard anyone like you for asking questions. If you must know, it's lime. And lime kills germs. It's to stop the hens getting any disease such as fowl pest or dropsy. If any of the hens got fowl pest, they could all be wiped out in a week. I hope and pray by the time you start going to school, you'll have learned to clean out the cabin for me. At least it'll be one job less I'll have to worry about,' she said, pushing me out of the cabin before her.

'Why is that hen lame and not able to walk properly?' I asked, pointing out a speckled hen that was hobbling around the street.

'She must have hurt herself trying to fly up on the roost or maybe the dog ran after her.'

'And why has she no feathers like the others?'

'Because she's getting old. Every year the old ones get what's called pin feathers, which means they lose their coat. All they're left with are a few spiked feathers. And then they stop laying altogether.'

The old hens were easy enough to identify. A lot of them were raggedy looking and found it hard to fly up onto the roosts. Because they couldn't fly they'd sleep on the ground with their heads under their wings: but the ducks were always picking on them trying to keep them away from their own corner.'

Shortly before I was due to start school, Mrs O'Brien suddenly called me in from the garden.

'Do you think you'd be able to take care of the house while I go up to the corpse house?'

'What's a corpse house?'

'A corpse house is when someone is dead and they hold a wake in the house.

Kilby's wife Mary, up the street is dead. Margaret next door is just after telling me. She was old…and sick for a long time. Poor Kilby has no one belonging to him and I'd like to help him clean up the house. Margaret and I will have to lay her body out unless somebody else does it: maybe Nurse Finnegan or someone, but I doubt it. Anyway, Margaret said she'd help me. She's sending Frank down to Johnston's to ask Daddy if he'll call in to Harry Ryan's on his way home, to pick up a coffin. It will save him having to go down again with the horse and cart. Will you be all right on your own, do you think?' she asked; a concerned look on her face.

'You have nothing to do except keep a sod of turf on the fire… and an eye on the chickens and don't let the dog go near them in case they get frightened…' she added, by way of encouragement.

'You can go; I'll look after the chickens,' I replied eagerly, at the thought of having the place to myself. Mrs O'Brien had often left me playing on my own around the street for a minute or two while she went to the well or had a quiet word with Margaret Collins across the garden hedge, but I was never left minding the house on my own.

'And another thing, don't let the cat in whatever you do or he'll scutter under the bed like he did last week. I'd bring you with me, a grá, but a corpse house is no place for the likes of you. Daddy should be home shortly. Make sure not to let the fire out because he'll want to wash and shave when he comes home.'

'I'll look after the chickens and I'll keep the door closed so the cat can't get in,' I said.

'You can have a bit of bread and jam, if you're hungry,' she added, as she began loosening her apron strings.

She made her way hurriedly up to Kilby's house carrying a scrubbing brush, a bar of carbolic soap and two towels with her.

I was delighted to be left minding the house. I could hardly believe my luck. I had the chickens, the cat and Bonzo to myself. If Bonzo was around the house, the cat wouldn't come in. But if Bonzo and I were going somewhere and the cat saw us he'd hop down off the window, jump over the half door and into the house. Once when Mrs O'Brien, had two lovely herrings washed and salted on a plate in the back kitchen ready for cooking, the cat sneaked in, jumped up on the table and dragged one of the herrings away with him.

Mrs O'Brien had said Bonzo was old and good for nothing and that she didn't think she'd bother with a dog ever again because their dogs were always getting poisoned. That was why he had to be tied up most of the time. I really liked Bonzo. He was a kind dog with sad brown eyes, but he would always wag his tail and give just one bark whenever I came home from Johnston's. He was bone idle and liked to spend a lot of time under the table where he'd follow my every move with his slumbering eyes. But the minute I'd go out the door, he'd try and follow me. At night, we'd tie him out beside the reek of turf in case he'd wee-wee in the house; or poo-poo under the table.

The first thing I did when Mrs O'Brien was gone was to give the cat a saucer of milk outside the back door. I would have loved to have let him into the house where I could have had some fun with him but I was afraid he might scutter under the bed. I tried playing with him outside the back door but he ran away. After that, I played with the dog by throwing sticks which he'd go after but would never bring back to me. I brought in two buckets of turf and kept a sod of turf on the fire. I sat down for a minute and began wondering if there was anything nice in the house besides bread and jam that I could eat? After all I was left in charge. And if I was going to keep an eye on the chickens, the house and the cat, then I was entitled to something nice, I figured. I went through every drawer and press in the house but could find nothing of interest. I looked in the bottom half of the dresser. There I saw a full packet of biscuits in a small biscuit tin, an orange and a bar of Fry's chocolate. I was afraid to attack the biscuits as they weren't opened and because there was only one orange and one bar of chocolate in the press I didn't think it was safe to attack them either as Mrs O'Brien was bound to miss them. I found a half a packet of sultanas and I ate most of them, making sure to leave just a few as I closed the bag again. Despite having a good feed of sultanas, I was still hungry. There were three biscuit tins sitting on top of the dresser that really intrigued me. I pulled over a chair and with great work I managed to take down the one in the middle which was a round tin. It was a lovely looking tin with a picture of a beautiful girl in a white dress. She had lovely blond ringlets and an everlasting smile. She was holding a biscuit in her right hand and had already taken a bite out of it. I shook the tin eagerly. There were biscuits in it all right but it was very hard to open. Finally with great effort, I managed to prise the lid off but it flew across the kitchen and rolled around the concrete floor creating an awful racket. But I got an ever bigger shock when I looked in the tin: there was nothing in it except two old polish brushes; a tin of black shoe polish and an auld rag. I had to jump down quickly to put the lid back on and leave it back up on the dresser before Mrs O'Brien came home. To do that, I had to step from the chair onto the bottom half of the dresser. It was very dangerous but I had to do it otherwise Mrs O'Brien would know I was at the tins. I turned the tin around a bit so she wouldn't notice the dint in the lid. I was afraid to try any of the other tins and decided it was safer to have a slice of bread and jam.

Now that my belly was full, I thought I'd surprise Mrs O'Brien by tying up the dog and closing in the chickens for the night. That way she wouldn't have to do much when she came home from the corpse house. By now the chickens were fairly big and it was no problem at all to round them up. All I had to do was call them. They came flitting across the garden along with the clocker. But then all the hens, ducks and geese, as well as the one turkey came running: they too wanted to be fed, though they had been fed earlier. I had a terrible job to shoo them all away while I drove the clocker and the chickens into the hens' cabin. I closed the cabin door for a minute and ran into the house and brought out a thick crust of bread as a special treat for the chickens. I tried feeding them a few crumbs at a time but the clocker jumped up at me and tried to snatch the crust out of my hand and I had to throw it down otherwise she would have pecked me. I got an awful fright when she jumped up at me. Still I was delighted to be doing such an important job. It felt wonderful to be in charge of everything while Mrs O'Brien was away. I knew the chickens couldn't wait to snuggle up beneath their mother's wings in the box and I couldn't wait to see them all jostling to get in under her. But as the chickens were getting bigger by the day, they could no longer hide themselves fully under her wing. It was so funny to see six little heads peeping out at me, I laughed out loud. It was as if the clocker had one big head, with six smaller heads growing out of her back: all of them looking in different directions. After studying their antics for a while, I closed them in by propping the stone against the board. I went into the house and sat down beside the fire and waited for Mrs O'Brien to come home. Already there were people walking and cycling by our house on their way to the corpse house. After a while I saw Mrs O'Brien coming down the street in an awful hurry. She came down to see if I was alright and to get a clean pair of sheets for Kilby's bed. She would be back after a while she said. I stood outside and watched her walk up the street, past all the houses. Ours was the first house, Margaret Collins's was second; Mickey Billy's, with the wicked geese was third; Annie Tobin's was fourth and Kilby's was fifth – the last house before the well. My favourite houses were the Collins's and Tobin's. Sometimes when Mrs O'Brien brought me with her to the well, we'd meet Annie or Margaret coming back with a bucket or two of their own. Very often Annie or Margaret would bring me into their house to give me an apple or an orange. No one in the village had much to do with the Mickey Billy's because they liked to keep to themselves. If I met Mrs Mickey Billy Comer – as people called her because there was another family of Mickey Billy's in Lakeland South – she'd grunt at me while keeping her head down. Mrs O'Brien said they were as odd as two left shoes and that they never spoke to anyone except when it suited them. They were always dressed in rags and looked very poor. They had an awful lot of geese around their house which was poorly thatched and looked as if it could do with a new roof. Every day I used to see the geese attacking people as they walked or cycled up the street. And I didn't like it when I had to go to the well with Mrs O'Brien as the gander and the rest of the geese would come out and attack us, their outstretched yellow beaks hissing as they tried to nip us on the legs. Mrs O'Brien said they did it because the geese were protecting their goslings, but our geese were not like them at all and we had six goslings. Mrs O'Brien always carried a bit of a stick with her when she was going to the well, in case they got too cross. Sometimes I'd see Mickey Billy or his wife laughing at us as they peeped out from behind a stable door which they were meant to be cleaning out. As well as that, every single day we could hear them shouting and fighting with each other, mostly over the cattle, which were often left unattended all day long as they grazed their way right through the village, thereby mucking up the road.

'For God's sake woman, will you go out and stay with the cattle.' Straight away Mrs Billy would shout back, 'Aaaah, kiss me arse; look after them yourself.'

One morning, as Mrs O'Brien and I were coming down from the well we could hear Mrs Billy screaming as if being attacked by some hideous animal, 'Aggh, aggh, aggh,' followed by a plea for mercy, 'Give over, give over.'

Now as I looked up the street, all was quiet. I thought about playing ball against the gable end of the house but then I spotted the wheel beside the horse's stable and decided to play with that instead. When I first arrived in Lakeland, Ned had given me an old bicycle wheel to play with. It was an old rusty wheel with no tyre or tube or anything on it; nothing except a few wire spokes. He had shown me how to roll the wheel down the road. To keep it rolling, I had to keep running after it. After a while, I learnt to drive the wheel with a stick which was great fun altogether. I loved playing with the wheel as it sped off down the narrow road, bobbing and weaving and bouncing and clanging all over the rough cobble stoned road as I ran after it in my bare feet.

Most evenings, I rolled the wheel down the road as far as the lake and back up again. It was so much better than playing with the metal bottle tops I remembered playing with in the Home. They were tiny by comparison and would roll under tables and dressers or disappear down gully holes in the playground.

It was great when I rolled the wheel really fast down the road with the stick. I could then use the stick to slow the wheel down by resting it lightly on the rim. Better still was when I used the point of the stick to touch the spokes of the wheel as it sped along the road. It made a lovely whirring sound as it began to slow down and went ping when it hit the last spoke and the wheel wobbled and fell.

Soon I realised it was getting dark and that perhaps I should go back and mind the house. On the way, I decided to close in the hens and geese in case a fox came and stole them. The geese and one turkey had their own cabin out near the reek of turf, which was nothing more than a two sheets of galvanized tin across a low wall. We used another half sheet to close them in, by propping a stick against it. It was very dark in the house and I didn't know how to light the table lamp. Besides, I was afraid if I went near the lamp, I might break the shade which was very delicate. I had seen Mrs O'Brien accidentally knock it over on the table one evening where it broke in two halves; and it took her ages to get another glass shade to suit the lamp. The only light I had in the house came from the fire and that wasn't very good. So I threw down a few sods of turf and waited for it to kindle, but it took a long, long time.

I was overcome with a growing fear that I might be left on my own for the night. And when I heard a mouse in the press behind me, where we kept the flour, I decided it was a lot safer to close out the front door in case another mouse came in. Then I decided to go to bed. I was only in bed a short time when I heard Mrs O'Brien opening the front door. She was holding aloft a storm lamp which she had brought down from the corpse house.

'It only me, a grá,' she said aloud, as she entered the house. And as she stuck her head round the door of my room with the storm lamp, I could see shadows dancing on the walls.

'You must be in bed, are you?' she called out, holding the lamp aloft

'I am,' I answered as I sat up in bed delighted to see her.

'You know something, you're a great lad altogether. I see you've closed the hens' cabin.'

'And I closed in the chickens and the geese and I tied the dog,' I said proudly.

'Musha, good on you!'

'And I kept a fire on for Daddy,' I added, 'but he didn't come home yet.'

'Lord, I don't know what I do without you. You must be kilt wondering where I was and why Daddy hasn't come home. It's because he's still in the town waiting for Harry Ryan to get the coffin ready. He'll be bringing the coffin straight up to the corpse house when he comes. I have to go back up for another little while, because there are people coming and going all the time. Margaret and I have to make tea and sandwiches and the devil know what for them. Do you think you'll be alright on your own for another while or are you afraid?' she asked, as she held the storm lamp over my bed so that she could see me.

I didn't know what to say. I was terrified at the thought of staying in the house on my own. But as she had lavished such praise on me for closing the hens and the chickens I didn't like to say anything.

'Will you be all right on your own do you think? I'll close the front door after me,' she added, as if to reassure me that I'd be safe; that I had nothing to fear.

'I won't be too long. Is that all right?'

Unable to say anything, I nodded my head.

'Daddy will probably go back up and stay in the corpse house for the night when he's washed and shaved, but I'll come home the minute Margaret and I have finished cleaning up. Nurse Geraghty is coming down to help us: and the minute she comes down I'll come home. I won't leave you on your own.'

She left the room and closed the door behind her. I turned over and buried my head in the pillow and tried to hide the awful fear of being alone in a dark room, a dark house and an even darker world, outside, where people died and their friends and neighbours had to tidy up the house after them. Why couldn't they tidy up the house while the people were alive, I wondered? If they did, I wouldn't have to stay on my own. It was horrible lying in bed having to listen to weird noises outside the house. I could clearly hear people walking past our house while others appeared to loiter outside my bedroom window, sniggering and whispering. What would I do if they made a mistake and came into our house, I wondered? It was terrible, lying there in the dark not knowing what to do. Despite my anxiety, I must have fallen asleep because the next thing I remember was being woken in the morning by Mrs O'Brien.

My father was still in the corpse house. He had stayed there all night. He was still up there by the time we'd finished our breakfast. Then he came home and milked the cows and fed the calves. When he'd finished milking, Mrs O'Brien took down a badly cracked cup off the side of the dresser and put a blob of butter into it. She broke a large duck egg into it and whisked it with a fork before placing it on some glowing cinders on the hearth.

'What are you doing with the cup?' I asked.

'I'm cooking an egg for your father? Have you never seen that before?'

I shook my head, I hadn't. I stood watching her stirring the egg vigorously every time it sizzled.

'You're supposed to heat it slowly and keep stirring it, otherwise it will burn and won't taste nice,' she said, as she added some salt and pepper and gave me a little taste of it. It was lovely; like no egg I had ever tasted before.

While my father was having his breakfast, I had to sweep up the pig meal Mrs O'Brien had spilled in the back kitchen while she was mixing gruel in the pigs bucket. I also had to sweep the main kitchen floor and dust all the chairs. She was forever saying if I dusted them properly I'd be able to see myself in them. And if I couldn't see myself in them, then they were only half polished.

Then she said she'd let out the hens and feed them if I'd let out the chickens. But when I opened the box to let the chickens out I got an almighty shock. Nearly all the chickens were dead. Only the clocker showed any sign of life as she stepped blindly into the light. She was almost too weak to stand as her sweat soaked feathers showed that she was close to suffocation. All of the chickens were trampled to death with the exception of two whose eye lids faintly flickered. They were the only two chickens to show any signs of life even though they looked as if they too were dead. The chickens had been walked and soiled upon during the night and it sickened me to see the state of them. Before I had time to recover, Mrs O'Brien came in to the cabin; she was checking to see were there many eggs and when she saw me standing there and the clocker on her own, she let out an awful sigh, 'Aggh Jesus, Mary and Joseph, don't say a rat got at me chickens?' Stooping down to take a closer look she screamed at me, 'Jesus…Mary and Joseph you've smothered me beautiful chickens!'

At that moment, I thought my heart would stop as I watched her reach into the box to pull out a lifeless chicken by the leg. 'Get out of my sight before I kill you,' she shouted, a look of horror on her face. I ran terrified into the house not knowing what to do or where to go. A minute later, she brought in the half dead chickens and put them lying on a sheet of newspaper beside the fire to try and revive them, while I stood watching from the safety of the back kitchen. After a minute, she picked up the two chicks and began dipping their little beaks into a saucer of water. She began shouting at me again as the two chicks suddenly shook their heads and began to take tiny sips of water. When she thought the chickens were coming round, she put them into the turf basket beside the fire to dry them out. She looked angrily at me and said,

'How many times have I told you not to close them in too tight or they'd smother? How many?' she repeated, as she stamped her foot on the ground. 'Jesus, Mary and Joseph do you realise what you've done? You've smothered me precious chickens; and all because I had to go away for a few hours. What sort of an amadawn are you at all?… that…that can't be trusted to do a simple job? Answer me will you?' she bellowed, as I stood trembling, in the back kitchen

I wanted to plead, that I didn't know, but I was so shocked I couldn't even open my mouth. I could not believe that my great efforts at minding the chickens had turned into such a disaster. And when I wasn't able to answer, she came charging for me like a bull and grabbed me by the scruff of the neck and pushed me out the door in front of her. We made our way out to the hens' cabin where I had to stand and watch as she examined the rest of the chickens for any signs of life. I began to cry at the thought of what she was going to do next. I knew by the expression on her face that she was ready to kill me.

'Why in the name of God did you have to close the lid so tight? Why? Answer me will you and not be standing there like a simpleton?' she screamed at me again when she realised there was no hope.

'I was afraid the rats might get them,' I pleaded, as I tried to wipe away the tears with the sleeve of my jumper. In truth, I was as devastated as she was at the loss of our lovely chickens. They had given me so such pleasure. Day after day I'd watched them flying up on their mother's back as she nestled in the garden. Now the clocker began to wander around the cabin in bewilderment at the sudden loss of her brood. Every now and again, she'd begin calling frantically, tuck-tuck, tuck-tuck, tuck-tuck, as if she had unearthed some food for them. But there was no response: nothing except a heap of stinking soiled carcases that Mrs O'Brien began pulling out of the box.

'Ah… rats me backside. I've lost nine chickens without a rat or a cat going next or near them. Go down the garden there and bring up the wheel barrow so I can throw these dirty rotten things into it. And dig a hole in the bottom the garden so I can bury them…' she ordered, 'that is if you're able to do anything right.'

And because I wasn't moving quickly enough she pushed me out of the cabin before her, saying, 'How you could be so stupid, I'll never, never know! To think I've lost an entire clutch of chickens and I after rearing them for the last three weeks.'

Frantically, I ran around the garden in circles, trying to remember where I'd left the wheelbarrow. Eventually I found it. While she was digging a hole in the bottom of the garden, I had to run and get half a bucket of lime. When the hole was deep enough, she tipped the contents of the wheelbarrow into it and sprinkled the lime over the chickens and covered it over with soil. She trampled the soil underfoot and heaped the rest of the clay over them.

As I followed her into the house, I couldn't help but look back at the heap of clay. I could not believe that the chickens that were running around the evening before were now dead and buried. And I wished with all my heart that I could bring them all back to life. But I couldn't. It was the first time I'd been asked to do anything around the house: the first time I'd been left in charge. Those chickens were the only friends I ever had. I loved them more than anything in the world. Despite my best efforts, the tears rained down my cheeks. I'd been asked to mind the chickens for an hour or two. But I had failed. Miserably

Chapter Four

It was early September when Mrs O'Brien escorted me down by the lake the first day I went to school. The school was situated at the end of Lakeland road that formed a T junction on the edge of the town. There, she introduced me to Mrs Patterson who was in charge of the infants. Every morning, Mrs Patterson drove up from Ballinlough in her brand new Morris Minor car, DI 6465 and inched it ever so close to the school wall. She was a stout pleasant looking woman. She shook hands with me and assured Mrs O'Brien that I'd be fine, even though I was reluctant to say anything. I was dressed in a pair of short trousers, a short sleeved shirt and a pair of brown open sandals with adjustable buckles. I'd a new school bag slung over my shoulder which Mrs O'Brien had made for me.

During the summer, most of the pupils went to school in their bare feet. Before the week was out, I too was running round in my bare feet like everyone else. Mrs O'Brien thought it was a Godsend. Now she could keep the sandals for when I'd be going to Mass.

In the evenings when I'd come home from school, I'd have to take off my good clothes and put on my duds as Mrs O'Brien called them and a pair of wellingtons. Then she'd give me a fine plate of potatoes with a mug of fresh milk. She'd peel the potatoes for me, cut them up, add a lump of butter and sprinkle a little salt on them. But once a week she'd make a lovely pot of Colcannon by draining and mashing the potatoes: she'd add a little boiled cabbage, chopped onions, some salt and pepper and mix it all up adding some milk until it was nice and soft. Then she'd scoop a good dollop of it out onto a dinner plate, shape it out like a giant soup bowl; decorate it with a lump of butter and away I'd go; devouring it to my heart's content while she started quizzing me.

'Well, how did you get on today?'

'Fine!'

'Did you get any slaps?'

'No. But E J Lyons did. The teacher gave him three slaps'.

'Why? What did he do wrong?'

'He was bold.'

'Troth, I hope you're behaving yourself; because if it's a thing I ever hear that you're bold in school and by the Lord God Almighty, I'll leather the daylights out of you. Do you hear that?'

Having received such a stark warning, I generally acknowledged her avowed threat by nodding my head, knowing that she could punish me far worse than any teacher ever could. Despite that, I'd still tell Mrs O'Brien everything that happened.

'And did anyone else get slapped?'

'John Keaveney. He got three slaps as well.'

'Oh! And why did she slap him?'

'Michael Fannon was pulling my hair and John Keaveney was trying to stop him.'

'And why was he pulling your hair?'

'I dunno. He just did.'

After my dinner, it was down to the every day ritual of doing my jobs. But having failed to look after the chickens properly, I was never again left in charge of the house. And as there was no one around to keep an eye on me, Mrs O'Brien tended to bring me with her wherever she went; be it visiting, shopping or simply going to the well. By bringing me with her, she knew I couldn't do any harm.

The well was at the end of the road, just past the last house in our village. The road through the village was called the street, though it was nothing more than a glorified dirt track full of stones, patches of grass, grit and dust where the hens liked to ruffle their feathers beneath the scorching sun The grass patches were fertilised on a daily basis by the comings and goings of farm animals, as well as hens, ducks and geese.

Sometimes Margaret Collins or Annie Tobin would be at the well when we'd get there. When they'd see Mrs O'Brien coming, they'd wait for her to join them; then the three of them would sit on the wall of the well and talk for ages. The women would laugh and swap stories and discuss the latest gossip from the town. They'd ridicule everyone in the parish from the Parish Priest – who was death down on drink – to Doctor Roland, who couldn't get enough of it. And with a nod and a wink in my general direction, they'd lower their voices and start whispering about the most eligible bachelor in the parish and where they themselves thought they had gone wrong.

'Well I know one thing… if I had my life over again I'd choose a different road. There has to be something better than drawing water from the well three hundred and sixty five days a year,' sighed Mrs O'Brien.

'Well I couldn't agree more. Imagine if we lived in the town, we could turn on a tap and have all the water we wanted.'

In the early months after my arrival, most of what was said around the village well went over my head. I was living in a world of my own, exploring every contour of the square shaped walls that formed the well and the river beside it, where Kilby's wife was said to have thrown in the horse's tacklings after a frightful row and where the river disappeared down a swallow hole.

Despite that, I couldn't help but build up little pictures in my head of all the leading characters in the town and what they did for a living. The main shopkeepers delivered sacks of Indian meal and flour to the people of the parish, and in return they collected the eggs. But no one collected the eggs from the village of Lakeland, because it was only a stone's throw from the town.

Listening to the women of the village talking around the well every day, I soon learned that the people looked after the parish priest in monetary terms: and in return the doctor and the parish priest looked after the people in medical and moral terms and if between the two of them they couldn't save you from dying, then you were on your way to either Heaven, Hell or Purgatory; depending on what sort of a sinner you were.

* * * *

The following summer in the midst of a searing hot spell, Mrs O'Brien and I made our way to the well. Margaret Collins was already there, struggling to team a bucket of water.

'Hello Margaret. Isn't it a wonderful day altogether?'

'Musha, Kate you wouldn't know whither it is or not,' said Margaret stopping to draw her breath after emptying some water from one bucket to another which she'd left standing on the well. 'The trouble with the good weather is that the well runs dry very quickly.'

'Yes, I know… and I hate that green slimy scum that comes up with the bucket every time you try to draw it out!'

'Ah! I wouldn't mind the scum at all. It's the frogs and the tadpoles I hate,' said Margaret as she coiled the rope in one hand and let go of the bucket with the other as I leaned in quickly to see my shadow in the clear pool down below. I was just in time to see two small frogs trying to climb up the slimy walls as Margaret's bucket plummeted down to the bottom; before slowing submerging itself and half-filling up with water as Margaret began to hoist it ever upwards until she landed it safely on the ledge. Then drawing a deep breath, she looked across at me and said, 'Mind yourself there John a grá, and don't be looking in like that, the Lord save us you could fall in.'

'Look it! The devil is stuck within him,' said Mrs O'Brien, angrily, as she pulled me away in case I fell in.

'How many times do I have to tell you not to be lookin' in like that: how many…?'

'Yes! Keep away from the well like a good lad. We don't want you to end up like Stokes the tinker,' added Margaret, as she smiled kindly at me.

I stood on the road with my two hands behind my back, as Margaret stood surveying the dark slimy entrails.

'You'd think the men would get together and do something about it. The

Lord have mercy on my man: he was always promising to clean it, but sure he never did.'

'And I don't know how many times I mentioned it to Ned. I said in the honour of God would you ever do something with it before we're all poisoned. And do you know what he said? Sure-a-biteen-of-frog-spawn won't kill you: isn't it alright the way it is? Now, that's men for you!'

'Men! Oh! Stop it will you. Don't ever ask them to do anything. It's no wonder Kilby's wife threw the tacklings into the river? Sure he must have been an awful yoke to live with. How in the name of God did she stick it so long?' asked Margaret with a furrowed brow, the fringes of her red hair glinting in the midday sun.

'Well God only knows. She's gone to Heaven now the poor creature and by the looks of things, it won't be too long until Kilby's after her. Ned was telling me he's gone to the dogs entirely since she died. He won't shave or get up out of bed or anything.'

'Well, he must have got up yesterday or the day before because he's after selling the last two calves he had to Wheeler.'

'Swear your solemn oath?'

'That I may drop dead this minute! I saw Wheeler yesterday evening and me coming home from the town. He was driving the calves out of that field beside your Górt Mór'

'And was anybody with him?'

'There was another man with him, an odd looking character. He didn't look like a jobber to me. He's a pair of green wellingtons with holes in them and a piece of wire around his waist, holding up his trousers. I think I've seen him before. I've a feeling he's from over around Ballyglass.'

'Well… that's a good one,' gasped Mrs O'Brien in astonishment.

'Wait until I tell Ned. Take care did he give the cattle away for nothing. According to Ned, Kilby's gone in the head since Mary dies. I've only been talking to him once or twice since. But Ned goes up to see him every evening. He was telling Doctor Roland about him. Roland said he should be sent to the mental in Ballinasloe: that he's not fit to be let out.'

'Well that's a good one. It's Roland himself that should be in Ballinasloe,' laughed Margaret.

'Did you hear what he said to Patsy Ganly in Cunneely's pub the other night?'

'No, I didn't, said Mrs O'Brien as she rested herself on the ledge opposite Margaret.

'Seemingly the doctor had asked Patsy to do a bit of painting and decorating around the dispensary. "Wallpaper and paint hides a lot of your dirty work," says the doctor to Patsy. Quick as a flash Patsy says back, "and what about the spade and shovel? It covers all your dirty work? Anything I do Doctor Roland, is above board."'

'O Sacred Heart of Jesus! Did he say that?' asked Mrs O'Brien.

'He did! He did! And wasn't he right. Sure that man's not fit to be a doctor and him drunk as a stick every night of the week. He was footless they said, when he tackled Patsy. What's worse he drove home,' said Margaret as she undid the green ribbon she had around her curly locks and tied her hair back off her freckled face.

'He'll be going on until he kills someone with that bloody car; or kills himself.'

'Arrah you couldn't kill the likes of him. But faith Patsy was well able for him.'

'Good man Patsy,' said Mrs O'Brien with a gleam in her eye, before moving on to some other topic she'd gleaned from a visitor to our house.

Hardly a day went by that a visitor didn't call to our house: it might be Colleen nipping in for a few minutes on her way to the town or it might be a neighbour or a friend. Sometimes Mrs O'Brien would have to curtail her visit to the well when she'd see somebody approaching our house from the town end. If it wasn't a friend or a neighbour, it might be the tinker woman, the chimney sweep, the insurance man, the rate collector, a government surveyor, or nuns collecting money for the black babies in South Africa. But no matter who it was, they always carried news of one sort or another. If it was a neighbour or a family friend they'd be brought into the house and I'd be told to run outside and play. I knew this was a way of getting rid of me while they discussed everything and anything. After a while, I resented being chased out of the house and I devised a little secret plan of my own so that I too could be privy to what was being said. I'd leave the house and make believe I was playing in the back garden. Instead, I'd make my way round to the front bedroom window, where the cat would jump down off the sill and I'd jump up. There I'd quietly listen to everything that was being said. Thought I never really knew what the visitors were talking about most of the time, I still found their conversations interesting, particularly if they said something nice about me. And I'd flee to the back of the house as soon as I'd hear the chairs being pushed back on the floor.

As Mrs O'Brien made her way down from the well, she stopped like she always did and said, 'John'een, I nearly whipped. If there's one thing I hate in this world, its having to trudge up and down to that cursed well three hundred and sixty five days a year. Would you ever give me a hand, like a good lad; and see if you can carry one of the buckets for me: if only a few yards?'

She sighed as she straightened her headscarf, re-adjusted her skirt and apron before picking up the bucket while I attempted to carry the second one, but it was too heavy and awkward and I couldn't carry it very far.

'Ah leave it down a grá, before you spill it.'

But it wasn't long before she bought a little can in the town and from that day on she'd fill the can with water and I too had to carry my share down from the well. It wasn't something I enjoyed but I had to do it. I much preferred going off with Ned somewhere in the horse and cart which meant I didn't have to go to the well.

When Ned wasn't busy saving hay or turf, he'd be busy helping Snowy and Tom Farrell with their crops and they in turn would help him. When the hay and turf was saved, it was time to get ready for the harvest.

Barley was the first of the crops to be cut, followed by the oats. If the barley wasn't fit for cutting by the 15th of August then you were considered a poor farmer. It meant you hadn't sown early enough. Everything revolved around the feast of Our Lady which was on the fifteenth. On the eve of the fifteenth, men and women from all over the parish took it upon themselves to walk to Knock as a penance for their sins. They'd commence walking to the shrine at Knock – twenty miles away – late in the evening and walk all through the night and arrive in time for six o'clock Mass in the morning: thereby gaining a plenary indulgence. Then they'd turn round and walk back home again. Some people even took it upon themselves to walk in their bare feet as a special penance for their sins. Mr and Mrs O'Brien did neither. They preferred to cycle to Knock when it suited them – or as they liked to say themselves, when they had the time.

* * * *

The field of barley opposite the lake was ready for harvesting. It was my first time to see it being done. I ran barefooted along the headland, feeling the soft green grass beneath my feet while Ned stood whetting the scythe. The rasping sound of farmers whetting their scythes could be heard for miles around. Soon Ned showed me how to walk backwards in front of him and to hold the rod as he mowed the barley. I held the rod – as the long eight foot stick was called – gently against the top of the corn which made it easier for him to cut. It was a glorious sight to see the gentle summer breeze rippling through the golden corn creating magical waves across the entire field. But for the mower it was a nightmare as very often the wind would sway the corn back over the blade causing it to ravel, which made it very difficult to take out. Mrs O'Brien followed Ned and took out each ledge as it was being cut: neatly lifting and sifting enough barley to make a nice sized sheaf. Then quick as a flash she'd pick up a dozen blades of corn, whip them around the middle, tie them; and throw it out from her, thereby forming a neat row right down the field. On and on it went all day until there were ten, twenty, thirty, forty rows of sheaves the entire length of the field: all waiting to be stooked. But if it looked like rain, Ned would not cut more than five or six ledges at a time before stooking it. I loved it when they started stooking as it gave me a break from holding the rod and generally signalled it was nearing tea time. I helped to make the stooks by carrying or dragging in the sheaves so that my mother and father could stand them on their end. The only thing I didn't like was walking barefoot on the razor sharp stubbles, and the spikelets on top of the barley that would stick to your shirt and jumper and were almost impossible to remove. I could hardly walk as the coarse stubbles cut the undersides of my toes forcing me to hobble around the field. Still, I preferred gathering up the sheaves to walking backwards all day, whilst holding the rod.

To make a stook, my mother and father would pick up four sheaves of corn – two under each arm. They'd stand four or five sheaves against each other at an angle of forty five degrees. And to head the stooks they'd pick up a single sheaf, turn it upside down and spread the bottom of it like a skirt around the stook before tying the two single sheaves firmly to each other like lovers wrapping their arms round each other: thereby protecting the stook from the wind and rain. The stooks were made in long straight lines, making them easier to count when it came to stacking.

Two weeks later when the barley was considered seasoned, my mother and father would begin stacking. This time they'd pick up the whole stook – though clumsy and awkward – were light as a feather. They'd carry the stooks to where they were going to build the stack. They'd build each stack by making a bigger version of the stook, gradually adding more sheaves until they had created a circular base about six foot in diameter. From there on up, they'd gradually drew the shelves into the centre of the stack until the whole thing came to a narrow point about eight or ten foot off the ground. To head the stack they took four sheaves, turned them upside down and tied them to each other the same way as in the stook, thus protecting all the grain which was built into the centre of the stack.

After my parents had gone down early one morning, to finish the stacking, my father turned to my mother and said,

'Isn't it a bitch how that fella has to be going back to school and the oats ready for cutting? Maybe we should keep him at home. It would make things a hell of a lot easier.'

'Ah, stop it will you? He'll go back to school on Monday the same as everybody else whether you like it or not. I don't want Sergeant Boyle calling to the house because we haven't sent him to school.'

As soon as we arrived back at the house, my father tackled up the horse and cart and went to the bog for a load of turf. I was hoping he would bring me for a ride in the cart but he told me to stay at home and to help my mother. It was around two o'clock when I heard Tommy the postman propping his bicycle outside the front door. I knew instinctively it was him. I almost collided with him as he lifted the flap of his bag and took out a letter on entering. As he ruffled my hair and said, 'God save all here,' I hung around the door, trying to keep out of my mother's way

'Jesus, Tommy, me heart! You frightened the living daylights out of me,' she said holding a hand to her chest as she looked up from the table where she was making her second cake.

'Arrah… blast it to hell is that all you have for me?' she asked, in mock disappointment.'

'That's all Mrs O'Brien! That's all I'm afraid.' said Tommy as he prepared to remove the cumbersome bag from around his sagging shoulders.

As Mrs O'Brien recovered her composure, she picked up the letter and looked at it for a moment, before deciding, 'That's probably Ned's gun licence. He keeps renewing it every year, thought he hasn't shot anything in… I don't know when. I was half expecting something from America because we've not heard from uncle Paddy in ages.'

'Well I'm sorry, that's all I have today Kate! Maybe tomorrow,' he sighed contentedly as he removed his postman's hat and began mopping his sweaty brow with a white handkerchief. He hung his hat on the corner of Mrs O'Brien's armchair along with the mail bag: his large sinewy hands and rugged complexion testimony to his many years on the road. He sat down and removed the bicycle clips from the bottom of his trousers before settling back in Mrs O'Brien's armchair.

'Take the weight off you feet now a grá until I make you a mug of tea; only I'll have to stick the kettle on. We're only just in; we were stacking the barley; but you're in no hurry, I'm sure?'

'Well the devil-a-hurry. No hurry in the wide earthly world: because I know if I go back to that bloody office too early, they'll expect me to finish early every day and maybe cut me wages. It's all very fine on a day like today when I haven't a lot to do: but as you know, there are days when I'm put to the pin of me collar to finish me round.'

'Ah sure, don't I know! Rest yourself now anyway. You're lucky; I've a nice bit of apple tart I baked this morning. Would you like a bit of bread and jam to go with it?'

'No. No thanks! A mug-a-tea and a bit of apple tart will suit me fine because Herself will have the dinner ready when I go home. Sylvester and one of the girls might spend an hour or two in the bog with me this evening. I want to try and gather up the last of the turf, while the weather's good.'

'Lord wouldn't it be great. You mustn't know yourself with all the help you have?'

'Well, 'tis wonderful surely. Sylvester is a bloody topper. He looks a delicate sort of a lad'een and yet he's gathered most of the turf on his own. Between one thing and another… by the time I get home and change me clothes and go to the bog, the day is damn near gone. But Sylvester, he'd do more in a few hours than the rest of us put together. Still, I'd like to make the effort before they all start back to school.'

'Oh sure, how old is he now? He must be eleven or twelve?'

'Eleven, eleven… going on twelve.'

'I was thinking that. I wish to the Lord God that I had someone that age.'

'And you will, you will, with the help of God. Wait till John Paschal grows up,' he said, nodding his head in my general direction as I hung around the front door.

'I suppose you're right,' acknowledged Mrs O'Brien.

'At least we have that much to look forward to. I'm glad now we got him, because we'd like to have someone to look after us as we get older. Tell me have you any news?' asked Mrs O'Brien, after a moment's reflection, knowing that if there was anything worth knowing Tommy would have it. She felt privileged that she had first hand knowledge of all the comings and goings in the parish, because Tommy liked nothing more than to sit down beside the fire divulging secrets while having a mug of tea in our house which was the last on his daily round.

'Well begod then Kate I have!' he replied cheerfully.

'As fine-a-bit of news as you're likely to hear in a long day's walk,' he added, as he plucked a cigarette from his newly opened packet of twenty *Players*, having already disposed of an empty packet. And as he held the cigarette in his mouth, he slowly began to rummage in his pockets for a box of matches, knowing that Mrs O'Brien was hanging on to his every word. Then, as he flicked the spent match into the fire and joyously inhaled a lungful of smoke, he sat back contentedly, threw one leg over the other before continuing,

'Mrs O'Brien, I'm pleased to inform you that your hard working daughter Colleen has just received a registered letter from Snowy: and he's in fine fettle by all accounts...'

'Is it a registered letter you said?' asked Mrs O'Brien, a look of astonishment on her face, 'Already?' she added, as she stopped for a moment before continuing to put the sugar bowl, the milk and apple tart on the table.

'Be damn but, yes! A registered letter! As I said to Colleen, Snowy, must be as fine a man as ever stood in shoe leather.'

'Well, thanks be-to-the-great-God Almighty, for that! So he must be working, is he, if he's managed to send her a registered letter, so soon: and he only gone, what...a fortnight, yesterday?'

'Oh he's working alright,' acknowledged Tommy, joyously, as he expelled two jets of blue smoke via his flared nostrils.

'And like that now,' he began slowly, 'poor Colleen couldn't wait to find out whether he was working or not. So the minute she signed the receipt, I threw the registered letter on the table. Naturally enough she opened it. But what happened next, Kate, will stay with me for a long, long time. If I hadn't seen it with my own two eyes I would not have believed it.'

'What?' asked Mrs O'Brien, with a look of consternation?

'Colleen opened the letter and took out, five crisp twenty pound notes. I'm telling you Mrs O'Brien, the sight of those notes will stay with me for many a long day. The poor creature stood looking at me, her mouth half open, the money still in her hand. Now! There's news for you Mrs O'Brien!'

'Jesus, Mary and Holy St Joseph, Tommy: a hundred pounds! Is it pulling me leg you are?' asked Mrs O'Brien, shocked that Snowy could accumulate so vast a sum in so short a time.

'A hundred pounds…amn't I telling you? Five crisp twenty pound notes!' repeated Tommy, as he leant forward in his chair to try and redress the personal nature of the disclosure.

'Now, what ever you do, don't let on I said anything. For God's sake, Kate don't let on,' said Tommy, aloud, as he extended the nicotine stained hand cupping the cigarette, to emphasise the point. Then lowering his voice to an audible whisper he continued, 'I know it's none of my business what any man does. But I knew you'd be anxious to know how he was getting on: or if Colleen had heard from him. Besides, where in Ireland would you find a man like that, I ask you… where?

'Well where is right,' agreed Mrs O'Brien, with a glowing look of satisfaction.

Then reverting to his usual self, he began to elaborate in a more relaxed tone of voice.

'He's beyond in Manchester working like a nigger: that's where he is, while his good lady wife is above in Woodlawn running the show.'

'Well, that's a bloody good one and I thought he was a good for nothing… so-an-so.'

'Well…I know he's your son-in-law and all that, Kate…but in truth, that's what I thought … a bloody wastrel! But it just shows you, how wrong a man can be.'

'God… I still can't believe it. A hundred pounds! Colleen must be delighted?'

'Delighted; delighted altogether! Out in the street, she was, mixing a barrowful of concrete when I called. I'm telling you; you wouldn't find her equal in the whole of Ireland.'

'Well thanks be-to-the-great-God almighty that he's working, anyway.' It's a blessing he didn't bother with any oats this year and they doing up the house,' said Mrs O'Brien, pleasantly, as she began to pour out a mug of tea for Tommy. 'He'd be a long time above in Woodlawn before he'd save that kind of money.'

'Well not if he worked his backside to the bone, would he see the colour of it. Ah but sure I always said it, we'd have been better off if we'd stayed under British rule: instead of letting that gang of…of….playboys and tricksters above in Dáil Éireann run the country.'

'Well… I don't know about that. But England must be a great country altogether when a man can save that kind of money? Wait until Ned hears it? It will drive him mad entirely because he does have notions of going over again. He used to work in the coalmines: and he thinks if he went over again, he'd get his old job back. But as I do say to him, he should have more sense and stay at home, a man of his age. And anyway, I wouldn't like to be left here on my own. Here! Enjoy this,' she said, handing Tommy a mug of tea and a slice of apple tart on a small decorative plate which he carefully balanced on his knee while he left the mug on the hob and took command of the plate.

'Well the blessing of God on you, Mam. I was looking forward to a mug of tea this last hour. I don't like saying it, but you know, some people would never think of asking, if you had a mouth on you.'

'Troth don't I know it well. But I bet they wouldn't be shy about asking if you had a letter,' replied Mrs O'Brien, as she began tidying up the table.

'Ha ha! You never spoke a truer word! Some people would demand a letter off you. And they wouldn't be shy about asking for it either. "Oh where's my letter? Are you sure it's not in your bag. Can't you have another look," they'd say. They must think I'm a pure eejit altogether,' he smirked thoughtfully to himself, as he savoured the juice seeping apple pie, devouring it with relish. When he had a few mouthfuls of it gone, he added gleefully, 'and there's a man that's home from Manchester, Peter Cornell. I was talking to auld Jim, only an hour ago. "I believe Peter is home. They tell me he's doing awfully well for himself in Manchester" says I.

"Blast me but he is," says Jim. "He owns half Manchester. He has men coming to him every day of the week, looking for work. He has lodging houses... and riding schools... and the devil knows what over there. Blast me but he has a car that he bought beyond in America. It's that long he had to bring it into the town the other night, just to turn it below in the square."'

'Ah, you're joking,' laughed Mrs O'Brien.

'You know Annie was telling me yesterday evening how there was supposed to be some young fella home from England with a big car, but she didn't know who it was. It must have been him? She heard that the car was as long as two houses. What harm but I wasn't inclined to believe her. He's supposed to be a fine cut of a fella, with a new suit and the hair oiled to the last.

'So, is it any wonder... Jim would so proud of him?' she said, as she dried her hands on the tea towel.

'Well, no wonder. And didn't auld Jim himself, behave well and rear seven of them, all on his own? I remember them as little kid'eens: and they running around the street; the arse hanging out of their trousers. No, but it's what some of them had no bloody trousers at all,' said Tommy, finishing the last of his tea.

'I know! Isn't that how half the country was reared?' replied Mrs O'Brien, as she lifted the lid off the three legged oven with the fire tongs and checked to see if the cake was baked by sticking a knife into it. There was still a trace of dough on the knife so she replaced the lid, put a few more coals under the oven and finished off by placing a few more coals on the lid.

'The ones that get everything, Tommy, grow up to be good for nothings.

It's the ones that haven't a pot to piss in or a bit to put in their mouths that do well when they go away,' she sighed, straightened her back.

'Sure Jim must be getting the pension now, is he?' she asked as an afterthought.

'Oh he is! He is! Auld Jim is pushing on, you know. I think he's seventy one this year. He only started getting the pension last year. Aaah… but he's a cute hoor you know; he'd never let on. But I know, from working in the Post Office.'

Mrs O'Brien cocked her ear for a second as she was about to throw a few more sods on the fire. She was listening to the rumbling of a cart coming up the road at the back of the house. She looked questioningly at Tommy for a second, 'I think that must be my man I hear,' she said. The words no sooner out of her mouth than I rushed out to see if it was Daddy. When I came back in to tell them it was, Tommy said,

'Well young man. How are you today? I dunno did I speak to you earlier?'

'Fine thanks.'

'Ye must have all the turf near home, have ye?'

I didn't know what to say, so I said nothing as I went outside the door again where I knew I could listen.

'We have, more or less. That's a load or two he'd left in the bog, because it wasn't dry; 'twas cut late.

'Be damn but, isn't John Paschal turning out to be a grand quiet lad? Weren't ye lucky to get him?

'Well thanks be-to-God Almighty, everything worked out grand. Ned is fond of him and likes bringing him to the bog. But, I'd be afraid he'd fall into a bog hole or something, because he's on the go all the time.'

'Arrah the devil-a-thing 'ill happen him. And won't he be a great help to ye when he gets a bit older?'

'Well, with the help of God. He loves helping in the bog and he's as happy as Larry. And I like having him here; he's very handy around the place. But sure he'll be back in school on Monday, just when we'll be getting busy with the oats. We could do with him around the place for another week – if it was only to call Ned in for the dinner or bring a bottle of tea down to the field. I must see where he is now and give him a bit to eat in case he goes to the bog with Ned.'

'I best start knocking a step or two out of it myself,' said Tommy, as I appeared at the door knowing I'd now be let go for a spin in the cart.

'Oh there you are! Listen, you'd better eat something a grá if you're going to the bog or you'll be starving by the time you get home,' said Mrs O'Brien as Tommy began to fold the bottom of his uniform trousers before slipping the bicycle clips back on. Turning round, he reached for his hat and bag and having straightened his uniform he perched his crested hat on his thin greying skull and went towards the door.

'Well the blessing of God on ye Mam. I'll see ye tomorrow with the help of God.'

'Good luck Tommy and thanks.'

I stood out in the street and watched Tommy as he slowly wound his way down the leafy lane and around the corner. I ran back in, to get ready for another jaunt in the horse and cart before school on Monday. Going back to school was something I didn't want to think about. But now that the summer holidays were over I didn't have any choice.

Chapter Five

A week after I was back in school, I came home to find Colleen in our house. Every other day, she'd nip down across the fields, to see her mother. They had a great welcome for me as I walked in the door. And as Mrs O'Brien began putting my dinner on the table, Colleen set up the churn on a chair in the middle of the floor and began winding the churn for her. When at last the butter broke, she began to wash down the blobs off the inside of the churn with cold water, before scooping it all out into a large wooden dish with a butter spade.

'How are ye getting on with the house?' asked Colleen's mother as she took over the churn and began draining the buttermilk out of the butter.

'Oh don't mention it. I thought they'd have it finished by now. But the way things are going I'll be lucky if they have it finished by Christmas. There's always something new wanted. The builder said he'd have to lower the front wall of the house if I wanted to turn the house into a dormer. And I thought it would be a straight forward job to put on a new roof and put in a few windows. I wish to God they started the job when they were supposed to. I'm terrified it'll rain and destroy everything. But the bathroom is coming on well, though it's going to cost more than I thought,' added Colleen as she dipped a large penny biscuit into her mug of tea.

'Ah! Bad cess to yourself and your bathroom, 'tis far from bathrooms you were reared. Isn't an auld piss pot under the bed good enough for you and you having two children to rear and maybe another on the way.'

'Mam! Do you realise what you're saying? We had no choice but to put a new roof on the house. And amn't I as well to build on a bathroom while I'm at it. For years you've being saying you wished you had a decent lavatory in the house. If any one calls, you have to show them that makeshift lavatory across the street. Well I'm going to have a new bathroom and that's that.'

'Ah makeshift lavatory how are you! Isn't it plenty good enough for us? At least I can dance according to my music. How are you going to pay for the bathroom? How? You should learn to crawl before you walk,' said her mother, as she finished moulding the butter on the butter dish.

'And does Snowy know you're building a bathroom?'

'Of course he does! I wouldn't build it with out asking him. If he stays in England for the winter, won't we be able to pay for it. So what's there to worry about? He's on great money, you know.'

'Ah well. Suit yourself!' said Mrs O'Brien as she put the rest of the butter into a crock and carried it out to the back kitchen. Returning with two clean buckets' she tilted the milk churn and drained the buttermilk into them. She was in the back kitchen when I heard someone outside the front door..

'God save all here,' said Tommy the postman, catching us all unawares as he lifted the latch on the half door and let himself in.

'Musha Tommy you're welcome,' the two women said in unison.

'Aren't you the lucky girl Colleen; that I caught up with you? I thought I'd have to keep your few pounds until tomorrow,' said Tommy, delighted to be throwing the registered letter and receipt docket on the table, awaiting Colleen's signature.

'I thought about leaving it in your house but I couldn't without getting it signed. I was afraid to ask any of the men to sign it because between one thing and another it might get lost. It would be a devil entirely himself to send home a few pounds and you to lose it above in your house. I didn't let on I had any mail at all,' added Tommy, lowering his voice. 'so they were none the wiser. They told me you were gone to the town to order stuff. I was thinking I'd meet you on the way.'

'Tommy, I can't believe it. I wasn't expecting to hear from Snowy so soon: and a registered letter at that. God Almighty Tommy but he must be on great money altogether...' she said excitedly as she picked up the registered envelope and began looking at it.

'Will you have a mug of tea Tommy?' asked Mrs O'Brien, giving Colleen a look as if to say, whatever you do don't open that letter while he's here.

'Be damn but, Mrs O'Brien I won't. It's getting late. I should've been finished an hour ago. Besides, I've a bit of fencing to do. And what with the turf and oats and the devil knows what, I haven't time to bless myself.'

'Well nothing was ever more welcome,' said Colleen as she signed the receipt slip and looked at the registered letter again.

'You know I wrote to Snowy last week after I got the money. I said it would be great if he could send a hundred every week,' laughed Colleen.

'I only said it as a joke. Little did I know he'd be sending me another letter this week?'

As Colleen left the letter on the table and Tommy carefully slipped the receipt into his little black book and pushed it down into his breast pocket he said, 'Ladies! I've said it before and I'll say it again; Snowy Fox must be the best bloody man in Ireland. Running the country the likes of him should be; instead of that shower-a-trumps above in Dáil Éireann. He's only three weeks gone and already he's sent two registered letters home to you. He's a genius I'm telling you: a pure bloody genius. I don't know how he does it. I've been delivering post for the last thirty years and I've not seen anything like it. The man's a genius – when he puts his mind to it – a pure bloody genius. Colleen, you behaved bloody well to collar 'im. You should be proud of yourself?'

'Well, I am. As long as he keeps sending me money the devil-a-hair-I-care,' laughed Colleen, going out to the back kitchen to rinse out her mug.

'The man's a genius; a pure bloody genius, I tell you!'

'Oh he was always a great man for the money,' said Mrs O'Brien, an edge to her voice.

'But until now... he was more inclined to drink it than earn it.'

'Mother!' exclaimed Colleen, aloud, annoyed that her own mother was trying to spoil what was a wonderful compliment.

'Ah sure we're only talking!' replied Mrs O'Brien.

'Did you hear the Board of Works are starting on the new road next week?' she asked, in an effort to change the flow of the conversation.

'Be damn but, I did, I did. But I didn't hear what day.'

'Monday,' replied Mrs O'Brien, as she began to fill the kettle with water before hanging it on the fire.

'That's what one of the engineers told Ned yesterday.'

'Lord, won't it be a comfort to ye when it's finished; besides having to traipse in and out through that cursed flood?'

'Well that's as sure as you're there,' said Colleen.

'Well I'd best be off,' said Tommy, as he swung the mail bag to the side of his shoulder and turned for the door knowing he would not be seeing the contents of the registered letter.

'I believe Kilby's not too good?' he said as an after thought.

'Ah, isn't it hard on the poor auld devil. I told you the other day how he was raving; and going round the street and not a stitch on him, except the auld long johns. Roland came out to have a look at him and send him to Ballinasloe. Ned rang the hospital yesterday to enquire how he was. But they said he wasn't good. So I'm thinking... he could be there a while,' said Mrs O'Brien, as herself and Colleen escorted Tommy out the door..

'Look at it this way, isn't he in the right place?' said Tommy, as I went down into my bedroom to change my clothes.

'Well...I suppose he is...when he has no one belonging to him.'

'Well God bless ye. I'll see ye tomorrow with the help of God,' said Tommy, taking his bicycle from beneath my bedroom window.

'Yes. Well good luck Tommy. And thanks.'

When Colleen came back in she picked up the letter while her mother looked at her as if waiting for some startling news to emerge. I could see Colleen was desperate to open the letter but she didn't want anyone else to know what was in it.

'Well, how is he getting on?' asked Mrs O'Brien, her hands on her hips.

'Who?' asked Colleen, a puzzled expression on her face?

'Ah! Who do you think? Is it trying to make a fool of me you are? Isn't that from Snowy? How is he getting on?'

'How do I know? I didn't open it yet: did I?' replied Colleen, holding the registered letter firmly to her bosom. The women glared at one another as I emerged quietly from the room.

'Well blast it to hell, are you going to open it or not; or what's wrong with you? Isn't Tommy gone now? Open it in the name of God until we see how he is or what he's up to.'

With a sigh of resignation and an overpowering sense of excitement, Colleen peeled back the sealed flap on the registered envelope and pulled out another white envelope that had something written on it. Colleen looked at the white envelope for a second.

'What is it? What does it say?' asked Mrs O'Brien, curiosity getting the better of her.

Colleen's face melted and broke into a broad smile as she read,

'I'll send more money next week. Love Máirtín.

'Jesus Mary and Holy St Joseph,' said Mrs O'Brien, 'Where's he getting all the bloody money?'

'Where do you think?' retorted Colleen angrily.

'He's up at six o'clock every morning and doesn't get home till late?'

Colleen tore open the white envelope and pulled out a thick wad wrapped in a single sheet of writing paper. When she unfolded it, she was left holding a wad of... newspaper clippings, each the size of a twenty pound note. The colour drained from her cheeks as she stood; her mouth half-open. I could see by her that something was seriously wrong. For a moment, she stood fingering the newspaper clippings in bewilderment. Seeing her mother's face, she grabbed the registered envelope and threw the entire contents into the fire. She seized her cardigan from the back of the chair and ran out the door without saying a word.

Mrs O'Brien, who had been watching her every move, didn't know which way to turn. 'What is it?' What's wrong?' she asked, before rushing over to see if she could rescue anything from the fire. But it was too late. The so called money was already in flames. Turning quickly she went out after Colleen, shouting, 'What's wrong with you? What in the name of God are you at?'

But Colleen had already hopped on her bicycle and was speeding helter skelter off down the road. The two of us stood watching her cycling around the corner, like Shay Elliott in the Tour De France.

'Well that's the damndest thing yet,' sighed Mrs O'Brien, in exasperation. 'That beats all ever I saw.' After a moment's reflection back in the house, she added, humorously to herself, 'I was thinking 'twas too bloody good to last. Talk about clipping her wings!'

* * * *

Mrs O'Brien was making tea and sandwiches as she got ready to go down to

Johnston's. When everything was ready, she lifted me up on the carrier of the bicycle and cycled down through the town to Johnston's, where Daddy was stacking oats on his own, using a short wooden ladder to head the stacks.

Again, I had to help by handing him the sheaves while Mrs O'Brien started gathering in all the stooks. They wanted to get as much done as they could before it rained. Tomorrow could be wet, they said.

It was another three days before we could finish stacking the oats and weeks before we were ready to bring it home. I loved it when my father and Tom Farrell lifted me up on the cart load of oats. There I sat tight, holding onto the rope that held down the load, as the cart lurched and rolled over the rough cobble stones and forced its way along the narrow lane as I ducked my head to avoid the overhanging branches as the load left a trail of golden straw clinging to the hedgerows. As night was falling and Tom Farrell headed the last of the stacks, he looked up at the waxing moon, drew a breath of chilly air and said,

'I'm telling you, we'll have frost before morning. It'll soon be time to start digging the spuds.'

Tom was right.

Every evening around the same time it grew that bit chillier. And each day as soon as I'd come home from school, I'd have to pick the pooreens* in the big field opposite the lake. As my father dug the potatoes he'd leave the small ones after him – or pooreens as they were called – for me to pick up when I'd come home from school. It broke my heart each evening to come home and see the long rows waiting to be picked up. I had a small bucket for the job but it was still back breaking work having to bend down all the time. It was a job I hated more than any other. Sometimes I'd stand on the pooreens and bury them underfoot so I wouldn't have to carry them all to the potato bag. Other times, I'd straighten my back for a minute to stare spellbound as flocks of wild ducks flew in over my head on their way to the lake. It was a magical sight to see them zooming in overhead at breathtaking speed often circling the lake two or three times before deciding where to land. Other times they'd climb higher and higher as if going away altogether before finally deciding to come down on the lake. A few minutes later, I'd straighten my back again on hearing the swishing sound of wings overhead as a flock of swans flew in, in v formation. They only ever circled once, before coming down to ski along the icy water with their yellow webbed feet. But the evening chill often forced me to keep working, however, much I wanted to study nature. The evenings often turning so cold, my fingers would turn numb as a crisp ground frost set in. And I'd pray with all my heart that my father would finish early; to give me a hand picking the pooreens* before I'd die with the cold.

When he finally decided he'd done enough, he'd join me and together we'd bag the last of them and leave them on the headland to be brought home later with the horse and cart.

---

* Pooreen (small potatoes)

Then as dusk set in he'd take the scythe and cut some long grass around the headland to cover the potatoes. He'd cover them with a good layer of grass and cover the grass with a layer of rushes he'd brought down in the cart, to keep the frost off the potatoes during the winter. Every two or three days as the pits grew longer and longer he'd built up a pyramid of soil about a foot deep round the potatoes to ensure their protection. His last task on leaving the field was to swing one of the many bags up on his back to carry home for the pigs, while I walked alongside carrying his top coat.

And because we had a good crop of potatoes it took weeks to dig them as the days grew shorter and the weather colder. But I loved it when it was raining, heavy. It meant I'd have the evening to myself with no pooreens to pick.

If it was a real bad day, my father would spend hours repairing farm implements in the cart house. When he'd that done, he'd come in and sit by the fire, waiting for it to clear. If it did, he'd put on his coat and go down and start digging again while I stayed at home to help around the house. But very often our daily chores were interrupted by Tommy the postman.

As soon as Tommy came in, I'd be ordered to do some meaningless task in the garden but I knew it was a ruse, just to get me out of the house. After a hurried job, I'd sneak round to the front where I could listen outside my bedroom window.

But it was news from afar that caught my attention late one afternoon: news that one could never ever forget.

'…Did you hear about Peter Cornell?'

'No! Don't tell me he's home again?' said Mrs O'Brien.

'No, no…the poor creature he's not and more's the pity. He was killed beyond in Manchester yesterday.'

'Oh sweet Jesus, is it Jim's Peter, you're talking about?'

'I'm afraid so. Jim's gone over to Manchester today. Seems the poor lad got an awful death. He was down in the yard – where he keeps his lorries – burning auld rubbish or something when a can of petrol blew up in his face.'

'Oh the Lord God Almighty may save us, but that's terrible!' sighed Mrs O'Brien.

'Terrible! Terrible altogether,' echoed Tommy

'Jesus, Mary and Joseph, but that'll kill poor Jim? He was so proud of Peter.'

'He was then! He was then… so proud of him!'

'And he was only home here, what… not long ago?'

'I know! I know! It's so hard to believe what can happen. Sure he couldn't be very old? What age would he be at all, twenty six …twenty seven?'

'Let me think… I'd say he must be going on twenty seven, if not twenty eight. Oh God, that's terrible news altogether, Tommy,' lamented Mrs O'Brien, her voice beginning to waver.

'That Peter was the grandest fella that ever stood in two shoes. He was so obliging. He used to help Ned turn the cattle in off the road when he'd be bringing them home from the fair.'

'Ah sure where would he leave it, the poor creature? Weren't all them Cornells decent people, ever? As decent a family as you'd meet in a long day's walk. Sure auld Jim, he'd give you the shirt off his back. Signs were on him, they all got on well in England. They say that Peter was a millionaire... that he owned half Manchester. He had riding stables, lorries, lodging houses and everything.'

'I wonder will they bring him home?'

'That, I couldn't tell you Missus. Some say he got married, not long since, to some English lass. But I'm not inclined to believe that. If he did, auld Jim would have gone over for the wedding. And he never mentioned anything like that to me. But like everything else, Peter might have gone off and tied the knot in some registry office: who knows? Peter wasn't one for showing off you know. Look at the way he built himself up and there wasn't a word about it. If it wasn't for that big car of his, we'd never known he was in it,' said Tommy.

'Aw well now, I won't be the better of that for weeks. And I wonder was there anyone else with him, any of the brothers or anyone when it happened?

'That, I don't know. It was Harry Ryan told me. I met him as he was coming out from Castlerea there a couple of hours ago. He was after bringing auld Jim to the station. It was Sergeant Boyle who got word late last night. Harry Ryan and Sergeant Boyle went up to break the news ... and poor Jim thrown above in bed in that auld shack of a house. Harry Ryan said it took them ages to get him down to open the door.'

'Oh God Almighty Tommy, wait till Ned hears this? His heart will be broke entirely. He thinks the world of auld Jim you know. He's so obliging. Ned never did a hand's turn round the place for him that poor Jim didn't offer to pay him; or give him a day in the bog for it.'

News of the tragedy spread like wildfire through the parish. And because Peter had recently got married to an English girl, she wanted him buried in Manchester where she'd be near his grave. He was buried in Southern Cemetery, Tommy said. A few family relatives went over. But there was a special Mass for Peter in Williamstown. The day before the Mass when auld Jim came home from England, he called unexpectedly to our house, while I sat at the table doing my homework. He told Mrs O'Brien about the funeral.

'...Blast me Missus... but I couldn't stop crying... to see his six brothers carrying the coffin and the crowd of people. Two hundred workers formed a guard of honour. They took it in turns to carry his coffin all the way to the graveyard. And though I was sittin' in the car, I thought we'd never reach the graveyard,' he sobbed, as he took a handkerchief from his pocket, removed his thick rimmed glasses and dried his eyes while Mrs O'Brien pulled a white handkerchief from the sleeve of her cardigan and shed a tear in sympathy.

'Ah well, may God Almighty help you, a grá. It must have been awful hard for you… to go over there to Manchester; to go through all that and he doing so well for himself?'

'I wished the Good Lord had taken me instead, Missus' he lamented, shaking his weary head.

'What use am I now to anyone, at the latter end of me days? And he with a beautiful young wife…and a child on the way.'

'Ah the Lord Almighty save us… and save us from all harm… and how is she taking it the poor creature?' asked Mrs O'Brien, giving auld Jim a large glass of whiskey.

'Would you like a drop of water in that?'

'Bad! Bad! No Mam…no. 'Tis grand the way it is,' he said, turning his glass away. A drop'een-a-whiskey is the only thing that'll ease… the pain. Elisabeth, the poor, poor thing'een is as beautiful a girl as ever came out of God's creation,' croaked auld Jim, shaking his head in sorrow.

As they were talking, my father came down from Pairc Nuá where he'd been fencing. The two men looked at each other in silence for a moment and as my father went towards him auld Jim rose slowly and my father hugged him as you would a friend and patted him gently on the shoulder, whispering sincerely, 'I'm sorry for your troubles Jim. I'm sorry.'

There was an awkward silence for a moment as Jim shook his head in acknowledgement and my father pulled down a chair and poor Jim sat down, trying desperately to curtail his heartfelt grief.

'I was just asking him… before you came in, did he know how it happened,' whispered Mrs O'Brien sympathetically, trying to lighten the burden as auld Jim sat in a sombre mood looking into the fire. Again nobody said anything as Mrs O'Brien got herself a chair and sat in front of the fire. Finally, auld Jim took a good slug and pulled himself together.

'Blast it if anyone knows rightly. He was tidying up the yard and trying to start a ... Oh God… I can't get that awful word out-a-me-head. They think…,' gasped auld Jim choking back the tears, '… someone must have put petrol in the can. No one knows rightly what happened. The police said Peter might have thought he was using paraffin. The lorry drivers said he was so careful about everything. He'd warn the drivers time and time again not to lie under a lorry in case anything happened. Instead… it happened … to him.'

There was a long strained silence while auld Jim tried to recover.

'I was so proud of him. There were two lads with him when it … But sure they couldn't… do a thing,' said auld Jim, as he threw back his head and fought to control his emotions. And as he did so, Mrs O'Brien took out her handkerchief and dried a tear once more. Jim raised his hand and bottomed the glass with one gulp then wiped his nose on the sleeve of his jacket as Mrs O'Brien signalled for me to go to go outside and play.

This time I did not listen. I went into the garden not knowing what to do. It was the first time I had seen a grown man cry and somehow it didn't seem right. Only girls and babies cried, I thought. And though I was no longer at the window I could hear Mrs O'Brien offering auld Jim another shot of whiskey as I came round by the kitchen window with a bucket of turf. And as I heaped up the turf basket near the back door, she asked my father would he have a drop and he said he would. They were still talking about Peter; how he built himself up, but I wasn't interested anymore. All I could think about was; what it must have been like to die in a fire. I already knew what it was like to touch a live coal. I had seen my father pick up a burning sod, after it fell on the hearth and throw it back on the fire with his bare hand. And I foolishly thought I could do the same when no one was looking. Instead my fingers got burned and broke into big white blisters that were very, very sore.

After that visit, Jim never stood in our house again. But my father would go and visit him every now and again. Sometimes I used to see poor Jim in the town going from one pub to another; bowed and bent as he struggled to see where he was going. Occasionally, after a good drink, he'd stagger home using his bicycle as an aid, with its precious cargo of bread, corn beef and whiskey hanging on the handlebars.

Tommy the postman said his other sons wanted to bring him over to Manchester, to live with them, but he wouldn't go.

'Blast me Tommy, but I wouldn't trade me home for a pot-a-gold. I want to end me days where I've had so many happy memories. Little did I know I was rich when I was poor; with me gang-a-childer' round me...till her herself died... giving birth.'

Hardly a day went by that Tommy didn't call, where he'd have news of one sort or another for Mrs O'Brien: while I'd be out in the fields helping my father. Later, when my lessons were done and before I'd go to bed she'd warm up a saucepan of Goody* for me; sprinkling a good spoon of sugar on it.

Thankfully I didn't have to help my father every evening. Sometimes he'd have to go to a pig or cattle fair, to buy stock for himself or Colleen. I loved that because when he'd come home, he'd bring me sweets and pull a blood soaked brown paper parcel out of his coat pocket which always turned out to be a piece of fresh liver together with a cow's heart. The heart would be kept for the next day's dinner, but the liver would be thrown on the pan to sizzle that evening.

Other times he might be helping Tom Farrell or Colleen and would not come home until very late. When that happened, Mrs O'Brien and I would have to do all the work before I'd begin my lessons. One evening while I was feeding the calves, my father came up and said, 'You'd better go to bed early

---

*   *Goody (boiled milk and bread).*

tonight. I need you to be up early in the morning to help me drive the cattle to the fair in Glan.'

Unable to conceal my excitement I said, 'What time are we going?'

'Well...' he said thoughtfully, as he began to rummage in his pockets for his pipe and tobacco, '...we'd want to be up around half past four anyway, to be on the road by five.'

I couldn't believe my luck. I was going to be off school for the day and wouldn't have to deal with the subject of algebra which I hated with all my heart because I could never understand it. I loved English, History, Geography and Religion, but I hated Algebra. I knew if we managed to sell the cattle I'd get money to buy sweets for having helped bring the cattle to the fair and that was another bonus. I had only ever been to a cattle fair in Williamstown, but that was only down the road compared to Glenamaddy or Ballinlough which were supposed to be miles away. They were the two venues people brought their pigs or cattle to if they could not sell them in Williamstown.

I was fast asleep when my mother called me for my breakfast. I got dressed as quickly as I could as my father was already up. He had his breakfast eaten and was already putting on his hat and coat, making sure to bring his pipe and tobacco with him. When I'd finished eating, I grabbed my coat and went outside with him where the moon shone like a brand new shilling, casting a glow over the entire landscape.

Ned handed me one of two sticks while he held the flash lamp and turned the cattle out of the field behind the hens' cabin and down the road towards the lake. It was very chilly at that hour of the morning but thankfully there was no frost. We were bringing five, two year old, red white-head bullocks to the fair. When we reached the main road, beside the school, we had to turn the cattle up the road towards Glenamaddy. Once they set foot on the main road, the cattle never ever stopped running. We both had to run after them to try and keep up.

Every now and again, my father would tell me to hop in over the ditch and run on ahead so I could stand at the head of the next laneway or by-road to stop the cattle going the wrong way. Despite that, they'd turn into somebody's front garden and I'd have to chase after them and drive them back out again, while my father stood guarding the road. Rounding a bend I thought I recognised Nan Little's, country shop, but I wasn't sure as it wasn't yet daybreak. Nan Little's, was a well known country shop where Mrs O'Brien had brought me on her bike when she was stuck for something which she could not get in the town.

As we drove on, I soon found it was not easy to keep ahead of the cattle. I was gasping for breath as I continued to jump over barbed wire fences and briar ditches that tore my clothes. As well as that, my two feet were soaked because there were holes in my wellingtons that my mother didn't yet know about. I was terrified she'd find out because the wellingtons were supposed to be brand new, though I'd been wearing them for God's knows how long. If she found out there were holes in them she'd blow a gasket entirely and give me a clatter across the lug because the wellingtons were supposed to last me forever. When she finds out, she'll have to bring them down to Johnny Smyth's garage to get them patched or else she'll have to go into Tommy Glynn's to buy me a new pair: and that wasn't good.

We were making great progress until we reached Cloonminda crossroads. There we had to turn right and the minute we did, the cattle started going wild altogether because there were lots of other farmers streaming out of by-roads with cattle bound for the fair. And in an effort to keep the cattle apart, we were forced to stall our cattle on the road for a minute or two to let the others gain access to the main road. But our cattle wouldn't stand still and in their excitement they jumped straight over a barbed wire fence and down into a big field of sugar beet. The field was wet and mucky as I ran frantically after the cattle trying to force them back out onto the road. But the cattle wouldn't go back out for me, no matter what I did. One bullock would go one way and another, the other; so that it took two or three farmers, my father and myself, an age to get the cattle back out on the road. Once we got going again, it seemed much easier as the road was now crammed with mad lowing cattle all going in the same direction. After all I'd been through I was soaked to the skin, my feet were squelching and the holes in my wellingtons were three times bigger than when I'd started out. Despite that, the sweat was pouring off me after all the running.

When we arrived in Glenamaddy, we took up a position outside the Garda barracks which was close to the centre of the town. I had to stand facing the Garda Barracks and mind the cattle. They were hemmed in on either side by other cattle. Some farmers had designated wooden pens outside shops, pubs and hardware stores. But we had no pen and it was my job to mind our cattle while my father laughed and joked with farmers nearby. I was terrified I wouldn't be able to mind them on my own as they began to puck other animals out of the way; threatening to run amok. But a kindly farmer nearby give our cattle several good wallops and they soon stood exactly where they were, with steam rising from their heaving flanks as jobbers went round prodding and goading their hind quarters, with long canes to assess their merits. Everything was grand until one or two tractors and trailers started to inch their way slowly through the town upsetting everybody's cattle including our own. Some farmers began shouting and swearing at the drivers as the tractors forced some cattle to infiltrate other herds.

'Damn and feck you whoever you are. You think you'd get up out of bed in time and not be upsetting everyone: just because you've a little tractor'een under your arse doesn't mean you can drive over us.'

But the drivers didn't respond. They just drove on slowly, smiling and nodding at everyone until someone struck a wallop on the driver's door.

'Slow down, slow down! And watch where you're going... for feck's sake.'

For a second, the driver looked back, as if to say, do that once more and we'll see what'll happen.

Soon calm was restored as my father went walkabout, talking to other farmers to see if cattle prices were better than at the last fair in Williamstown. If prices were up, he'd sell: if not, he'd hold them over until the next fair in Williamstown. I secretly prayed that we'd sell; that I wouldn't have to go through the same torture bringing the cattle home again. Besides, I was perished with the cold, standing minding the cattle after sweating all morning. The sun was very slow to rise and there was nothing to eat: at least until we sold.

Several jobbers came to look at our cattle and to bid for them, but I could see my father wasn't a bit pleased and my heart sank. He point blank refused to put out his hand to accept any offer. Time and time again, I watched helplessly as a particular jobber walked away only to turn round and shout, 'Well! Ned, are you going to sell to me or not? A hundred and fifty pounds, that's my best offer!' When Ned refused to consider the offer, two friends of his whom I didn't know, grabbed his hand and forced him to hold it out like a man so that the jobber could make a bid. 'Damn the two of ye,' said one of the men, 'I never met two more cantankerous hoors in all me life. In the honour of God, let ye divide what's between ye? At the end of the day, what's ten pounds?'

'I'll tell you what it is…,' says the jobber coming back with serious intent. '…its bloody lion feed, when you haven't got it! That's what it is. To me it's the difference between a profit and a loss!'

'Ah damn you to hell…'tis only chicken feed to the likes of you. You'll still make a handsome profit, believe me, when you bring the cattle to the factory,' said Ned's friend.

After much cajoling, the men forced Ned and the cattle jobber to split the difference between them. But Ned had to agree to give the jobber back, ten bob good luck penny. After what seemed an eternity, Ned clinched the deal by holding out his hand while the jobber spat on his own palm and slapped Ned's open palm with a resounding slap, 'One hundred and sixty pounds, with ten bob, luck penny!'

'Done!' replied Ned, returning the slap with a vengeance.

'And I hope they'll be lucky for you.'

I was filled with elation that we'd sold. I would now have the run of the fair, while Ned waited to get paid and had a few pints-a-porter. But when he told me that we still had one bullock left because he wasn't good enough for the factory, I almost cried. The thought that we'd have to bring home the smallest bullock because we couldn't sell him was mind-boggling. I'd have to stand outside the Garda Barracks minding him all day while Ned drove the other four up the street to where they were being loaded onto a lorry at the far end of the town.

It was almost eleven o'clock; the fair was in full swing. And though the sun was out, I thought my two feet would fall off me with the cold. I'd been standing in the same spot for almost four hours. Finally Ned came down the street towards me, smiling.

'Bejeepers John'een… we're in luck. I was talking to a man and he said I could put the bullock into a shed at the back of Dockery's pub, across from us.'

'But won't we have to bring him home?'

'We will, but I know a man who has a tractor and trailer and he said he'd bring the bullock home for me. But you wouldn't know; we might sell him yet.'

It was the most heart warming news I'd heard all morning. And I was in seventh heaven when Ned gave me two shillings and told me to go and get myself something to eat: that he'd take care of the bullock, as I'd done a great job all morning.

'Whatever you do, don't get lost. I have to go into Dockery's pub to get paid so if you're looking for me you'll know where I am,' he said.

I ran straight up the town, bobbing and weaving my way excitedly through the maze of people, jack-shape* stalls and cattle. I bumped into two older lads from school who'd taken the day off to help their father. By now I was ravenous with the hunger so I went into a café where I'd seen people sitting down eating. I stood outside the window looking in for a long time before I got the courage to go in. A waitress showed me a table and I ordered a mug of tea and a sandwich. After a while, another waitress brought me the tea and sandwich. She stood smiling at me for a moment saying I a great fellow altogether. But I felt like running out the door as everyone seemed to be looking at me. I lowered my head and tucked my feet under me so they couldn't see the holes in my wellingtons. When I'd finished I went straight back to Dockery's pub in case my father was waiting for me: but he wasn't. He was standing at the bar with three other men laughing and joking, a pint of black porter in front of him.

'When are we going home?' I asked.

'Ah, you're time enough yet á Mach.** Sure I haven't seen the jobber at all yet.'

'No begob,' says one of the men, 'we haven't seen hair nor hide of him yet.'

'You may as well go off and enjoy yourself,' said my father as he lit his pipe.

'I can't go anywhere until I get paid.'

I ran up the street again, bought myself some sweets and spent the rest of the day going from one end of the town to the other; making sure to stop at every jack-shape stall, street trader, musician and ballad singer.

I watched men and women haggling over the price of boots, hats, overcoats and household goods. But it was Joyce's stall, with its fancy toys that really caught my eye. Later I passed a shop window and saw some lovely buns and scones on display. I decided to go in and buy two scones for my mother as they were only

---

* Jack shape *(clothes stall).*
** *á Mach (son).*

three pence each and I still had some money left over..

As the jack-shape* stalls were packing up, I went into Dockery's pub for the third or fourth time. The place was packed. I hung around waiting for my father to finish his drink so we could go home. But I didn't know if he was ever going to finish as there was nothing but pints of porter all along the counter. The noise seemed to be getting louder and louder as people were laughing and shouting at each other while one man started playing the accordion and another started singing. Suddenly the man who was singing started shouting for order. He banged his glass on the counter a few times and called for order and then he started singing.

There's a hairy ass fair in the county Clare.
In a place they call Spancill hill.
Where my brother James got a rap of a hames.
And poor Paddy they tried to kill.
They loaded him up in an ould ass and cart.
As along the road we passed.
Bad luck to the day I roamed away
to join with the tinker clan.

Chorus)

O'Sullivan John to the road you've gone
Far away from your native home.
You've gone with the tinker's daughter
All along the road to roam
O'Sullivan John you won't stick it long
Till your belly will soon be slack
Up along the ould road with your mighty load
And your tool box on your back.

When he had finished, he picked up an ash plant and suddenly hit a man in front of him a wallop across the shoulder saying,

'Paddy would you ever shut up and listen while a man's singing?'

Paddy said nothing but swung his hand back wildly, hitting the singer on the jaw which sent him flying. There were cheers as the singer fell to the ground. But he soon got up and made a lunge for Paddy. The noise was deafening as the whole pub started shouting and heckling; with people trying to egg them on while others tried to keep the men apart. But in the melee, tables and glasses went crashing to the ground sending little rivers of porter across the floor. By now the entire pub seemed to be heaving, first one way, then the other as the two men threatened to kill each other. I ran towards the door suddenly terrified, as I could see my father in the thick of the action. He was pleading with the singer to calm down, to calm down, not to spoil things;

saying, they all had a good day. After a great deal of pleading during which the men threatened to go to battle once more, the two men were forced to shake hands. Then they all ended up laughing while I felt like crying because I was so so tired, hanging round the front door waiting for my father, to go home.

I went back into the pub for what seemed like the hundredth time and heard a man say to my father,

'Ned, drink up if you want me to bring that bullock home for you. I have a gang-a-children at home, waiting for something to eat.'

'Well, if you have… don't let me stop you.'

The man backed the trailer into a shed at the rear of the pub and let down the ramp. They separated the cattle and loaded the bullock, with the aid of a yard light as it was now dark. My father asked the driver would he mind waiting a minute while he went across the road to the butchers.

Going home I sat on the mudguard of the tractor, while my father stood on the draw bar, leaning in talking to the driver. I began to wish we had a tractor and trailer of our own so we could bring cattle to the fair instead of having to walk them miles and miles. But I knew we'd never ever be able to afford one. Only big farmers could afford a tractor.

When we got home, Mrs O'Brien was waiting at the door with a flash lamp. We unloaded the bullock and turned him into the same field we'd taken him out of that morning. My father shoved a few bob into the driver's fist though he didn't want to take it. I watched the fading lights of the tractor as it disappeared around the first corner, the trailer bouncing and rattling violently on the rough cobble stoned road. As soon as we went into the house, my father pulled a blood soaked brown paper parcel out of his coat pocket and left it on the table. This time, it was fresh liver, with lamb chops. It was then I realised I'd mislaid something. I'd lost the two scones I'd bought for my mother. I couldn't remember what I'd done with them. The last I could remember was having them with me in Dockery's pub before the row started. I recalled running for the door and realised I must have left them after me. Now I'd nothing to give her and felt bad: real bad. I told her what happened and she said, 'Ah what harm a grá. You did your best. But it was nice of you to think of me. Here, sit down a grá and have your dinner. You must be starving with the hunger? Suddenly she turned round to look at me again

'Jesus, Mary and Joseph are them holes I see in your wellingtons?'

I didn't know what to say as she led me towards the light to see if they were real.

'Well Lord God Almighty, but that's the damndest I ever saw! How did you manage to flitter them like that or when did it happen?'

I was terrified I'd be walloped despite the fact that she appeared to be in good humour.

'This morning,' I lied.

'I had to jump into a field after the cattle and they got caught in the wire.'

'Aaaah! You expect me to believe that! How well the lie wouldn't choke you! Well you can make do with them now for the next six months because I'm damned if I'm buying you another pair: and I only after buying them. Do you know something, you'd wear out the cross off an ass.'

After that little salvo, she remained silent while she put the dinners on the table.

I was delighted to see she had bacon and cabbage and potatoes ready for us. She peeled three potatoes for me and gave me a large mug of milk as my father hiccupped and told her how he managed to sell the cattle. She sat by the fire and asked if we had any news after the day; and when my father said he hadn't, she said,

'Well isn't it great. I wasn't outside the door at all and I have more news than either of you. Don't tell me you didn't hear about Dr. Roland?'

'What about him?' asked my father, eagerly.

'Don't say me you didn't hear… and you on the road all day?'

'Hear what?'

'Dr Roland was near kilt this morning on his way home from Galway. He crashed into a wall near Claregalway. Seemingly he went up yesterday to see the wife and children. Tommy the post was telling me. He met Sergeant Boyle on the road somewhere; and he was after telling him.'

'By cripps, that's the first I heard of it.'

'So now where would you be going? I always said drink would be the finish of him.'

'Did Tommy say he was drunk?' asked my father, as he tried balancing a sliver of butter on a potato wedge.

'Drunk? Well look it, I'm surprised at you. When did you ever see Roland sober?' asked Mrs O'Brien annoyed that he should even question her judgement, as she placed another sod of turf on the fire.

'I know… he drinks a lot,' acknowledged my father slowly.

'Crashing the car doesn't mean to say he was drunk. Something else could have happened?'

'Aaaah! Lord God Almighty. It would take someone like you to stand up for him.'

'And what makes you think I'm standing up for him? Just because he takes a drink doesn't mean to say he was drunk when he crashed the car?'

'Ah! I'll say no more. Why do you think the wife left him?'

'Ah…I dunno,' sighed my father wearily. 'From what I hear, he was damn glad to be shut of her.'

When I'd finished my dinner, I sat by the fire to warm myself. But I was no sooner sitting down than my mother said,

'John a grá, I think it's time for you to go to bed. Don't forget you've to be up for school in the morning. Make sure to wash your feet now before you go bed. You've had a long hard day. You must be worn out, after all the travelling?

As I stood outside the back door, peeing, I couldn't help but grieve for the loss of my two fine scones. And though I'd a great day at the fair, not being able to give my mother the two scones ruined everything. There was no knowing if I'd ever be able to buy anything like them again. Now I had nothing to look forward to: except school in the morning. I was tired and wanted to go to bed.

* * * *

I'd finished my homework and was doodling under the table lamp while my mother sat knitting by the fire: finishing off her Aran cardigan. I was trying to trace the shadow of my fingers onto a piece of paper. I was conscious of my mother sighing wearily as she stopped knitting for a moment.

'I dunno in the name of God what's keeping that man.'

I looked quizzically at her as she added, 'You know he should be home by now. It's a long time since ten o'clock this morning. I hope he hasn't met with an accident.' she sighed, more to herself than to me, as she swiftly exchanged the knitting needles from one hand to the other and started knitting again.'

'Where's Daddy?' I asked, not having given the subject of his absence any great thought.

'Ah…If I knew that I'd be… Shush! …Is that a car I hear …?'

She cocked her ear as the faint sound of a motor car could be heard approaching, and I raced out to see the headlights of a car approaching. I stood watching excitedly as my father got out of Harry Ryan's hackney. In the kitchen, I noticed there was a dark stain all around his mouth and his eyes appeared to glisten.

'Hello,' I said cheerfully, but he didn't say anything other than to ruffle my hair.

I stood and watched him as he sighed wearily and took off his hat and coat and hung them up with a great deal of effort.

Finally, after a long pause, my mother said, in a voice that was ice cold 'Well, how is he?

'Ah… the devil-a-loss on him,' he said, as he stumbled down by the fire and sat in his customary chair, his grey hair forming a broad silver bangle around the back of his head.

I could see my mother's dimple quivering as she cast a cold beady eye on him while he looked into the fire and began rummaging in his pocket for his pipe and tobacco.

'And the devil-a-loss on you, by the looks of you: Harry Ryan and yourself must have had a great time … on the beer, no doubt?'

'Well… it would be a devil entirely if I couldn't go as far as Ballinasloe to see Kilby without having a-drop'een-a-porter.'

'Ah! A-drop'een-a-porter-me-arse! On the batter all day, more like! It's a miracle yourself and Ryan made it home at all; that ye didn't end up like Dr Roland. What harm but Harry Ryan is supposed to be a hackney driver. But where did you get the money, that's what I'd like to know?'

My father said nothing as he began lighting his pipe with a bit of paper. And as he sat back savouring the delights of a refreshing smoke, my mother took the argument to him once more.

'I know one thing; you won't go far on the price of half a quarter of tobacco: that's the third half a quarter you've started this week… I'm beginning to think you must have got a better price for them cattle than what you told me.'

My father turned his head, a look of venom in his eyes, as my mother stood up, to put a boiled egg on for him, thereby avoiding his look of distain.

'How do you mean, a better price?'

'Ah! How do you mean, a better price, me arse! You must take me for an awful fool altogether: and I buying you a half a quarter of tobacco every week, out of my hard earned egg money. According to yourself, you never have a penny. Yet when it comes to having a smoke, you always seem to find the price of it, somewhere; thinking I wouldn't notice. But faith I notice. I see everything that goes on in this house.'

'Well, whatever I got for the cattle, you got every last penny of it. But of course it's never enough… and if I got twice as much for them it wouldn't be enough. I'm entitled to nothing, is that it?' asked my father, a glazed look in his eyes as he turned and spat into the fire. A spit that hung momentarily suspended like a spider's web before it broke and hung from his chin like a finely spun silk thread. A quick swipe with the back of his hand and all trace of the revolting phlegm was gone.

'I never said what you gave me wasn't enough. Never! I'd do many a thing but I wouldn't stoop that low. I know that you're entitled to a decent smoke and all that. But when I have to give you the price of the hackney to go to Ballinasloe, I don't expect to see you coming home oiled to the gills,' said my mother in a wicked tone of voice'

'And what was I supposed to do… when Harry Ryan…and Kilby wanted to treat me? Act the altar boy, I suppose?'

'Ah, Altar boy, me-backside!' shouted my mother loudly, as I began to get afraid at the sound of their raised voices. I went and sat on one of the chairs beside my bedroom door, close to tears. I hated to hear them shouting.

'And why would Harry Ryan and Kilby want to treat the likes of you? Two out and out drunkards; who'd…who'd… drink porter out of an auld piss pot if they could get it. And for what, for going up to Ballinasloe to see a man who isn't right in the head, is that it? That hasn't a roof over his head… a penny to his name or a pot to piss in,' she replied with venom.

'Ah Musha God help you. A lot you know about treating people,' sighed Ned, as he spat into the fire again.

'Well Jesus, Mary and Holy St Joseph, may God forgive you: and all I've done for you... going on thirty years,' said my mother as she stood to lift the egg that was bubbling away in the pea tin on the fire.

'Oh dear-o-dear,' sighed my father deeply, as he put the pipe back into his pocket and turned to look at the table, part of which had been set all evening waiting for him to come home. As my mother dropped the egg into the egg cup, he got up from the fire and made his way to the table, while my mother went back to finish off her knitting.

After a prolonged period of strained silence, when only the sound of my mother's knitting needles could be heard clicking, away rhythmically, my father said,

'Well, I'm glad I went up to see him anyway...' And when my mother didn't respond he added after another long pause, '...Kilby asked ... if I'd take care of his funeral.'

'His funeral!' exclaimed my mother as she stopped knitting. 'Well, Jesus, Mary and Joseph! Is that all that's bothering him? And what did you say?'

'What could I say? Except that I would,' answered my father as he tried for the third time to lift a bit of butter out of the butter dish.

'And who's going to pay for it?' asked my mother, a look of horror on her face as the dimple on her chin began to dance once more.

'Ah...what does it matter...who's going to pay for it? Who's going to bury him? That's more to the point. That's all he was worried about.'

'And sure Lord God Almighty the man has nothing?'

'I know... he has nothing. But still...isn't he a neighbour? We can hardly bury him in a pauper's grave.

'I know he's a neighbour...and so was Mary. But I think it's a bit much asking you to take care of his burial; after all we did for Mary.'

As my father wiped his mouth with a tea towel and pushed his chair away from the table, he looked at her quizzically and said. 'what did we do but what anyone would do... clean up the house up a bit?'

'But anyone didn't clean up the house a bit; except muggins here... and Margaret Collins: that's what I'm coming at. It's an awful bloody thing if we have to go buying a coffin and paying for a funeral out of our own hard earned money and we not having two pennies to rub together. It would be alright if he had something belonging to him; an animal or two; but no: he has nothing. Like a lot before him, he drank every thing he ever had, knowing there would always be some fool to take care of his burial.'

'Well... tis agreed now anyway,' sighed my father as he sat down by the fire again and swiped his chin with the sleeve of his jacket before reaching for his pipe once more.

'Harry Ryan said he'd take care of the coffin if I'd take care of the burial. And if we couldn't drink to that, then I don't know why we living at all: especially when Kilby said he'd treat us.'

'You mean to say ye were drinking in the Hospital?'

'Ah... how could we drink in the Hospital? We went across the road,' replied my father as he spat into the fire once more before attempting to light his pipe.

'You mean to say, they let Kilby out of the Hospital... for a drink... and he not supposed to be right in the head; not fit to let outside the front door?'

'Fit or not, he came out with us. But he only had the one. One of the porters came with us and brought him back.

After digesting everything that had been said, my mother flattened out the back of her newly finished cardigan and replied contemptuously, 'Well... yourself and Harry Ryan made up for him anyway'

My father sat back thoughtfully while emitting great blasts of smoke from his crooked stemmed pipe as it rested on his spittle stained chin.

'There wasn't much else we could do...except to stay in the pub. Everything had to be written down. Someone had to take responsibility for him... it seems... in case anything happened him. They had to get someone to sign the papers along with us: a solicitor, a peace commissioner or someone..' After another period of prolonged silence, he added, as he leant forward in a relaxed mode, his elbows on his knees as he spread his hands to absorb of the heat of the glowing fire, 'Sure we might be dead before him. Who knows?'

With a deep sigh of resignation, my mother folded up her knitting and stood up to clear away the dishes..

'John... I think it's time for you to go to bed. Would you like me to warm a drop of milk for you?'

'No thanks,' I said, feeling it wasn't a good time to ask for anything; though I would have given anything for a thick slick of bread with a mug of warm milk. I knew if I got the chance I'd sprinkle two spoons of sugar on the bread just to try it out, as John Keaveney had told me it was the nicest thing he had ever tasted: that he had two slices of bread with sugar on it, every single night before he went to bed.

Reluctantly I slid off my chair and went outside the back door to pee. Bolting the back door after me, I said good night and I went quietly to my room. And as I lay curled up in bed I realised there was much to think about: Kilby who wasn't right in the head and who wanted my father to bury him: the sight of the wild ducks coming down on the lake and the young heifer that was due to calf, soon.

And to crown it all, Christmas was, but around the corner.

Chapter Six

The winter days were so short it was hard to get everything done in our house before nightfall. Monday was wash day. And because it was so cold, Mrs O'Brien would bring the galvanised bath into the house and set it up on two chairs so she could wash the clothes in the kitchen. She'd boil several pots of water and pour them into the bath, put the clothes steeping for a few minutes, get the washboard and start scrubbing them with a thick bar of red carbolic soap. Sometimes she'd leave the dirty clothes steeping: and if they were really dirty – like Ned's shirts and socks – she'd boil them for an hour before scrubbing them and then she'd rinse them all out in a bath of cold water before hanging them on the blackthorn hedge. It was an awful messy job and when everything was washed she'd sweep the suds out the front door and go to the well for more water so she could start cooking the dinner. As soon as dinner was over, she'd turn to me – if I was at home – and say, 'Would you ever run outside and play in the garden, while I try and get forty winks.'

She'd go up to the room and bring down an old plaid shawl, wrap it round herself and settle down in her favourite armchair. After an hour or so, she'd call me in and together we'd have a nice mug of tea and a piece of apple tart or sweet cake. She'd drink her tea out of an old earthenware mug while I'd drink mine out of a tin mug; one that I couldn't break, because according to her, I'd break the cross off an ass.

Tuesday was the day for making the churn. The minute I'd come home from school, she'd have everything ready and waiting. As soon as I'd eaten my dinner, I'd sit down and make the churn for her. When the butter was made and all the implements were washed and scalded, it was time for her to go to the well, again. As soon as I'd get her gone, I'd spread two spoons of sugar on a thick slice of bread and gobble it all up, though I'd be just after having had my dinner. But I had to be very careful because Mrs O'Brien was forever giving out about the amount of sugar we were using.

'I don't know in the name of God how we go through so much sugar. We'll just have to cut down or else start drinking less tea. Before, I used to manage on 2 lbs a week, now I seem to need 3 if not 4lbs. And it's not as if I'm making apple tarts every bloody day.'

By the time she'd come back from the well, I'd have the turf basket in the corner, filled, which made it look good. Then she might say, 'Look, will you run down as far as the town and get me 2 lbs of cooking apples, a packet of bread soda and 2 lbs of sugar in Harry Ryan's. Do you think you'll be able to make your way through the flood with the shopping or will you have to go through the field?'

'I'll be able to go through, with my wellingtons,' I'd say, hoping I wouldn't have to go through the field with the shopping. It was all right going through the field and climbing over the ditch with my school bag over my shoulder, but shopping was different. Besides, the field was very mucky on account of having dug the potatoes.

'Maybe you'd better go across the field all the same…to be on the safe side. I wouldn't like to think you'd get wet. Anyway, it's too dangerous to be going through that flood now that it's rising again.'

As winter progressed, the flood on the road rose higher and higher; driven by a cold north easterly breeze. The rippling waves, carried broken reeds out from the lake and built up a brown bank along the side of the road. And if it wasn't for the ditch holding back the flood our potato field would have been entirely flooded. The ever expanding lake was now home to a multitude of ducks, swans and geese. In the early evening, ducks could be heard going; quack, quack, quack, followed by mellower tones from the evening skies; herr-onk, herr-onk, herr-onk, announcing the arrival of yet more swans. The resident swans would always serenely bow their heads, welcoming them joyously, honk… honk.

On Sunday mornings, my mother wearing a long grey coat and matching headscarf would cross the field down by the lake in her wellingtons, before changing into her bootees. But if it was a High Mass she was going to, she'd wear her black coat, with a mink stole and black hat with a shiny gold hat pin. When she wore her hat and coat I thought she looked very ladylike, a bit like Princess Grace of Monaco, whose picture I'd seen several times in *The Connaught Tribune*.

While she was gone to Mass, I'd help my father to cook the breakfast. Sunday mornings in our house were very special. It was the only morning we ever had a fry. Watching my father preparing the sausages, I soon learned that timing was everything. And because she was always cold after coming in from Mass, my mother would be none too pleased if the breakfast wasn't ready. And being fond of the sausages myself I was eager to help.

'Can we put on the sausages now?' I'd ask, watching the lump of rendering slowly melting in the pan.

'Ah, we best wait a while. We don't want to have them too cooked, otherwise they won't taste nice,' he'd say, peeling the last of the individual wrapping off of the new packet of Donnelly's sausages, carefully laying them out on a plate. When everything was set, he'd stand at the back door of the house looking out across the fields.

'What are you looking at?'

'I'm looking to see to if anyone is going home from Mass. If there is, I'll know Mass is over and we can put down the sausages. Why don't you bring out a chair here and keep an eye out. When you see people passing over the road, you can tell me,'

I remember the first time I stood on the chair looking out across the fields.

'Daddy, there's a man on a bike. He's cycling along the road.... Oh and there another man. And there's two more. Oh, and there's a woman with a red headscarf. She's passing them all out.'

My father laughed as he said, 'You'd better get down and rinse out the teapot... before Mammy comes home, while I cook the sausages.'

Ten minutes later my mother would come in the back door, taking off her headscarf and overcoat, before attempting to warm herself by the fire.

'Jesus, Mary and Holy St Joseph, my feet are perished. In the honour of God have ye the tay wet, until I try and warm meself?'

'The kettle is boiled, I'm making the tea now,' I'd say, as my father poured the boiling water into the teapot for me.

After a while, my mother would come round to the latest topic of conversation,

'Jesus Mary and Joseph, but it's an awful morning out there. I know one thing for sure, if I have to go through that flood another winter, I'll die with the cold. What harm, but I thought Fr Murphy would never stop talking. He went on and on and on.'

My father would listen, taking it all in as he turned the sausages one last time to ensure they were well cooked and served sizzling hot.

'What was he on about, this time?'

'Ah I don't know rightly. I couldn't hear two words he was saying because I stayed at the back of the church so I'd be first out when Mass was over. Nan Little was telling me somebody was supposed to have cut the tail off Brody McHugh's ass: and that the priest put a curse on the one that did it. He said the hand that carried out such cruel act would die and wither before the year was out. So there you are now you have it all.'

'By cripps. It's a wonder he wasn't on about money,' said my father as he divided out the sausages.

'Damn but, I think he mentioned that too at some stage. But like I said, I couldn't hear two words he was saying. Only for Nan Little I'd know nothing.'

'Believe me he did,' sighed my father as he sat down at the head of the table.

While they were talking, I mopped up the gravy with a crust of bread, slowly circling the last of my three sausages round the plate like a dinky car so I could relish the lingering flavour of Donnelly's sausages. They were so tasty

I wanted to preserve the last sausage as long as possible. My father always had the biggest share, five, while my mother had four and I had three.

Only when Colleen or one of the neighbours brought us something special, like a coil of home made black pudding or a fresh piece of liver could we afford a feast like that. Our Sunday morning sausages were far nicer than the boiled egg, which was what my parents had every other day of the week. My father would always give me the top of his duck egg, though I'd have my own mug-a-porridge and a thick cut of bread and jam.

As soon as Sunday morning breakfast was over, my father and I would start getting ready for second Mass. He'd start by shaving himself inside the open back door where he could see himself properly in a hand held mirror. For a long as I could remember, he'd been using a cut throat razor which he used to sharpen every Saturday night by rubbing it on a strop that hung on the side of the dresser. When he could no longer knock a shave out of the cut throat he began to use *Mac's smile* blades. And when they needed sharpening, he'd take an old jam jar out of the press and spent ten minutes sliding the blade over and back inside of the glass, like a pendulum on a grandfather clock. Every couple of minutes he'd turn the blade over and repeat the exercise until he deemed the blade sharp enough to shave.

Having finished shaving himself, he'd get my mother to pin a white shirt collar onto the back of his old striped shirt, with a silver stud. He'd button the front of his freshly starched collar, put on his suit and tie, then his hat and overcoat. But he'd not consider himself fully dressed until he had his gold watch and chain hanging across the front of his waistcoat

While he was getting ready, I too would have washed and changed. Last thing we'd slip our rosary beads into our pockets, put on our dirty wellingtons, stuff our good shoes into a bag so we could change into them the far side of the flood; and off we'd go. But before either of us would be let outside the front door, my mother would insist on brushing down our topcoats, making sure not to leave a speck in sight. Then she'd stand in front of my father; straighten his hat, so that he looked a bit like Humphrey Bogart in the film Casablanca. Then she'd say, 'Off with ye now.'

All day Sunday – particularly in the afternoon – the echoing sounds of gun fire could be heard as fowlers, dogs at their heels, roamed the countryside in search of game. There were lots of ducks on the lake but they were too far out and usually took off as the first shot rang out. Besides, men like Sergeant Boyle, didn't like shooting ducks on the water. It was unsporting he said. A useless exercise as no one had a dog good enough to retrieve a fallen bird.

And as the first shot rang out, I'd race down to the bottom of our garden where I could watch the fowlers in two and threes as they circled the lake. Meanwhile, my father would be keeping an eye on his stock, concerned about the likelihood of the black heifer calving, as he checked her for signs of softening around the hind quarters.

'…I think she'll soon calve,' he said to my mother, as he buttered a slice of bread and cut another chunk of *Calvita* cheese as we sat having our evening tea.

'She seems a lot softer around the hindquarters today. I think I'd better keep an eye on her tonight.'

'You said the same thing about the red cow, if you remember: an' she kept us up every night for a week, before she calved.'

'Well,' sighed my father, as he gave a loud burp, 'it's hard to be right all the time.'

'I don't mind when she calves, so long as she's safe. Anyway, there's plenty of oil in the storm lamp in case we need it. But I hope to God she calves during the day; and that we won't have to be troubling the neighbours, again. I'll keep an eye on her while you're visiting. You can look at her then when you come home.'

'Ah, I mightn't bother going anywhere. I think it's going to come wet,' said my father as he took out his false teeth and cleaned his gums. He put back the teeth and stood up to go and sit by the fire where he was reading *The Adventures of Huckleberry Finn* by Mark Twain. It was the only book in our house. It was the one I had chosen in Williamstown library because my teacher Mrs Patterson had recommended it.

The following morning he was still keeping an eye on the heifer as he drove her into the field beside the hens' cabin along with the other two cows. For two days and nights, he kept checking up on her in case she'd calf unknown to him. The third evening after we'd put her into the stable for the night, I was helping my mother with the dishes when my father came in out of the rain and said,

'She's just after making a water bag.'

'Oh! Thanks be to God! John, will you run up and get the flash lamp that's on the chair above in my room, like a good lad.'

I went out to the stable along with my mother to hold the flash lamp, while my father hung the storm lamp on the back wall of the stable. When I saw the cow lying down I thought she was dying: that there must be something wrong with her because she was bellowing all the time. There was a big thing like a balloon sticking out of her backside. I was very, very frightened and asked my father,

'What's wrong with her?'

'Nothing, except that she's going to calve.'

'And why is there a balloon tied to her tail?'

My mother and father laughed.

'Lord isn't it great to be innocent,' my father said.

'That's not a balloon, that's a water bag. It's full of water and will burst in a few minutes. Then she'll have another water bag after about twenty minutes or maybe half an hour and when that bursts, you'll be able to see two feet sticking out. When that happens I'll want you to hold the flash lamp while we try to pull the calf out.'

Half an hour later when the second water bag had burst, I could see two black hooves sticking out of the cow as she lay bellowing on her side. To me it was a fierce distressing sound as I watched my father take down a coiled rope he had hanging on the back wall. He laid the rope out on the straw and then doubled it over, carefully matching the two ends together. He picked up the doubled end and doubled it over again and slipped the loop he had formed over the black hooves, tightened it. He told me to stand to one side, out of the way; and to shine the light on the heifer. I was really frightened standing there, shining the light. I could no longer see my mother or father, but I could hear them slipping and sliding behind me as they tried to pull the calf; stopping and starting every few minutes. Every time I shone the light on their faces they gave out to me.

'In the honour of God, will you keep that cursed light away from us and shine it on the cow so we can see what we are doing,' said my mother, angrily.

After a while my father rolled up his sleeves as he knelt down to examine the cow.

'She doesn't seem to be giving us much help. Maybe the calf's turned the wrong way. Shine that light here a minute,' he said as he tried to push his hand in beside the hooves.

'It seems to be turned the right way,' he said, as he rose to his feet and waited for the cow to start pushing again. When she did, her efforts were accompanied by long distressing bellows as her head lay flat on the ground and her topmost hind leg began to lift off the ground. After several failed attempts to pull the calf, my father said,

'I'd better get help; that's if there's anyone at home? Somehow or other I don't think we'll manage on our own.'

'Well, you'd better go quick! We'll wait inside till you come back. I don't want to be standing out here in the cold. But I'll keep an eye on her. You won't be long I'm sure. Thanks be to the Great God that you're here, that you didn't go visiting. I don't know what I'd do if I was on my own, especially with it being her first calf. I only hope we don't have to call the vet,' said my mother.

The three of us went back into the house. My father lit his pipe and began to put on his coat, hurriedly. It was starting to rain again. He was in two minds whether to go next door; to see if Margaret's lads were home or to go for John Madden.

Suddenly there was a loud knock on the door. And as father turned up the collar of his coat he opened the door.

'Hello Tom. Come on in. You couldn't have timed it better. I have a cow calving and I was going out to see if I could get someone to give me a hand.'

Tom Farrell came in and my father closed the door after him with a sigh of relief.

'Won't I give you a hand, and two of them if you like,' said Tom humorously, his two hands stuck beneath the tail of his jacket as the corner of his mouth went bop and he expelled a blast of blue smoke from his spittle stained pipe which was identical to my father's.

'Well the blessin' of God on you,' said my mother as she began to wrap the headscarf around her head again.

'I could tell by the lowing, there was a cow in trouble somewhere. I could hear her as I was going over the road,' sniffed Tom knowingly, as he removed his pipe and tilted his head back emitting a powerful blast of smoke in the general direction of the ceiling.

'Well, are we glad to see you? It's a wonder you're out at all and the night that's in it?' said my mother.

'I was going to go rambling for an hour or two,' sniffed Tom. 'I thought to meself, wasn't I as well to go rambling as to be sitting at home on me own. But I had to stand under a bush to let that last shower pass when I thought I heard one of yer cows lowing. Says I to meself, that sounds like a baste in trouble. I was thinking it might be yours, but I wasn't sure. That's why I came round,' sniffed Tom again, as he stuck his pipe into the top pocket of his well worn jacket and asked, 'Have ye a flash lamp?'

Tom had the look of a seasoned farmer about him. He wore a pair of heavy hob nail boots, a pair of brown corduroy trousers, and a well worn jacket over a frayed plaid shirt that highlighted his barrel shaped chest. On his turnip shaped head, he'd an old peaked cap that seemed way too small for him. It was tilted down over his right eye and moulded to the shape of his head by the wear of all its years.. When he spoke, it was as if the words came through his nose with a snort. Yet I was keen to listen, because his carefully chosen words seemed to convey both knowledge and wisdom. His face had a jovial appearance, which added greatly to his heart warming sense of humour.

'I have. Can't John here hold it for us… because I'm thinking… it'll take the three of us all our time to pull the calf, because the heifer doesn't want to help,' said my father.'

'Troth then, if she doesn't help, there'll be no calf,' sniffed Tom. 'Maybe she's not ready. If she's not ready you're wasting your time. And haven't we this fella here,' smirked Tom, with a nod and a wink in my direction as he reached out and ruffled my hair, 'doesn't that make four of us?'

'Faith then it does,' acknowledged my father wistfully, as he headed for the back door.

'Can I wash me hands here?' asked Tom as he reached for the carbolic soap sitting on the back kitchen window.

'You can then,' said Mrs O'Brien handing him a towel,

'Sometimes they calf quicker if they're left alone for a while,' said Tom as we went out to the stable again. The heifer was still lying down, bellowing every now and again. Straight away Tom took off his jacket and rolled up his sleeves to examine her.

'Is this the heifer you were telling me about?' he asked, as he pushed his hand gently in beside the two hooves that were still sticking out of the uterus the same as they were earlier.

'It is. She's very small. I wouldn't have brought her to the bull at all, but one of Snowy's bullocks broke into the field: that's how she came to be in-calf.'

After checking the position of the calf, Tom said, 'She might be alright, you'd never know. We'll just have to give her time. It might be a bull calf. And if it is, it will be harder on her. Bulls can be a hell of a lot bigger; and harder again to pull, for a first time heifer. We'll wait a while and see what happens. We won't try anything until we see how she's getting on. When she starts pushing in earnest, then we'll start pulling.'

For a long time, the three of them stood talking because nothing seemed to be happening. Suddenly the cow started bellowing louder and louder as she struggled on the ground and began to calf in earnest. The three of them grabbed the rope, while I shone the lamp. They started pulling as hard as they could. But it seemed as if the calf hadn't moved an inch. Then as they began to pull a second or third time, the two feet began to get a bit longer but that was all. After a few minutes Tom said,

'We better take it easy. There's no sense in killing her. We're doing all right. We're making progress. Besides, it'll give her a chance to rest herself. When she's ready, she'll start pushing again and we'll start pulling.'

At that stage, it seemed to me as if the cow was ready to burst. Her belly was swollen and looked like a giant hairy mound. Her topmost hind leg was sticking up in the air, as if suspended by an invisible cord.

At that point, the cow gave a long distressing moan. Again she tried desperately to calf as the men began pulling for all they were worth almost knocked my mother in the process as they slipped and slithered on the muck and urine hidden beneath the bedding. Struggling to gain a foothold, they lurched this way and that; swaying with the rope as they pulled with all their might. Miraculously the calf's head began to appear as Tom's cap fell off and he gasped hoarsely, 'we're winning; we're winning: keep pulling, keep pulling let ye.' By now my mother had regained her balance and was pulling manfully with them.

I shivered nervously amid all the excitement as the shoulders of the calf began to appear and the cow's backside seemed to expand beyond all imagining when suddenly the great burden of stress seemed to abate and the rest of the calf slid out of the cow on a tidal wave of slimy liquid followed by a mixture of blood and water. When the new born calf slid out, it had a slimy veil covering its body. Tom Farrell moved quickly and removed the slime from around the calf's nose and slipped his finger into the side of its mouth to make sure the airways were clear and that the calf could begin to breathe of its own accord. He grabbed a fistful of clean hay and began rubbing its coat vigorously, whilst my father began removing the rope from around the calf's hooves. When my mother saw the calf lying on the straw, she said joyously and with great pride,

'Well the Blessing of God on ye men. I don't know where on God's earth we'd be without ye? Lord, but it's a fine calf, I wonder what is it?'

Tom quickly and expertly turned the calf around so that it now faced its mother and for the first time the cow lifted her head in recognition that she had finally given birth. She gave a soft instinctive low to let the new born calf know she was there, as my father lifted the calf's tail to see what it was.

'Ah, I was thinking. It's a bull all right. Only for you, Tom, I'm thinking we'd be in trouble. You can't bate someone who knows what they're doing. Thanks be to God, you came at the right time. I doubt if she'd have calved on her own.'

'Troth then, she would.' sniffed Tom, as my mother handed him his cap which he slapped down on his bald head, adding, 'She'd have calved alright... but 'tis a dead calf she'd have. It would have taken that lady all night and maybe half the morning to calf on her own. That calf would have smothered if it was left in her too long.'

Seeing the new born calf beside her, the cow stood up and strained her neck on the chain to try and reach it. The two men pushed the calf a little closer so that she could nurse him. Straight away, she began licking and cleaning the calf over and over and over again until its dark coat was gleaming. Running her long tongue ever upwards she soon had the calf eager to stand up. After several failed attempts, the calf finally made it up on to its long wobbly legs. For a moment it looked as if it was going to fall down again, but then it steadied itself and established a firm foot hold by splaying its long legs, before tottering nervously, instinctively towards the udder, as its mother gave a soft low of encouragement. Finally the calf stuck its white star forehead beneath the cow's swollen udder seeking one of her teats. And as the four of us stood looking on proudly, I almost cried with happiness. It was hard to believe such a miracle had taken place, right before my eyes. Looking out through the stable door I caught a glimpse of the new moon. Somehow it reminded me of the scene at the stable in Bethlehem, where Jesus was born; where the three wise men had come to the stable bearing gifts. It was part of what I was learning in school, which now made the whole subject of baby Jesus easier to understand.

When my father was satisfied everything was fine, he threw an extra bit of hay to the cow, closed the stable door and we all went back into the house to wash ourselves. My mother made sure Tom was first by handing him a towel while she went to put the kettle on. When we'd all finished washing our hands, we sat round the fire and she brought two glasses and two bottles of stout down from the room and left them on the table. She uncorked the bottles before giving them to the men.

'You wouldn't want to let Fr Murphy see you with them bottles,' sniffed Tom with a twinkle in his eye.

'What makes you say that?' asked my mother.

'Did you not hear the rumpus he caused last Friday… with Mrs Maguire, from Kilbeg…?'

'Arrah blast it; sure we hear nothing. Don't tell me there's more, after what he said at Mass on Sunday.'

'Troth then there is,' sniggered Tom, derisively. 'Sure he puts a curse on someone every day of the week.'

'Well I don't know how it is, but we never seem to hear a thing from one end of the week to the other. Though I was at first Mass on Sunday, I wasn't talking to a sinner, except Nan Little: and she never said anything about it. She told me about McHugh's ass alright, but that was all,' said my mother as she made a small pot tea for the two of us and began cutting and buttering a few slices of currant bread.

'Sure 'tis the talk of the Parish…,' sniffed Tom, with delight, as his great hairy chest heaved with the humour of it all: the bottle suspended at an acute angle as he was about to pour it into his glass. '…I don't think I ever laughed as much in all me life,' he heaved, joyously.

'Musha, tell us what happened?' pleaded my mother seriously; facing Tom, her hands on her hips.

'Ah 'twas what… last Friday… Mrs Maguire came into the town to do her shopping, like she always does. You know she cycles in every Friday morning around ten o'clock to collects the pension for herself and Jim. I do see her passing every week. If you'd a clock, you could set it with her. She always goes into Cunneely's of a Friday. Anyway it seems they were getting ready for the thresher on Saturday morning. Seemingly Jim told her to bring home four bottles of stout. And between itself and the shopping she was loaded down to the hilt: with bags hanging either side of the handlebars. And it wouldn't be the first time she had them. Anyway she was walking up the hill opposite the doctor's house and who did she meet, but Fr, Murphy,' tittered Tom.

'Jesus, Mary and Holy St Joseph,' gasped my mother in glorious anticipation, as she sat down for a minute, lest she miss anything.

'Hello Kathleen. You've been shopping I see. What have you in the bags?' sniffed Tom humorously, impersonating the priest. 'Kathleen…! I'm surprised at you… you of all people, meddling with the devil's brew. Has the devil been prompting you; has he?' asked the priest; looking at the bottles. 'Kathleen, how many times do I have to tell the people that drink is the curse of all evil and the ruination of family homes every where. I forbid you to bring those bottles home. So I'll relieve you of your burden and put you out of your misery. What in God's name were you thinking, Kathleen... and you supposed to be a good Catholic?' With that didn't he take the four bottles and smash them on the side of the road, leaving Kathleen there, shaking like a leaf.'

'Oh... he never did?'

'That I may drop dead this minute,' said Tom, his two eyes bulging in his head.

'And did she not say anything to him?' asked my mother. 'If it was me, I think I'd kill 'im.'

'But don't you know Kathleen? Sure she wouldn't say boo to a goose?'

'Well, Lord God Almighty, but that was awful. She must have been mortified?'

My father was smiling to himself as he threw the piece of paper he was after lighting his pipe with, into the fire, 'Ah, I wouldn't wonder at anything that man would do.'

'Ah well Jesus, Mary and Joseph that bates everything. That bates all ever I heard,' said my mother, as she handed Tom a plate with three thick slices of currant bread slathered with butter.

'Would you like mug of tea to go with it?'

'No Mam,' sniffed Tom, humorously, holding up the glass and reaching for a slice of the currant bread, 'I'll stick with the devil's brew. Sure you heard nothing at all yet,' snorted Tom, cheerfully, as he devoured half a slice in one mouthful.

'I wonder what did the bould Jim say or did she tell him? He wouldn't take too kindly to that, I'm thinking?' said my father putting the glass of stout to his head.

'Troth then he didn't take too kindly to it. He did what any right man would do. He went into the garden and cut a good decent ash plant and came up to the town. He went into Cunneely's pub and ordered four bottles-a-stout. Then he cycled across the square and up to the priest's house and left the four bottles down on the gravel in front of the house and knocked on the door...' chuckled Tom, taking great satisfaction in prolonging the story as he devoured another slice of currant bread and washed it down with a good slug of porter. '...He knocked on the door again and again: but of course there was no answer. Jim got fierce annoyed when he thought there was no one home, so he started kicking the door; creating a hullabaloo. And the next bloody next thing, didn't the priest open one of the windows upstairs and stick out his head. He said, "what's goin' on down there? What's goin' on?" He hadn't seen Jim because he'd gone around the back of the house to see if anyone was home. The next thing Jim appeared. "I'll tell you what's goin' on. The devil himself is goin' round this parish disguised as a priest. He broke four bottles-a-stout today belonging to my wife. I ordered those bottles and I'm ordering you now – the self same devil himself – to come down here and break them in front of me. I dare you to come down. Come on! Come on down! And we'll see if you're half the man you were earlier. Come on! I dare you! See if the cloth will save you?" But faith he didn't come down; even though Jim kicked the door again and again,' smirked Tom, as he left the empty bottle on the floor beside him and took the pipe out of his pocket.

'He knew a hell of a lot more than to come down. Jim would kill him you know. He'd warp that ash plant across his back if he got half-a-chance. He has a fierce temper you know!' smiled Tom as he tried to clear the stem of his pipe by blowing in to it. When that didn't work, he plucked a feather out of the goose quill that was thrown on the hob and cleared it. He put the pipe back together, struck a match and began smoking again.

'If he has a temper itself, he did the right thing. That was an awful thing to do; and she after paying for the bottles and everything,' said my mother as she pulled down a chair and took up her knitting where she'd left off the night before. I sat at the table drawing, trying not to miss a single word.

'Lord weren't we blest when we had Fr Geraghty: and we didn't know it. We thought he was too quiet. But with this fella…there's no knowing what he'll say or do,' added my mother, her needles picking up speed as they began clicking away rhythmically.

'Aaaah! He won't be here much longer. He'll be moved! Wait'll the bishop gets wind of it,' snorted Tom, with indignation.

'Well the-devil-a-move. For all you know the bishop could be just as bad,' suggested my father.

'Sure they're only a crowd of tricksters, the same as they ever were. I dunno do you remember Fr Madden or not… he was the parish priest here around…ah it must be near forty years ago.'

'Ah no. That was long before my time,' replied my mother.

'Ah sure he was a holy terror entirely. Shortly before he was transferred out of this parish, he'd arranged for Louis McGuire and meself to be sent to the reformatory school in Letterfrack. He reckoned we were the biggest trouble makers in the parish. He'd a horse and carriage arranged to bring us away on the Saturday evening. There was supposed to have been three from Ballymoe and two from Cloonfad going with us,' smirked Tom humorously.

'Something must have happened because he was transferred out of the parish on the Friday morning and there wasn't another word about it.'

'By cripps! I'm surprised at you Tom; I didn't know you were a trouble maker,' replied my father jokingly.

'And neither did I,' snorted Tom, wittingly. 'What harm but I used to hear our John saying, he came home from England one time and a few of them cycled into Castlerea of a Christmas Eve to get confessions; and to do a bit-a-shopping. And between one thing and another they ended up on the beer: they didn't go to confessions at all. By the time the four of them got back to Williamstown, 'twas too late. What did they do then but go up and knock on the curate's door and it nearly twelve o'clock at night. Fr Flanagan was the curate at the time; he was gettin' ready for midnight Mass. He said "what's troubling ye?"

"Is there any chance you could hear our confessions", they said. And what did he do, but say, "kneel down there let yez, and I'll give ye absolution: yer intentions are honourable." The four boys knelt down in the street and he raised a hand over them in blessing and there wasn't another word about it. Which goes to show, if the man with the white collar is with you, you have nothing to fear…but if he's against you, you'd better watch out,' chuckled Tom, as he put his pipe away and shoved the cap to the back of his head.

Looking at me, my mother said,

'Listen here; have you your lessons done or what are you at?'

'I've just finished.'

'Well about time! I don't want you coming home here tomorrow telling me that you forgot your lessons… or that you hadn't time to do them.'

'At the rate you're growing, the teacher will soon be afraid of you,' said Tom as I stood up from the table.

Turning to Tom, my mother said proudly, 'Oh he's fairly growing alright! It's no bother to him now to run as far as the town for a few messages. What's more, he'd be back while I'd be thinking about it. He comes with me every Friday and helps me to carry the eggs down to Ryan's.. I don't know where we'd be without him. And of course he's expecting Santa. But whether he'll come to this house or not is another thing. He's a bit big for Santa, but we'll see.'

'Ah, Santa doesn't care how big you are. It's how good you are: that's what he's interested in,' said Tom much to my relief as I slowly put my things into my school bag lest I miss anything.

'The devil-a-one of you will feel until he's able to do everything round the place. Then ye can go off to Galway on yer holidays and he'll mind the house for ye.'

'Ah! Galway how are you! I'm here now going on thirty years and I've never even had a day off: never mind a holiday,' said my mother, moving uncomfortably at the mere thought that she could afford such a luxury. Having come to the end of a knitting row, she swiftly changed the needles round. Her chin began to move erratically as she sat in silent contemplation, while my father grunted wearily to show he was not impressed by the remark.

'Troth then…Galway isn't all it's cracked up to be, I'll bet,' he said, after a slight hesitation, having removed the spittle stained pipe from his mouth to spit into the fire where the offending phlegm sizzled.

'Whether it is or not, I never got the chance to find out,' retorted my mother, sharply. 'But I know one thing for sure and certain, if I had me life over again I choose a different road. What gets me is; it's the same old thing day in day out, three hundred and sixty five days a year.'

Tom sighed deeply in the corner, pulled the cap down in to its customary position and said, 'I think now; I'd best be off: or me own fire 'ill be gone out. I'll see ye again with the help of God.'

'And what hurry is on you?' asked my father, well aware that Tom was leaving early because my mother was in one of her moods.

When he saw Tom getting up, he too rose solemnly.

'Well, thanks for your help anyway. You know you couldn't have come at a better time.'

'Well the blessing of God on you for calling. You were a great help,' reiterated my mother.

'Sure 'twas no bother. I'd only be sittin' at home… or beyond in John Tarmey's, talking auld rubbish.'

'Well! I dunno about that!' replied my father..

I followed the two of them out to the street while my mother began tidying up the house.

'It looks like we'll have more rain,' said my father looking up at the dark cloud that threatened to glide across the face of the moon as stars twinkled in another wise clear blue sky.

'Troth then we will and plenty. And we'll be lucky if we don't get a bit of Jack Frost before morning. I'd best step it out before that shower comes,' said Tom studying the massive cloud sweeping in from the east.'

'Ah please God you'll be at home before it comes. Good night Tom.'

'Good night,' said Tom, tilting his head slightly against the strengthening breeze. He set off walking down the dark road, with its tall ghost like trees creaking on the naked hedgerows. For a moment my father and I stood watching him: his two hands tucked beneath the tail of his jacket as he began to plod his way home.

'Where does he live,' I asked.

'He lives the other side of the town. Do you know where the doctor's house is?'

'Is that the big house up on the hill?

'It is. Tom lives in that little house on the right before you go up the hill.'

As we went back into the house my mother said,

'John! Don't you think it's time for bed? It's very late for you to be up. If I'd known it was that time you wouldn't have been let stay up, I'm telling you that.'

I went straight to bed so as not to annoy my mother and I began to dream of our new baby calf, Santa Claus and the wonderful things I might get for Christmas.

Chapter Seven

Christmas Eve 1954

It was the eve of the great feast. A heavy white frost lay on the ground as the dense fog slowly lifted: to be replaced by thin wisps of blue smoke from the village chimneys as they crept slowly skywards where a plane crossed the broad expanse of the universe, glinting like a jewel in the early morning sun. The village street was a frozen quagmire of muck and sludge. But now it was beginning to melt beneath the warming sun. Yet there was an icy chill as the white frosted ice puddles on the potholed road, creaked, cracked and crunched under the weight of animal hooves as farmers everywhere went about their chores; herding cattle to and fro before making one last trip to the town for the festive season.

From early morning, everything that happened in our house was geared towards making it an enjoyable Christmas. Early in November, my mother had made the first of four Christmas cakes: a porter, a Dundee, an Irish whiskey and a rich fruit cake to carry us over the festive season. She wanted to make them early, so that the cakes would have plenty of time to mature, she said. As well as making four cakes for ourselves, she made two extra porter cakes, one for Colleen and one for the new priest's housekeeper, Nora Keeffe, whom she gave a can of butter milk to, every week.

By now the bottom half of the dresser was full with Christmas shopping. There were tins of peaches, strawberries, pears and mixed fruit. There were small tins of prunes, pots of blackcurrant jam and marmalade as well as tins of treacle and syrup. There were numerous packets of *Bird's Instant Whip, Bird's Custard* and *Bird's Jelly De Luxe*. And as a special treat for Christmas, there was a large bottle of Irel coffee and two tins of Jacob's biscuits. There were several 2lb packs of tea and sugar as well as two Swiss rolls in readiness for any unexpected visitors. And above in the bedroom under the bed, were two cases of stout, two bottles of whiskey, a bottle of port, a bottle of sherry and half a dozen Babychams. The decorative china that had sat gathering dust on the dresser most of the year had been taken down and washed along with the three Willow plates.

As my father was due to go working for the Board of Works after Christmas

– drawing cart loads of stone for the new road – he tackled up the horse and cart and went down to the potato field, opposite the lake, for a load of potatoes. He also had to pull enough carrots, parsnips and turnips for Christmas and the New Year. He was going to bring home enough potatoes and vegetables to last a few weeks, he said. He didn't want to have to be opening up the potato pit again, especially if he was going to be busy with the horse and cart. He had to clean out the stables; and put fresh bedding under the cattle while I had to clean out from under the hens, ducks and geese. My mother asked my father if he'd go to the town for a bag of pig meal. There was enough pig meal to last a week or two, but she'd feel a lot happier if we had another bag as he wouldn't have time to do it once he started working on the road, she said.

Earlier in the morning, she had made a bowl of sherry trifle which I had helped to stir, with a long spoon. Occasionally, I dipped my finger in to taste the mouth watering syrup, when she wasn't looking. After that she set about making bread and onion stuffing for the turkey. The turkey had been killed and plucked and left to hang on a nail in the back kitchen for seven days. When she had the turkey cleaned and ready she preserved the giblets in two vinegar jars which she then left up on a shelf in the back kitchen.

'We'll be damn glad to eat them in middle of January,' she said.

I felt I was lucky as I'd been given easy jobs to do around the house: jobs like, washing up, sweeping the floor, dusting the chairs and mixing the sherry trifle. After that I helped her grate the bread crusts she'd been saving up all week. But I had to peel and cut two big onions which stung my eyes and made them water.

'Arrah, what's wrong with you? Why are you crying?' she asked. She was laughing at me and I didn't like that at all.

'I'm not crying! It's the onions! They're stinging my eyes.'

'Look! I'll finish them myself if you're going to puss about it. Go out and fill four bags of dry turf for me. And make sure it's dry whatever you do. Daddy will carry them in for me later. And then you might wash your face and tidy yourself up a bit and comb that rotten head of yours and run up as far as Colleen's. She said if I sent you up she'd try and do something with your hair. Find out if she needs anything for tomorrow, a saucepan or anything and ask her if she knows what time Snowy's coming home.'

I was excited at the thought of going up to Colleen's, it being Christmas Eve. But I wasn't too happy at the thoughts of having to race past Mickey Billy's geese and Colleen's cattle. The problem with running up across the boggy fields to Colleen's house was her cattle. I was not afraid of our cattle at all, they were very quiet, but Colleen's were wild. As soon as ever they'd see me, they'd come running after me. Very often I had to sneak along by the ditch because I knew that if they spotted me they'd come running like mad and I'd have to climb up on the ditch and walk along the top despite the presence of barbed wire, furze, and thorn bushes. I could not go into the adjoining field because Margaret Collins had a big black bull that was always looking at me. Sometimes he'd start walking towards me, and I'd have to run like hell in case he came after me.

I filled the four turf bags as fast as I could and I sprinted up past Mickey Billy's geese, past the well and then I climbed in over the ditch and ran up the length of the first field towards the boggy field where Colleen's cattle were all lying down. I crouched along by the ditch so they wouldn't see me, and then I ran the last hundred yards into the next field and safety before the cattle saw me.

Like my mother, Colleen too was busy, getting ready for Christmas. She had a lovely slated roof on her house and a brand new bathroom. As soon as I set foot inside the back door, she cut a few slices of bread and jam and gave them to Una, Sadie, Kevin and myself. She told us all to get out of her sight, while she stuffed the goose.

'I'll call you in John, when I'm ready to cut your hair.'

I was delighted. I was anxious to talk to Una and Sadie to find out what they were expecting, from Santa. It was only when I started talking to them that I realised how stupid I was. They were expecting to get presents that I had no earthly interest in. Dolls and dolls' houses and combs and hair slides; whereas I was expecting to get a motor car or a football.

After a while Colleen called me in and told me to sit down with my back to the fire. She began cutting my hair with a hair machine. It felt horrible as Colleen tried to run the machine up the back of my head but it kept getting stuck in my hair and pinching me.

'Well blast this machine anyway; it's pure useless. Maybe it needs oiling. I'm sorry John… I'm not used to this. If Máirtín was here, he'd know how to work it,' said Colleen, blowing into the hair machine, trying to unclog it. To take my mind off the ordeal, I said,

'Mammy told me to ask, what time's Máirtín coming home; and if you need any saucepans for tomorrow.'

'Huh! That'll be the day that I'll know what time that fella's coming. He could walk in that door any minute a grá. Then again he mightn't come until tomorrow It all depends on the sailings. And knowing him he'll leave everything until the last minute. You can tell Mammy I'm alright. I think I have everything. If I need anything, can't I run down in the morning?'

While I was getting my hair cut, Una and Sadie stood watching. And I was really embarrassed when Una told her mother how I wrote to Santa asking for a motor car, a pair of football boots and a packet of sweets. I'd only said that to them to make it sound good: now I was horrified they were telling their mother.

'Is that true?' asked Colleen.

'Yes,' I croaked, barely able to open my mouth.

'That's an awful lot to expect off the poor man. And what will happen if you get nothing?'

I was almost stuck to the chair. I hadn't thought of that,

'Well… what are you going to do?' reiterated Colleen, as she stood agog in front of me, looking me straight in the eye, the machine in her hand.

'I don't know,' I mumbled.

'Huh! There you are now…and you thought you were ready for Christmas. I've told my two ladies that if they ask Santa for too much, they'll get nothing at all. Santa doesn't like children that ask for too much. I think meself, you're better off not asking for anything. Then if you get something, it'll be a surprise? Well… wouldn't it?' she said, looking at me again.

Somehow I hadn't thought of that either and I felt bad for having told such blatant lies to the girls. All I could do was sit there in silence as it suddenly dawned on me that I might get nothing. I was being too greedy; expecting a motor car and a pair of football boots. When I didn't respond, Colleen sighed deeply, and said, 'Well I dunno what to say to you. Tell me, what were you really expecting?' as she again tried cutting my hair.

'A motor car,' I said, careful not to mention any word of the football boots or the jersey or the sweets that I was expecting. Again I winced as the hair machine got stuck behind my ear and pinched me for the third or forth time.

'Oh sorry! Sorry! I think this auld machine is bunched. One minute it's grand and the next… it's…'

'Ow,' I cried aloud, as the machine brought a tear to my eye.

'Ah, I'll finish it with the scissors. And even that isn't great. I could cut off your ear and you'd end up like that fella…what's his name… the painter. Anyway, it's near done now. I wouldn't have tried cutting it at all, if I knew the machine was that bad. But Mammy said your hair was getting too long; that you might turn into a girl if we didn't cut it. If she doesn't like it, you can come up again when Máirtín comes home and he'll finish it off.'

When I got home, my mother took one look at my new haircut and said, 'Well, God Almighty, but you look like something the cat dragged in. Is that the best she could do?'

'She had to stop the machine because it was pinching me.'

'Aaaah! And why did she start cuttin' it, if she couldn't finish the bloody thing? Sure 'tis only a kiss me arse job. When's Snowy – I mean Máirtín – coming home; or do you know?'

'Colleen said he could come any time, today or tomorrow.'

'And sure that's no answer. I could have guessed that meself. If he comes home today and it's not too late, I'll have to get him to cut your hair, again. You can't go to Mass on Christmas day, looking like that.'

My father arrived home from the town with the pig meal and began bringing in the turf that I'd filled earlier. He left the four bags inside the back door and went out to give some oats to the horse. We brought the three cows in early but only two of them needed milking, the other one was in-calf. I stood and watched as my father put the chain around each of their necks in the stalls before he started feeding them. When I saw my father giving the cows and calves extra hay along with a few heads of cabbage, I asked,

'Why are you giving cabbage to the cows?'

'And why not, isn't it Christmas? Wouldn't you like them to have plenty to eat, the same as us?'

I nodded in agreement. And as my father stopped to light his pipe, he added. 'Anyway, they haven't much milk this time of the year and if I don't feed them well they'll have nothing at all. And if it wasn't for the cows we wouldn't have any milk, or butter or bread or money to buy anything in the town. It's the same with the calves. If I don't feed them well, I can't expect to get a good price when I sell them?'

When he'd finished milking the cows, I helped him to carry the four small buckets to feed the suck calves which were in two small pens at the back of the stable. I helped him feed the pigs while my mother ironed our shirts and polished our shoes and boiled the Christmas pudding and got all the vegetables and potatoes ready for Christmas day.

'I don't want to have to do a tap tomorrow,' she said, as she put the vegetables into one of the small skillets and left them steeping overnight.'

It was pitch dark outside and almost six o'clock in the evening. My mother was setting the table for our tea. She spread a white cloth on the table and brought down the good table lamp that she always kept on the mantle piece above in her room. It had a beautiful decorative brass base supporting its tall brass tower and around its waist was a large circular ceramic bowl. The bowl itself was green with heavily embossed roses all the way round it. On the side of the bowl was a silver screw-on lid where you poured in the paraffin. On top of the bowl were two wick holders that had two circular adjusters on the side so that you could turn the wicks up or down when you wanted to adjust the flame. And over the double wick holder was a tall glass funnel about sixteen inches high and over that again was a crystal shade etched with intertwining vines and leaves. As she prepared to get everything ready for our Christmas feast, she took off the shade and the glass funnel, turned up the wicks and lit the lamp with the box of matches she always kept on the front window. A gold flame shot up straight away and a thin plume of black smoke started billowing towards the ceiling. She had to turn the wick down quickly to stop the smoke before she slotted the glass funnel and shade back on. Then she set the table with the best china in the house. She brought down the silver cutlery that was locked away in a special case on top of the wardrobe in her room. She polished all the spoons, knives and forks before she laid them on the table. Soon there were slices of cold ham and tomatoes on the table as well as brown bread, Christmas cake, sherry trifle, and peaches. When everything was set, she lit three white candles and placed them on the three front windows of the house as a sign there was room for a visitor at the inn: the same as when the three wise men came to the stable in Bethlehem where Jesus was born.

'I think now it's time to turn up the lamp,' she said, and when she did the house looked like magic as the twin flames in the lamp began to flicker casting beautiful shadows on the walls and ceiling. My mother and father and I looked like giants as we went around the kitchen and I gave a saucer of milk to the cat outside the back door. The shadow of my head stretched half way across the ceiling. Even when I sat on the three legged stool between the two armchairs either side of the fire my head was still half way up the chimney breast. By now every door in the house was closed to keep in the heat. My mother was rinsing out the teapot and getting ready to wet the tea when there was a gentle knock on the door. Before any of us had time to react, Tommy the postman lifted the latch and looked in before opening the bottom half of the door.

'God save all here and a happy Christmas to ye,'

He had a big black cape over his shoulders. It was dripping wet as he reached under it to uncover his mailbag.

'Musha Tommy a grá, are you still on the road? I thought when it was so late you hadn't anything for us. You must be perished with the cold after that awful shower? Will you have a cup of tea?'

'Begod Mam, I won't, not this evening,' replied Tommy as he threw two letters on the corner of the table. 'Herself and the children will be waiting for me. It's gone very cold. I'm thinking we'll have snow; so I won't be delaying.'

'If we do itself, it would be better than that bloody rain,' said my father.

'Well God knows it would. Anything's better than that bloody rain as you say,' said Tommy trying to swing the bag round, beneath his cape. Then looking at me in earnest, he added. 'Santa is supposed to be coming to my house tonight… but I don't know if he'll come or not because our chimney was never cleaned. Mongan, the chimney sweep was supposed to come last week; but of course he never came.'

Looking seriously at me, my father said, 'Did you hear that, John'een. It's a bloody good job we got ours cleaned. But whether he comes or not is another thing.'

'Ah Please God he'll come, he'll come,' said Tommy as he adjusted his cape and turned for the door.

'Wait a minute,' said my mother as she reached across the table to the window sill, where she had two packets of cigarettes ready and waiting. 'Here you are now. Have a decent smoke for the Christmas. I'd offer you a drop of whiskey but I know you don't touch it. So I'm afraid, a few cigarettes is all I can offer you.'

With a look of appreciation, Tommy said,

'Mrs O'Brien, there was no need for that. Look at the way you've treated me all year, with tea and cakes and the devil knows what. Sure I must be costing ye a fortune. On me solemn oath, it's what I should be treating ye! I have ye robbed, drinking and eating, night noon and morning?'

'Ah stop your nonsense, will you, and all the news you bring from England and America,' said my mother.

'Ah...at the end of the day, what is it, but a drop'een-a-tay: and you having to cycle round the country in all kinds of weather,' added my father standing, waiting to escort Tommy out.

'Well the blessing of God on ye. I hope ye'll never be short and that ye'll all be still alive, this time next year.'

'And the same to you, Tommy. I wish you a happy Christmas and a prosperous New Year,' said my father as we escorted him out the door.

Outside, I strained my eyes to see if I could see any sign of Santa but all I could see were heavy clouds spanning the earth. It was so cold my body trembled and I wondered how Santa and his reindeers could possibly keep warm as he sped around the world delivering parcels. Only an exceptionally great man could do something like that I thought. I was glad I had come to my senses and decided I only wanted a motor car because there was no way Santa would have room in his bag for everything I wanted. A motor car was better than nothing, I thought. When the postman turned on his flash lamp and cycled off down the road, I asked my father,

'Does Santa go across the sky like an aeroplane?'

'He does.'

'And how will he know where I live? He might go down Mickey Billy's chimney and leave my present there?'

My mother and father laughed, as they closed the door and we all came into the warmth of the kitchen, 'But I thought you wrote to Santa? Did you not tell him where you lived?' asked my mother with a questioning gaze.

'I did,' I assured her, though I was beginning to doubt whether I had sent him the right letter. I had written several letters in an attempt to get what I wanted.

'Well... if you did, you must have put your address on the letter: so he can't go to the wrong house, can he?' queried my father, thoughtfully, as my mother tore open the two letters Tommy had thrown on the table. She took the card out of each envelope and read them aloud before putting them with the rest of the cards that were strung on a piece of twine over the fireplace, while a few cards were strung across the top of the dresser, with another half dozen on the window sill.

Despite that assurance from my father, I couldn't remember writing the address on Santa's letter. It was then I realized I was great for asking but not so good when it came to writing things down. Addresses were too long and complicated for my liking. All I could remember doing was asking for a motor car and a football and maybe a packet of sweets. Now I was worried that I might get nothing at all. Just when I thought we were all ready to sit down to have our tea, my mother suggested we say the rosary, first; to get it over with. Every night we knelt down and said the rosary in front of the fire. And regardless of whether anybody called to the house or not we finished the rosary. If anybody called while we were in the midst of it, they'd be invited in and expected to join in the prayers.

My mother and father always knelt with their backs to the fire, one each side while I was made to kneel in the middle. My father led the prayers while my mother and I responded while saying the Five Mysteries. One night they'd say the five Joyful Mysteries; the following night the five Sorrowful Mysteries; the third night the five Glorious Mysteries and I could never remember which ones were which. One night Snowy called to our house after we'd started saying the rosary. He didn't seem too interested but joined in nonetheless. When it came to his turn, he was supposed to say, 'The fourth Sorrowful Mystery; the Carrying of the Cross.'. But Snowy couldn't remember it, so he simply said; 'The fourth Sorrowful Mystery... ... is a bit of a mystery,' winking slyly at me as he carried on.

We had to say the five decades of the rosary.. We had to say the Trimming of the rosary which meant we prayed to all the Saints and sinners pleading for their support, and we prayed for the sick and the infirm and rounded it all off by praying for the dead.

By the time we'd sat at the table, I'd forgotten all about Santa. We blessed ourselves while my mother gave out the prayers: 'Blessed O Lord and these thy gifts, which of thy bounty, we're about to receive, through Christ Our Lord, Amen,' before encouraging us to, 'Eat up now let ye. There's plenty of everything in the house; and let us be thankful to God that we have full and plenty: that we're not starving... like them poor babies in South Africa.'

We had lovely feed and washed it all down with dainty cups of tea. About an hour later, after we had everything cleared off the table and were relaxing in front of the fire, telling stories, my father said, he'd go rambling for a while. I was sitting at the table looking through a copy of the monthly Messenger; a small religious magazine with a lovely red cover; that my mother got from the priest's housekeeper, Nora Keeffe. I liked reading it as it showed pictures of starving babies and people with leprosy being cared for by Irish priests on the foreign missions. And because it was Christmas, the magazine had lovely coloured pictures of famous priests and nuns on the front and back cover. Inside the magazine were lots of little stories and pictures of people all over the world who'd been cured of terrible diseases, while others were pleading for our continued help and support. When I grew tired looking at their ingrained haggard features, I rested my head on the table and wondered would Santa Claus ever come to my aid by sliding down the chimney; and if he did, what would he bring. I was still trying to figure out what he might do when my mother said,

'Now that we're doing nothing, I think I'll get you to hold the wool. I'd like to have another ball of wool ready for when I start knitting after Christmas. Slowly I got up from the table so she could hang a hank of red wool across my outstretched arms. I had to stand in front of her, holding the wool, while she began winding it into a big ball. We had just finished the first ball and were about to start the second when there was a fierce commotion outside the front door. It sounded as if something heavy had just fallen from the sky and landed outside our front door. It was followed by a loud aggressive knock that nearly made me jump out of my skin. I stood rooted to the ground, terrified.

'Well glory be to God Almighty! Who's knocking at this hour of the night?' she said, as she stood up hesitantly. As she went to the door she turned and said, 'God would it ever be Santa, do you think? We'd better go and see who it is.' She caught me by the hand and brought me reluctantly towards the door. And because the door wasn't opened quick enough there was another loud knock.

'God Almighty… but they must be in an awful hurry.'

She opened the door and attempted to look out into the black night when a gruff voice said, 'Is this where John lives?'

My mother turned to me and said, 'It's Santa. He's looking for you.'

I nearly died when she pushed me forward.

'That's Santa. Tell him who you are.' I was too petrified to say anything. When I didn't respond, she said, 'For God's sake tell him who you are or he'll go away and give you nothing.'

It was Santa alright, from what I could see of him. He was dressed in a long red coat and white beard. And from the faint light of the kitchen, I could just about see him rummaging around in a big canvas bag, so I bravely shouted,

'Yes, it's me.'

The next thing a gloved hand thrust itself towards me and handed me a turnip. I recoiled in horror at the sight of the turnip.

'No! No!' I cried aloud, stricken with fear that that was all I was going to get and threw the turnip back in disgust.

Santa laughed at me, ', Hoh, ho. I must have given you the wrong present. A turnip! Hoh, ho, that turnip is meant for another boy, he does nothing around the house.'

This time Santa handed me a cardboard box tied with a string. I said, 'Thanks very much.' Then he turned and disappeared into the night. My mother closed out the door and stood looking at me.

'Lord, aren't you the lucky boy that spoke up; otherwise he'd have gone away and you'd have got nothing. What did he bring you?' asked my mother, as she looked at me holding what looked like a shoe box.

I left the box down on the table and tried to open it but it was too well tied. My mother got the scissors that were hanging on the side of the dresser and cut the twine for me. I opened the box and when I saw what was inside it took my breath away. It was a red metallic car like nothing I had ever seen before. It had a long nose, but the most pleasing aspect of it was that the bonnet was ridged which showed off its two gleaming head lamps to perfection. It had beautiful wire spoked wheels with the letter F emblazoned on each wheel and on the front of the bonnet was written the word Ford. It was everything I could have dreamed of. Beside the car in the box was a bag of mixed sweets. My mother took the sweets and left them up on the dresser, saying

'I think we'll keep these now until tomorrow, because you've had enough sweet things already; what with fruit and Christmas cake and everything. They might only sicken you a grá and you going to bed.'

I never said a word. I was too mesmerized by the sight of my new car. It had a butterfly type winder on the right hand side. My mother took the car from me, wound it up and left it on the ground where it sped across the floor and under the table. I dived in after it and with her help I wound it up again and watched it drive all round the floor. It crashed into the dresser, spun around and kept going until it hit my bedroom door. It was the nicest Christmas present I ever got. I stayed up half the night playing with the car and when my father come home I told him everything that had happened: how I'd heard the awful racket outside the front door and how I thought I could see Santa's reindeers standing beside the hens' cabin, waiting; and that that must have been the awful racket I'd heard before he knocked on the door.

My mother said it was time to go to bed. When I did, I could hardly sleep. I couldn't wait to get up in the morning, to show my new car to Una and Sadie.

But when I woke on Christmas morning and looked out I saw the most incredible sight I'd ever seen. It was snowing outside my bedroom window. I could hardly see Collins's thatched house across the way. I stood there at the window, hypnotised: watching millions of snow flakes falling as they kissed and hugged each other before tumbling lazily to the ground. Suddenly it stopped snowing and the sun began to appear. Then, a funny thing happened. A white rooster, standing on one leg emerged from the side of the hens' cabin. It ruffled the snow from its feathers, thereby exposing its coat of many colours. It was one of our Rhode Island Reds that had been out all night. Seeing him transform his overcoat was magic. One minute he was snow white, the next he was red and brown with a hint of green.

A blackbird flew low across our garden and landed beneath the hedge. It began hopping along, uprooting moss and withered leaves with its yellow beak until it found a worm. It tugged and tugged, gobbling it down before it hopped along once more. For a moment it stood, its tail pointing upwards. Then another blackbird came and chased it away. It flew up and landed on the thatched roof of Collins's house. It stood looking all around as the snow began to melt. Water was dribbling from the base of the thatch, running down the scum covered green walls. I was just about to turn away from the window when a mini avalanche of snow slid off the thatched roof and went plomp! on the ground.

I started playing with my new car while my mother went to First Mass and my father did the jobs around the house.

By the time she arrived home, a lot of the snow had disappeared: the sun dissolving what little there was; and I wished with all my heart it would soon start snowing again. To add to my woes my mother said she couldn't make up her mind whether to let me go to Second Mass or not: because my hair was a holy show.

But my father said, 'What difference does it make?'

'Well, let me tell you it makes all the difference. I don't want to see everyone else's child neat and tidy... and this fella here traipsing down the church with a head on him... like...like... I don't knows what,'

'And can't he wear a cap?'

'He can. But he can hardly wear it walking down the aisle, can he?'

After much arguing, my mother decided to let me go on one condition.

'You're to stay beside your father at all times. Leave your cap on until you're inside the door and make sure to put it back on the minute you come out. You're not to mix with any of your friends; otherwise you'll be the talk of the parish. And if it wasn't for the fact that it's Christmas day and we're celebrating the birth of Baby Jesus, outside that front door you'd not be let go. Do you hear that?' she said turning up the collar of my coat.

Regardless of the flood, we had to wear our wellingtons to Mass on account of the slush and sludge. Going through the town, my father wished everyone a happy Christmas as they propped their bicycles outside shops and offices. Outside the church, some ladies alighted from their horse drawn carriages while the men tied their horses to the nearest lamp post.

My father and I stayed near the back of the church, about a third of the way down.

We were kneeling right next to the middle aisle on the men's side where we could see everything that was going on. Traditionally, the women of the parish knelt on the left hand side and the men on the right. Occasionally a man home on holidays would kneel beside his wife on the left hand side but this was very rare.

As I looked around, I could see a lot of my school friends making their way up to the front of the church where our teacher Mrs Patterson said we should go if we wanted to be good Catholics. Behind them, knelt the young men of the parish; their hair neatly oiled. Some wore heavy overcoats as they hurriedly genuflected and pushed their way into pews, hats and caps firmly held in their hands. All round me, were elderly men, some with their wellingtons on, with straggly wisps of hair swept across their egg shaped heads. They smiled toothlessly as they fingered their rosary beads and jockeyed for position with friends and neighbours.

Then I thought I heard a strange noise behind me. And when I looked round I saw an old man making his way down the centre aisle on his hands and knees. As soon as he passed, my father informed the man kneeling next to him that he was home from England: that the man had been injured during the war and had received a gold medal. The injured man wore brown leather gloves, brown trousers with knees patches and a check jacket with patches on the elbows. He too had well oiled hair.

By now the church was full, but people were coming in all the time: some of them, in the side door; and they had to go right up to the front because there was no place else for them.

On the women's side, all the school going girls knelt way up, in front of the altar. They wore caps while their mothers further back wore fancy hats with gold hat pins. And behind those were numerous women with fox and mink stoles wrapped around their shoulders, while the older women at the back of the church wore ordinary looking coats and scarves with wellingtons and galoshes. I could hear some of them whispering, Happy Christmas to each other as they took out their rosary beads and began to pray fervently. After a while I thought I could hear what sounded like an aeroplane or a motor car outside the church but I couldn't be sure as it sounded like nothing I had ever heard before. Shortly after that, a man and women came in the side door and went up to the front. The woman wore a white fur coat, a white hat with a feather sticking out of it. Everybody in the church seemed to be looking at the two of them. For a moment I thought the woman looked vaguely familiar and then I realized it was Colleen; and Snowy. He wore a black leather jacket and his dark wavy hair was neatly oiled. He looked as straight and as powerful as any of the Guards in the town. I could hear and see some of the women in the aisle across from me whispering and nudging each other, commenting on people's style. When the Mass bell began ringing, we all had to stand up.

I was anxious to meet Una and Sadie, to find out what Santa had brought them. But I couldn't see them. They must have gone to First Mass I thought, as they were not with their mother or father. I also wanted to meet my other friends from school but I knew that I couldn't go near them on account of my hair, which was supposed to be a holy show. I couldn't understand what all the fuss was about: my hair felt alright to me. But if my mother said to keep away from my friends, then I knew I had to, otherwise she'd have my guts for garters.

When Mass was over, I stuck close to my father and pulled the cap down over my ears as we all spilled out of the church. Mingling outside, people everywhere were full of the Christmas spirit. Even the sun was shining, which meant the last of the snow was fading away, fast. Around the church gate, people were shaking hands with well-to-do spalpins* who'd come home for

---

* *Spalpins (locals on holidays from England).*

the Christmas.

My father too stood outside, talking to a small group of men as they cast a cold critical eye on the visitors' up to date style. All of a sudden, we heard the roar of an engine down the street.

The noise of it made the hair stand on the back of my neck, as it went vroom, vroom, vroom. The men too stopped talking and craned their necks to see what it was.

Looking down the street we saw a man and a woman on a powerful motorbike. I knew straight away it was Colleen and Snowy. For a minute we all stared spellbound as the couple settled themselves before take off. It was the first time I had seen anybody on a motor bike. There were only three men in the parish with motorised transport; The doctor, Harry Ryan, and Johnny Smith. Each of them had a motor car, but they were living in the town and were considered an exception. No one else in the parish that I knew of had a motor car. The majority of the farmers went about their daily chores on horse back while the women cycled everywhere. We had no horse-trap or carriage but very often my father too would go about his daily chores on horse back.

Seeing Snowy and Colleen on a motorbike was like a scene from a film I'd seen in the Parochial Hall. I began to wonder if Santa had brought it to them, but I knew that couldn't be; Santa only ever brought presents to children.

'Begod Ned you're sound for the Christmas. You won't have to worry about the flood now that Snowy's home. He'll whip you in and out of Lakeland in no time,' said one of the men jokingly. Before my father had time to answer, the motor bike went vroom, vroom, vroom again as it took off and roared right past us as the tied horses reared their heads distressingly. Snowy, wearing a pair of goggles, sat frog-like on the motor bike, as did Colleen, clinging tightly to his waist as the powerful machine sent women fleeing either side of the road, where they stood looking on in anger.

When at last my father and I were walking home together, I asked him a question I'd wanted to ask for a long time.

'Why do some people call Una and Sadie's father Snowy, when his name is Máirtín?'

'Well...' he said after deliberating a moment, '...his proper name is Máirtín, but around here... everyone calls him Snowy,'

'But why?'

My father chuckled to himself, as again he deliberated.

'Ah, it's a long story. When he was a baby he was found by a ditch, after a heavy shower of snow.'

And who found him?'

'His mother, I think. She was supposed to have been on her way to the doctor when she found him. I dunno rightly. But she landed home with him anyway. And he's been called Snowy, ever since.'

'And is that why he has a patch of white hair on his forehead?'

'Ah no! That was caused by an accident. He was sitting on the cart when his father was bringing home a cartload of potatoes. He fell off the cart and cut his head. And ever since his hair's been white.'

'He was lucky. Only for his mother… he might never have been found.'

Again my father chuckled.

By the time we got home from Mass, my mother had the turkey roasting in the oven. She had a roaring fire down and every half hour she'd lift the lid and turn the turkey. There were three or four slices of fatty bacon sizzling with it, to help keep it moist. Replacing the lid she added a few more burning coals to the lid and bottom of the oven. Hanging on the crane over the fire were two skillets, boiling away, one with potatoes and one with vegetables.

When the dinner was over, my mother said, 'Now that we have our bellies full maybe the two of us will walk up across, seeing as Snowy hadn't the decency to call in and say hello on his way home from Mass.'

She had no sooner mentioned his name than who should come up the road but Snowy and Colleen on the motor bike.

They turned into the street where Snowy pushed one of the foot pedals down to the ground to support the bike. They were still in their good clothes but Colleen had a thick woollen scarf around her head instead of the small feathered hat, she'd worn to Mass. We all stood out in the street admiring the gleaming motorbike before turning to go back into the house.

'…And this is what he bought me for Christmas,' said Colleen, excitedly as she did a twirl, modelling her new fur coat in the kitchen.

'Well talk about style! Jesus Mary and Holy St Joseph, but where did you get it?' asked my mother turning to Máirtín, as she took the fur coat from Colleen, feeling the luxurious warmth of it, before trying it on.

'Where do you think?' asked Snowy, sarcastically, 'I got it in a pawn shop.'

'Aaaah… you did in me backside!' 'Did he?' asked my mother looking inquiringly at Colleen.

'Arrah not at all! Don't you know that fella long enough now not to believe one solitary word that comes out of his mouth? When I asked him how he knew what size I was, he told me he stood outside the shop all day until he saw a woman passing that looked like me. He asked her would she mind trying the coat on for him. And he reckons he asked another woman to wear it while he was going through customs, otherwise they'd have taken it off him in Dublin or made him pay duty on it. So I wouldn't wonder at all at anything he'd do. And the devil-a-hair I care, so long as I've got what I always wanted.'

'What will ye have to drink?' asked my father looking at Snowy, delighted to see him home again.

'Arrah, anything at all… a bottle of beer or stout – if you have it?' replied Snowy as he sat down beside the fire and started warming his large freckled hands and twirling the large gold ring on his finger..

Colleen sat down and had a glass of Babycham the other side of the fire while my mother proceeded to tell her all about Santa: and I in turn had to show her my new motor car. And because it was Christmas, Colleen asked Snowy to give her mother and father and myself a spin on the motor bike.

'…Is it what ye're trying to kill me? I wouldn't be seen dead near that thing…not even if I was paid,' said my mother, with an air of good humour.

'Troth then, we'll not pay you, said Snowy, joyously 'You can hump it or lump it.' 'Ned, you hop up here behind Colleen,' he indicated with a shake of his head.

I stood looking on as my father cautiously threw his leg over the back of the motorbike. Despite Colleen's best efforts to make room for him on the saddle, Ned ended up practically sitting on the mudguard, as a wisp of white smoke spat intermittently from the chrome exhaust.

'Jack, you hop up here in front, with me,' said Snowy, indicating he wanted me to sit on the petrol tank. He always referred to me as Jack, why I didn't know. But that didn't stop me lining up to take my place on the purring monster.

'John'een… you'd better be careful! Don't fall off that bloody machine what ever you do. Make sure you've a good hold,' said my mother as Snowy grabbed hold of me. He put me sitting on the gleaming petrol tank that had the initials BSA emblazoned on the tank. He told me to put my two feet out over the handlebars, to lie back and hold on to his outstretched arms.

We drove bumpily down the road towards the lake, through the slush and then very gently through the flood.

'If the flood was an inch higher we wouldn't have been able to go through it: it would have smothered the exhaust,' roared Snowy, trying to make himself heard about the roar of the engine. He drove the motorbike down through the town and then out the Dunmore Road for about a mile before turning round at Kilnalag crossroads. It was both terrifying and exciting watching the front wheel of the motor bike throwing up rivulets of water as we drove through the flood: but it was even more terrifying watching the road disappear so quickly beneath the front wheel as we drove along the main road: with the engine spitting and backfiring and going, vroom, vroom, vroom.

Soon Christmas was over, and it was back to the every day jobs of mucking out the pigs' cabin, the hens' cabin and the stables. Snowy and his motorbike were but a distant memory as he'd gone back to England: but he'd be coming home again he said. And with any bit of luck he'd have his motor bike, and I'd get another spin, I thought.

Now I was back in school preparing to make my First Communion, which was due to take place in Spring. I knew I had a long hard road ahead of me, learning my Catechism. If I didn't learn my Catechism off by heart then I couldn't make my First Holy Communion, Mrs Patterson said. And from what

I'd been told, making my First Holy Communion was going to be a joyous occasion. And that was something I didn't want to miss, above all else.

Chapter Eight

Mrs Patterson began her usual early morning roll call. When she called out my name in Irish I raised my hand and shouted, 'An Seo.'

It was the day after I'd helped my father to bring Colleen's cattle down to the fair in Williamstown. Mrs Patterson looked down at me and said,

'Where were you yesterday? Why weren't you in school?'

I stood up and said, 'Please Miss, I had to help my father bring cattle to the fair.'

'Well I hope you don't make a habit of it. You'd a very good attendance record up to yesterday. I was hoping you wouldn't let me down. The Inspector will be coming in shortly. You were one of only three pupils with an unbroken term…but I'm afraid… that's now down to two. Never mind. We'll just have to get on with it.'

My friends in school were anxious to hear all about the fair. They wanted to know if it was as good as Glenamaddy. I told them it was a lot better, just to make them feel jealous. Michael Fannon said that Glenamaddy wasn't a proper fair anyway. He said the best fair he was ever at was in Castlerea. But we all knew he was telling lies. My friends said, Fannon's father only goes to Castlerea because he likes to think he's a big farmer. Michael too thinks he's better than anybody else in school but we know he isn't. He's useless playing football, but if we don't let him play he calls us names.

I didn't like Michael Fannon at all and the thought of facing him in school every day upset me. I thought about staying away from school for a few days and hiding in the fields down by the lake. The only thing that stopped me was the cattle and the fear of getting caught. And because our village was so close to the school there weren't that many places I could hide. Somebody going in or out of the village might catch me, I thought.

Michael Fannon took great pleasure in taunting me if I favoured one side or the other playing football. He'd call me a pauper and a miserable bastard. Why he did it I didn't know. Somehow I knew I wasn't the same as everybody else and thought that that was why Fannon and his so called friends picked on me. I hated being called a pauper and a bastard. What those words meant I didn't know, except that it was something horrible. Sometimes my friends in third class would give me sweets, but if Fannon knew I'd been given something nice he'd take it off me. EJ Lyons said nobody could stop him because he was as thick in the head as he was around the arse. And that was how we came to nickname Michael Fannon, Fatso. John Keaveney said we should give Fatso a box in the mouth. We all laughed when EJ came up with the name. John said Fatso was like a big fat sausage. Again we all laughed. Everybody in our class liked John Keaveney. John would look at you with a twinkle in his eye when you sought his advice. If he couldn't come up with a ready made answer he'd say something funny like, 'I'll ask me grandfather; he knows everything, because he's over a hundred.'

Fatso was bigger and stronger than any one in our class. We were all afraid of him. And if I didn't give him what he'd ask for, he'd kick me and belt me into the ground. Everybody agreed, Fatso was too big for his boots

By the time my first Holy Communion came around, I'd done everything to stop Fatso tormenting me, but it was no use. The minute I'd try to stand up for myself he'd ask one of the bigger lads to help beat me up because I was considered a teacher's pet.

For weeks, Mrs Patterson had put us through our religious paces. And sometimes, first thing in the morning she'd look down to our class and say,

'Johnny Rodgers, I want you to go out and run up the school road and get me the biggest sally rod you can lay your hands on. And when you find it bring it back so than I can knock bit of sense into this crowd of heathens. And make sure it's a good strong one, not like the last one you brought in.'

When she said this I had no choice but to run up the school road. I knew exactly where the best sally rods were. My father cut a lot of them which he used as scallops to thatch the roof of our house. Every time the teacher asked me to get a sally rod, I was tormented because I didn't know what kind of a sally rod I should really get. If I got a nice light one – one that'd break easily – my friends would praise me. But I knew if I didn't get a good Sally rod, Mrs Patterson would give out to me and everyone in class would laugh at me. The fact that the teacher's pet was getting a good telling off was hilarious altogether. And of course there was always the danger that I could end up being the first one to get slapped with it; for talking.

Eventually I'd manage to get hold of a good sally rod: one that was neither too light nor two heavy. The minute Mrs Patterson got the sally rod into her hands she'd threaten EJ.

'EJ Lyons, if I have to go down to you, I'll bring the wrath of God down on that bobbling head of yours. Every time I turn my back, you're jig-acting. And if you think I'm bad, just wait until you go into Mr Feather's class.

Everyone in third class knew this was a serious threat. Mr Feathers was supposed to be a wicked teacher who loved using the cane. We dreaded the thought that all of us in third class would be going into him next year. Yet we couldn't wait to see how EJ would get on with Mr Feathers. EJ was not afraid of anyone, not even Mrs Patterson. Despite that, he was always getting slapped for jig-acting. When EJ got slapped, he'd blame me for having provided the rod in the first place. As a result we had a very serious discussion on how best to reduce the power of the sally rod. For some time John Keaveney had claimed that a single hair from a horse's tail, placed across the palm of the hand, would cut any rod in two even halves; thereby reducing all of our suffering. He swore time and again that this was the only solution. He claimed he got this tip from his grandfather and he knew because he was over a hundred.

The following day John brought in a grey strand of horse hair that was as long as your arm. He swore the hair would wrap itself round the sally rod the moment it struck the palm of the hand. But somehow or other that elusive hair could never be found when we needed it most

Two days before Our First Holy Communion, Mrs Patterson was checking to make sure everyone in third class knew how to make a good Confession. Time and time again she made us go over our prayers until we were blue in the face. We couldn't wait to make our First Holy Communion because we knew we'd be treated to an ice cream and maybe a few bob the minute we came out of the church. It was a tradition that children were treated by their parents no matter how poor their circumstances.

The morning of my First Holy communion was like a summer's day, though it was still only March. The road down by the lake was now dry and we could walk on it again. I was dressed in a grey sleeve-less jumper, a white short sleeved shirt, a red tie and grey jacket with a matching pair of short trousers, white socks and black shoes that my mother had bought for me. I felt like a king as I walked down to the town with her. She was wearing a long floral dress, a black hat with a gold hat pin and a hand knitted shawl round her shoulders. When we arrived outside the church we found that we were way too early. There were only a few people there, standing talking outside the church. They were waiting for Mrs Patterson and other pupils to arrive so we could all march down the middle aisle together. As more and more people began to arrive, my mother joined them while I slipped away quietly and began playing with my friends near by. Unknown to my mother I'd scrambled over a wall to get a ball that John Keaveney had accidentally kicked into the priest's garden. As I reached under a hedge to get the ball I spotted a blue egg on the ground, with brown speckled dots. I picked up the egg and brought it with me to show to my friends. Because it was blue I knew straight away it was a blackbird's egg and I wanted to impart this extraordinary knowledge to my friends. As I was standing outside the priest's wall showing the egg to John and EJ, Fatso Fannon came along and demanded to know what was going on. John ran back to his mother, while EJ stood watching Fatso. He put two fingers into his mouth and gave a loud wolf whistle to distract Fatso. But Fatso took no notice and I was left to deal with him on my own while EJ slipped quietly away. I'd already put my hand into my pocket before Fatso could see what I had. As he crowded me, I began to back away.

'What have you in your pocket?'

'Nothing.'

'Nothing! What do mean nothing? I saw you putting something into your pocket?'

'No, I didn't,' I replied, as Fatso closed in on me, a single streak of hair oil inching its way down his, fat, pimpled face.

'Show me what you have in your pocket.'

'I won't,'

'Show me, or I'll kill you!' said Fatso, menacingly

'I won't... show you. it's nothing,' I replied, hesitantly

'Then what were you showing Keaveney and Lyons?'

'It was nothing. I wasn't showing them anything. We were just talking.'

'You're a liar. I saw you put something into your pocket, Give it to me, you little pauper,' said Fatso, as he rested his hands either side of me on the low wall. 'Give it to me or I'll get one of the big lads to kill you.'

For no particular reason I got the feeling Fatso was bluffing: that he wouldn't really beat me up; and my mother standing, talking to her friends only yards away. Despite that assurance, I didn't want to take any chances. And as I stood there eyeing Fatso in his white shirt, peach coloured tie and grey pinstriped suit, I got an overwhelming desire to do something bad. Fatso saw the hesitation in my eyes, and as his thick skull closed in menacingly and I could smell his stale breath, he growled, 'Give me what you have in your pocket, you little pauper.'

While I was playing for time and desperately mapping out my escape route, I brazenly said, 'I'll give it to you... if you promise to leave me alone... forever'

'Forever?' smiled Fatso, as he began to sneer, 'Forever?' Suddenly he said, 'OK, OK I promise.'

'Close your eyes...and put out your hand.' I said, as I tried to psyche myself up to carry out a wicked deed.

'Why would I close my eyes? You twit!'

'Because... because... it's a surprise. And it won't be a surprise if you don't close your eyes,' I said, nervously.

Fatso closed his eyes and put out his hand as I stood watching him. Very slowly I took out the egg and held it in my hand for a split second and as I did so Fatso opened his eyes and asked, innocently,

'What is it? What is it?'

I put my hands behind my back and replied,

'It's a surprise. A surprise! I won't give it to you unless you close your eyes... I'll give it to you, but I wouldn't give it to anybody else,' I said, feeling it was now or never.

Fatso scrunched his eyes shut and quick as a flash I popped the blackbird's egg into the top pocket of his new suit; gave it a slap and before he knew what was happening the rotten egg exploded upwards with a horrifying stench as the gooey entrails of a dead bird spread over his suit and shirt. With lightening speed I ducked under his arm and ran for my life down the street. By now my mother was looking for me and if it wasn't for all the people present outside the church, I'd have got a clatter across the lug for having wandered off without her permission. Mrs Patterson and the other teachers were busy trying to round up the boys and girls making their First Communion before marshalling us down the middle aisle to our seats in front of the Altar. But there was no sign of Fatso Fannon

I was terrified I'd be blamed for holding everything up. And when Mrs Patterson and the other teachers asked if anyone knew where Michael Fannon was I thought my heart would never stop pounding. But no one said anything. For about five minutes there was pandemonium while the teachers tried desperately to locate Fatso. They knew he was there earlier. They'd seen him; they'd seen his mother. Where could he have gone? In the end, they had to go ahead without him and I felt a tremendous glow of satisfaction that I had caused my tormentor to miss out on the greatest day of his life, his First Holy Communion.

When the ceremony was finally over, and we were outside, word went round the town that Fatso Fannon had had a weakness. He was supposed to have slipped and fell on cow dung on the road: that there was a smell off him that would knock you and that his mother had had to bring him home, again. When John , EJ, and I heard this we laughed. We said it was good enough for him; he was only a guttersnipe anyway: and everyone hated guttersnipes.

Only John and EJ really knew what happened to Fatso; but they never said a word. Still, I couldn't relax. I half expected to be murdered when I went back to school on Monday. Somebody was bound to tell Mrs Patterson. Thankfully, nobody did. After that memorable encounter, Fatso Fannon kept well away from me and I was no longer afraid of him. For the first time in my life I began to enjoy going to school. And although Spring was well and truly in the air, the weather would sometimes turn bad. And when EJ hit Fatso on the puss with a snowball after an unexpected snow shower, I prayed that it would snow every single day: but it didn't. All it did was rain.

Chapter Nine

After a heavy winter of rain, sleet and snow, some of the houses in the village looked like tumble down shacks. The overhanging trees which were meant to protect the houses from the worst of the elements, instead acted as giant sprinklers ensuring the heaviest raindrops fell directly onto the houses. And as the faint stirrings of spring began to emerge, the grassy patches on the roofs of the houses gained a new lease of life. Not surprisingly, one corner of Kilby's house had succumbed to the elements. The sagging roof which had clung to the chimney breast for so long, had finally lost its grip and tumbled to the ground, thereby obliterating Kilby's only bedroom. And although the tall chimney breast stood proud and tall, it somehow looked eerie and naked, a sure sign it would never warm the hearthstone of Kilby's home again. The back wall of the house, once as white as the driven snow, looked as if it had been submerged in a sea of frog spawn. During the course of many winters, it had grown a film of green scum which has something to do with the grass on the roof and everything to do with the rain. And although Kilby himself was still confined to Ballinasloe mental hospital, it looked as if he no longer had a house to come home to. If he came home again, he'd have to sleep in the kitchen because there was no other room.

My mother said to Margaret, as they stood looking at the ruin on their way down from the well, 'Ah sure 'tis not fit for a dog never mind a human being. Maybe in God, they'll keep him in hospital, because if they don't... I'd hate to think I might have to look after him.'

'Well... I wouldn't mind looking after him... if I had to. But then again, when you look at it... our own house isn't much better? I don't know in the name of God what we'll do with it: whether to put a slated roof on it or thatch it again?' said Margaret as she picked up her two buckets of water. Together, the women made their way down the street trying to avoid the cow manure splattered on the road while I tried jumping over the little puddles only to land in the middle of them.

'Ah for God's sake, will you walk out in front; and not be destroying me,' said my mother turning round after I splattered her. Leaving the buckets down, she continued, 'At least you have someone to do it; not like me. Sure Frank is awful handy. He can turn his hand to anything.'

Frank was Margaret's youngest son. Often I'd see Frank cutting sally rods along the sides of the road in the evening after he'd come home from work. When he'd enough cut, he'd tie them in a bundle, swing them on his back and walk home. After working all day, he'd spend his evenings in the workshop, weaving the rods into baskets, bird cages and other useful things which he could sell at the fair. Any bits of sticks he'd left over he'd use to make garden cribs for catching birds in his front and back garden.

Once when Frank saw me looking at him through the hedge he invited me in to see the cribs. He had three bird cribs that looked like Chinese hats. I stood in awe as he set one of the cribs for the following morning. He began by slitting and pointing a short piece of stick that looked like a pencil. He tied a short piece of string round the pointed end and used it to prop up the crib while he tied a small piece of cheese to the other end of the string and placed it under the crib.

'Why are you putting cheese under it?'

'I'm using cheese to try and catch a few birds! Hopefully when the birds try to fly away with the cheese, the crib will fall and trap them. To encourage them, I'll spread a few grains of oats around the outside and with any bit of luck I'll have a Goldfinch by morning,' he said with a smile.

'What's a Goldfinch?'

'A Goldfinch is a beautiful bird that sings all the time. Some people go mad for them. There are lots of different finches but if I catch a Goldfinch, I can get a better price. Only thing is, they're very hard to catch. Some people catch Goldfinches by going out at night with a lamp. Sometimes you can see different birds when you shine a light into the bushes. Birds freeze the minute they see a light and if it's a Goldfinch you can reach in and catch it.'

When I said nothing, Frank looked at me and said, 'Now, are you happy?'

I shook my head, I was.

I often saw Frank catching Sparrows, Robins and Blue Tits but I never saw him catch a Goldfinch. If they weren't Goldfinches, he'd let them go again as they were no use to him. Frank had two Goldfinches in a cage that hung by the dresser. And he had two Greenfinches in another cage that was hanging in the back kitchen. I was surprised when I saw the state of their back kitchen. There was no ceiling; just some sticks and what looked like branches, holding up the thatched roof. And their kitchen roof was sagging down and looked much worse than ours. And like our back kitchen there were buckets of water and bags of turf, as well as other bags and boxes everywhere. One wall was lined with old bottles and tins, as well as old jam jars with lumps of goose grease, the same as we had. Sometimes, my father rubbed the goose grease on his knees before he went to bed so I knew what it was for.

Frank's mother would sometimes ask me to run to the town for a box of *Rinso* or *Blue* for washing and dyeing clothes while Frank and Malachy were away painting. As soon as I'd come back, she'd give me a cut of currant bread and jam or a silver threepenny bit for myself. I liked getting the silver Threepenny bit because it had a rabbit on it. The sixpence had a greyhound, the shilling, a bull, the two shilling piece, a fish and the half crown, a horse; which was my real favourite because a half a crown was an awful lot of money.

Whatever money I got, I always gave it my mother. If it was more than threepence, she'd put it in the post office for me, saying,

'We may as well save it and keep it for a rainy day.'

She'd slip the money into her purse and that would be the last I'd ever see of it.

* * * *

Frank and his brother Malachy were on their way home from work. Seeing their mother talking outside our house they slowed to a crawl and hopped off their bicycles.

'…Ah sure you couldn't keep that auld roof of ours thatched either. And now that the new road is nearly finished, we're thinking of building a new house near the head of that road…that's if we can get a grant. I was talking to Johnny Glynn the councillor and he said he'd do what he could for us,' said Margaret.

'A new house!' gasped my mother. 'God Almighty may save us, that's an awful surprise. And you never said anything about it?'

'I didn't… because we only made up our mind last week: isn't that right Malachy?'

'Yeah.'

'I wanted to wait until I'd see Johnny Glynn. Now that's he's going to help us apply for a grant, we're decided to go ahead…'.

'That's great news Mam,' said Malachy, leaning across his bicycle.

'But won't it cost ye a fortune?' queried my mother, a distinct air of jealously in her voice.

'It will. But what can we do? We have to do something! But it'll be only a small house: two bedrooms, with a kitchen and toilet.'

'But mammy, not if we build it ourselves,' intervened Frank as he rested his foot on the frame of the bicycle. Turning to his mother in earnest, he added, 'We were working it out Mam, Malachy and I could build it ourselves: and we could be living in it by Christmas. I'll show you the sketch we drew.'

'Arrah what do ye two know about building?' said Margaret angrily, dismissing her sons' idea as ludicrous.

'Mam! I'm telling you, we could build it ourselves,' insisted Frank, but his mother ignored him. Instead, she turned to my mother again, as the two lads dropped their heads and walked on home, huffed that their own mother wouldn't even listen to them.

'Ah look at the poor devils… you've upset them now…you shouldn't have said anything,' said my mother.

'Arrah they'll be alright! You know Frank; he's just like his father; the Lord have Mercy on him. He has no patience at all, always wanting to be doing things without thinking of the consequences. Anyway as I was saying, if we could ever get a council grant, we'd build a house near the head of the road. All our land would be around the new house then and we wouldn't have to be going in and out by the lake. We could let ye have our front and back garden; and that auld workshop if it's any good to ye. It'll be no use to us once we move out. We'd probably knock the shed and bring the stones out with us. If we did that, we could build a shed beside the new house. The other sheds are good for nothing ... but the workshop... it might come in handy for ye,' said Margaret.

'God...,' replied my mother, lost for words as she stood clutching the bottom half of her apron that held half a dozen eggs she was bringing in from the hens' cabin. '...I can hardly believe it. If we got that little workshop it would be great altogether. I must mention it to himself, I'm sure he'll buy it off ye.'

'Ah... we can talk about that later,' said Margaret, dismissing the idea with a wave of her hand. We haven't started building at all yet. And did you hear about Annie? She's talking about building.'

'Is it ...Annie Tobin?' my mother asked, flabbergasted.

'The very one!'

'Aaah, you're pulling me leg?'

'I'm not,' laughed Margaret heartily, seeing the shock on my mother's face. 'Annie herself told me that yesterday. But I never let on, we were thinking of building.'

'Well isn't she the witch. And I talking about Kilby's house only yesterday, and she never said a word.'

After that startling revelation, the conversation in our house was muted for days on end. It was as if a dark cloud hung over the house. Any time my mother attempted to broach the subject of doing something with our own house, my father would push back his chair and make for the door. Finally, after many heated arguments she managed to bring him round to discussing what we might do with it, as he sat reading *The Connaught Tribune*.

'...Anyway, it's long past time we did something with it. The rain's coming down in John's room; and as for the wallpaper... sure you couldn't keep it pasted.'

When he didn't respond in any way, she continued. 'If you ask me it's a waste of money buying any more wallpaper. And as for our own room...'

'But didn't Daddy fix the hole in the roof?' I suggested. I wanted to add my Penny hape-penny's* worth, even though I was supposed to be doing my

* *Penny hape-penny's (Penny and a half).*

116

lessons.

'I know he did a grá… but you can't make a silk purse out of a sow's lug…'

'I don't know what sort of misfortune I have….,' said my father angrily, folding *The Connaught Tribune* as he stood up. '…you're always complaining.'

My mother left down her knitting and looked at my father as he made for his top coat hanging on the wall beside my bedroom door. 'Look it! I'm not complaining in any shape or form! But if we don't do something about the house it'll soon be as bad as Kilby's. We'll be the laughing stock of the parish: that's all I'm saying!' she shouted, as my father slammed the half-door after him and went off visiting.

By now the roof of our house had become a major bone of contention. There were so many birds nesting in the thatch it resembled a shooting gallery. Blackbirds and Starlings were the main culprits, my father said. Every morning I could hear them chirping, long before I got up, as they flew in and out of their nests carrying worms and insects to feed the Scaltáns.*

But my father had far more pressing things on his mind than the roof of our house. Things like ploughing and harrowing and picking the stones off the fields. Already, the village landscape resembled a chess board with every second field being turned over to enable the farmers to begin sowing their crops.

Barley was the first crop to be sown, followed by oats and potatoes. When lea land was ploughed it had to be harrowed, then cross harrowed before it was fit for sowing. After that, the stones had to be picked off it or else rolled into the ground after the oats and barley had been sown. The potatoes too presented a formidable challenge before they could be sown. Farmers who opted for potato ridges had to settle the ridges with a spade before they could stick the potatoes. After that, they had to spread cartloads of farmyard manure all along the ridges. This was referred to as putting out the top dress. As a result, the road was a mess as it was littered with manure falling off the carts as it was being transported to fields and gardens, everywhere. And it was my job, when I came home from school every evening, to help spread the manure on the drills and ridges.

But spreading manure was the last thing on my mind as I landed home from school one evening. I couldn't wait to tell my mother about Sylvester Naughton.

Sylvester was Tommy the postman's son. He was supposed to be dying in hospital. Nobody in school knew whether it was true or not. He wasn't in school all week so we all figured it must be true. I couldn't wait to tell my mother. But as I entered the house I got an awful surprise. She was sitting on

* *Scaltáns (fledglings or young chicks).*

the floor with mounds of potatoes all around her. It was so unlike anything I had ever seen before.

She was sitting with her back to the wall, a scarf around her head, with a heavy sack thrown across her lap. She wore a pair of short wellingtons, a pair of glasses and looked totally out of character. There was a large bag of potatoes one side, a huge mound of potato slits the other and a heap of potato buds on her lap.

In her hand she'd a short knife that had a piece of cloth tied around the handle. I stood in bewilderment watching her reach into a canvas bag where she took out a handful of potatoes and left them on her lap. Picking up one of them she examined it carefully, broke off the bud with a flick of her thumb and began cutting the potato into four small pieces, throwing what was left of the potato into a bucket beside her.

'What are you doing?' I asked.

'What do you think I'm doing? I'm slitting. How do you think we grow potatoes if we don't slit them?'

I stood looking on, mesmerized at the heap of slits on the floor. It was as if my father had tipped up a cart-load of chopped potatoes.

Do you see that slit now,' she said, holding up a quarter of a potato. 'That will grow ten or twelve good potatoes when it's sown. And if you sow enough of them you will have a decent crop. I usually sit out beside the reek of turf which saves me having to carry the potatoes in but it's too cold to go outside yet: besides I'm not able for it any more.'

I looked on intrigued at her deft use of the knife.

'Would a potato not grow if you sowed it?' I asked, innocently.

'Of course it would. And I wish to the Lord God Almighty that I didn't have to slit them. Slitting and going to that cursed well are two jobs I hate more than anything in this world. But if I don't do it, who'll do it? Look at the state of me poor hands?' she said, holding them up. There were red blisters on her hands from all the slitting.

'Could Daddy not do it?'

'Musha God help you a grá. It's a man's world. And this is a woman's job – that's according to the men,' she sighed. 'Anyway, I think your father has enough to be doing. He's working with Tom Farrell so that's him gone for the next few days; as if I hadn't enough to do already, what with feeding the pigs and baking and washing and the devil knows what.'

'Why don't ye sow the big potatoes, then you wouldn't have to slit them?

'A Musha, why do you think? If we didn't slit them a grá, we wouldn't have any potatoes left to feed the pigs. And what would we do if we hadn't a potato for our dinner? That's why we have to slit them: the same as every other house in the parish. Do you see this Kerr Pink now,' she said holding up a large pink potato.

'I do.'

'And do you see them three or four buds that are starting to sprout?' she asked, as she broke off the buds.

'I do.'

'Well, a new bud will only grow where there's an eye in the potato. Each eye has a root that goes down to the bottom of the potato. If I cut this potato straight between the eyes I can make three or four seed potatoes out of it,' she said, deftly slitting the potato into something that resembled four quarters. 'The rest of it is no good, so I'll throw it into the bucket and we'll give them to the pigs. I'm trying to feed the pigs as best I can. We might be able to kill one of them later on, with the help of God.'

'Are we killing a pig?' I asked excitedly.

'If I can convince you father, but sure I might as well be talking to the wall. We used to kill a pig in this house every year, before you came. It saved us having to buy meat from Sean Mulryan. But your father would rather sell the pigs and get a few pounds for them.

'John Keavney said they killed a pig, once. He said it was horrible because the pig wouldn't stop screaming no matter what they did.'

Suddenly we heard a noise outside and the postman's head appeared over the half door. 'God Bless the work,' he said, as I rushed to open the half door but Tommy had it opened before me.

'Musha Tommy, how are you? And look at the cut of me and I trying to be slitting a few potatoes.' 'John, in the name of God will you go down to the room and change your clothes and not be standing there like a ploeta.* When you've that done, I want you to put the slits into these two bags I have here and you can help me to carry them outside,' said my mother, throwing the buds off her lap and rising to her feet. 'And sweep the floor while I put up your dinner,' she added, as Tommy threw a letter on the table with a deep sigh of resignation.

'Ah musha… Mrs O'Brien I don't know how I am,' said Tommy as he swung the mail bag round his shoulder.

'Oh, and what's troubling you?'

Ah, I dunno rightly. I feel as if I'm after being dealt a mortal blow,' said Tommy, a quiver in his voice.

'Aw Jesus Mary and Joseph, don't tell me you're sick?' You've been off for a few days.'

'It's worse than that Kate. If it was meself, I'd accept it. It's poor Sylvester…he's in hospital the poor creature,' said Tommy, emotionally.

I tried to pretend I was busy changing my clothes in the room but in truth I was more interested in discretely watching and listening, from behind my bedroom door.

---

* Pleota *(softie or simpleton).*

'Ah... I don't believe it. What's wrong with him?'

'He...he... has a hole in the heart...,' whispered Tommy, barely able to spit out the words. '... but keep it to yourself. I don't want the whole parish knowing. Nan Little and yourself are the only two I've told. We only found out ere yesterday. You know he was prone to blackouts, but we never suspected anything as serious as that. People can say what they like about Doctor Roland, but he put his finger on the button when we brought him to see him. 'Twas there about a year ago... Roland said to me, "that son of your is a walking time bomb. I can't detect a single heart beat, but obviously he's alive and kicking. I can't find a thing wrong with him. But if he gets another blackout I'll send him straight to the hospital." To tell you the truth Kate, I was beginning to think Roland was raving; until the other evening, when Sylvester got another blackout. He came round after a few minutes and I brought him up to Roland; and he brought him straight up to the Hospital.'

'Oh...but that was awful, Tommy? Won't you sit down a minute and I'll make you a nice cup-a-tea? You know I was wondering why you were off, because it's not like you. The sub-post didn't say where you were and I didn't like to ask him. I thought maybe you were sticking potatoes or something,' said my mother, reaching for the tea pot.

'Ah musha I won't. I'll give the tea a miss. I rather go home. Herself will be worried don't you know?'

'Oh...I know, I know. It must be awful hard on her. I do see herself and the children at Mass every Sunday, dressed up to the nines.'

'Bedamn but, yes! She loves dressing them up, showing them off. Sylvester was always her favourite,' Tommy tearfully replied, although he tried hard not to show it.'

'Glory be to God Almighty, do we ever know the hour or the day or what's around the corner? And what's the cause of it I wonder?'

'The devil-a-one knows. He's above there in the hospital now and the nurses tell me he's laughing and joking with them, the same as if he was at home. But the Head Doctor warned me... he could get another blackout; and not come out of it. Seemingly it's very rare; one in every... I don't know how many. To tell you the truth Kate, it feels like a death sentence.'

'Well may God Almighty help you. You know there isn't a day goes by but there's something. But to hear about a young fella like that? John often talks about him... how he's always playing football with the big lads and everything.'

'Why wouldn't he? Why wouldn't he? Aren't they always running round together – though they're not in the same class?'

'And what's going to happen now or do you know?'

The doctors think they should operate: but they are waiting to consult a heart specialist who's coming down from Dublin.'

'Oh well, that in itself should be a help. Well I hope to God that they make the right decision.'

'Well I hope so; I certainly hope so!' said Tommy, wearily as he went towards the door, followed by my mother.

After weeks of uncertainty, the doctors decided to operate, but they only gave him a ten per cent chance of survival. As things stood, he had no chance, they said. The operation, however, was not a success and he died three days later. The school was closed as a mark of respect. The pupils had to form a guard of honour as his coffin was carried through the town on its way to the church. The teachers made us line up on either side of the road as we waited for the cortége to arrive. We all had to stand arms' length apart and wear our black arm bands on the arm nearest the coffin. The funeral was so big it was an hour late. By the time it arrived, people were perished with the cold. Not only that but they were sad and lonesome at the loss of such a fine handsome young lad.

What made it worse was seeing Tommy alone in the front of the hearse as every man woman and child came out to show their respects, while his wife and children sat bleary eyed and grief stricken in the back of Harry Ryan's car. It was the same the following day as the children of the parish marched either side of the hearse as it made its way out to the graveyard. And as the priest read the final prayers and they lowered the coffin, I shed a tear as Sylvester's brothers and sisters cried uncontrollably. Tommy tried to comfort his sobbing wife as he held her in his arms: trying desperately not to show his emotions.

After Sylvester was laid to rest, people still inched their way forward paying their last respects. I stood beside my father and mother feeling the funeral would never be over as they stood talking to people, trying to come to terms with what had happened.

Though Tommy was back doing his rounds a few days later, he was only a shadow of the great man we once knew. Gone, was the lightness of step and his sense of humour. His hunched shoulders only served to augment his grey pallor as he struggled to cope with the loss of his eldest son. Thereafter, when ever my mother made him a cup of tea and their conversation inevitably turned to Sylvester; and what might have been, Tommy would take out a handkerchief to wipe away the tears.

My father meanwhile was working with Tom Farrell. That meant he'd put the bridle on the horse each morning before leading her to a low stone wall where he'd throw his leg over and ride bareback down to Tom's house. There, they'd yoke up the two horses and begin cutting the dykes as well as opening and closing the drills in the adjoining fields. As Tom only had himself to look after he didn't have to sow a lot of potatoes. Yet he liked having a few bags of Golden Wonders to sell when it came to Christmas, he said; along with an acre of sugar beet. Tom in turn would come to our house to help my father look after Colleen's farm, while Snowy was in England.

When Snowy came home and brought his motor bike with him, I could tell whether he was going in or out of the town from the sound of his motorbike as it sped along the road at the back of the lake. Occasionally I'd hear a car or lorry passing but Snowy's bike was so distinctive, I'd race to the bottom of the garden the minute I'd hear him, so I could watch which way he was going. Going into the town, he'd disappear from view for a few seconds as he flew past the wood; emerging the other side where he'd go roaring up Kilnalag hill at great speed, the bike glinting in the distance like a precious jewel.

Snowy and his motor bike was the talk of the parish wherever he went. He was known to stop along the road to offer a lift to some oddball who'd never set foot on a motor bike before. Those who availed of his kind offer usually ended up pleading for mercy, pleading to be let off. To add to their foreboding, Snowy would promise to take them on a decent run, the next time.

'...He's fit for anything. Did you hear what he did to Sergeant Boyle?' sniffed Tom Farrell, with a touch of hilarity, as he sat smoking in our house after a hard day's work.

'The-devil-a-hear,' said my father, as he leant forward and spat into the fire across from Tom, while I sat quietly doing my lessons.

'I believe it was great cráic* altogether. He met Sergeant Boyle in the town and he told him to hop on the bike, saying he'd give him a spin, round the square? Sure the Sergeant thought nothing of it and him walking up and down the town... on duty by the way.'

'Musha I wonder is that true?' interrupted my mother.

'True! Sure didn't I see it meself with me own two eyes,' sniffed Tom as he pulled the stem out of his pipe and cleared the blockage with one blast of his lungs, his ample chest heaving with the humour of it all. 'I was turning in the cows to go milking when I saw Snowy passing by the gate and Sergeant Boyle perched behind him, in full battle dress. But faith he wasn't long taking off the hat, because Snowy wouldn't stop. "Ah bejeepers, bejeepers, go easy, go easy!" But Snowy wouldn't stop until he had him landed within in Cashelray. "Come in and we'll have a drink" says Snowy. And who did they meet but a few fellas home from England. The next thing Snowy called for drinks for everyone and told the landlady that Sergeant Boyle was paying for it; saying it was his round. "I'm alright, I'm alright," pipes up a little man at the far end of the counter. "I know you're alright, you miserable fucker, but can't you drink a pint, seeing the Sergeant paying for it," says Snowy. "And with any bit-a-luck he'll summon you one of these days, for beating your wife."'

Listening to Tom describing the events, I was taken by his use of the word Cashelray. I knew he meant Castlerea which was the nearest large town to us.

'Musha I wonder did he say or do that?' gasped my mother, questioningly. I could see she was mortified Snowy could have behaved in such an ill manner

---

* Cráic *(fun)*.

while Ned's ageing jowl creased with unbridled joy as Tom continued.

'He did; and worse! Anyway, the upshot of it all was, they stayed drinking all day. I was talking to Mickey Hara and he said you should have seen Snowy the other night below in McHugh's pub, imitating the little man after he got the free drink from Sergeant Boyle. Snowy reckoned he couldn't see him behind-the-pint he was that small,' snorted Tom, as his powerful frame shuddered with the hilarity of it all. 'Snowy left home that morning to go to the town for a bag'een-a-flour. He knew if he went home at the end of the day without it, her ladyship wouldn't be too pleased. And what did he do before he left Cashelray, but buy a ten stone bag-a-flour. He threw it across the front of the motorbike and brought it home, drunk and all as he was. People thought 'twas a ghost...when they saw it flying ...'

'Ah...now... now I dunno about that?' said my mother, irritably. 'If you ask me, talk is cheap. Anyway, I don't know what Colleen ever saw in him. And what's worse he seems to have no notion of going back to England, where he might get a decent job: him coming home by the way, to work the land.'

'Land?' smiled my father, 'Sure he's not cut out for land. I think he'd rather work in hell, than work the land?'

'He would then!' agreed Tom.

'What possessed her to marry him then?' asked my mother giving my father a quizzical look, as she nestled the teapot amid the glowing embers on the hearth stone.

'And sure what's work or land got to do with it?' asked my father, perplexed, as Tom added his penny's worth,

'Ah, they'll get on. As my father – the Lord have mercy on him – used to say; we never died a winter yet. Look at the birds, they never did a-stroke-work in their life and doesn't the Good Lord clothe and feed them?'

'Ah clothe me backside?' Upon–my oath, Tom Farrell, the man that doesn't earn his living by the sweat of his brow, 'ill not last long, let me tell you that,' said my mother putting three mugs on the table.

'You know I used to hear our John saying, when he'd come home from England, that there were men over there, who never knew what it was to do a day's work. They were too intelligent he said. Somehow or other they could show you a simpler way to do a job. They were soon made foremen and they ended up earning twice as much as the men doing all the work. And if you said anything to the foreman, he'd soon tell you he was getting paid from the neck up while you were getting' paid from the shoulder down,' sniggered Tom, joyously 'Look at the job himself and Colleen have done on the house.'

'Well...it's alright I suppose,' agreed my mother, softening slightly. 'But who's going to pay for it?'

'Aaaah never mind... who'll pay for it!' said Tom as he took a thick slice of soda bread and jam that my mother had passed to him, 'They're young yet. It'll all be paid for, in God's own time. Money isn't everything you know!

Look at Tommy the post; and he working every day of his life! And what good is it to him, now?'

After a moment's silent reflection my father replied,

'I dunno…but 'tis true for you.'

I sat quietly at the table taking in everything that was being said. Tom Farrell had such a way with words I liked listening to him. I began to recall the night I went rambling with my father to John Tarmey's house. Tom was there too. There, the subject of Snowy and his motor bike was raised. John Tarmey sat hunched over the fire, expressing his opinion, while quietly stroking Shep, his faithful dog.

'…The man's good for nothing! Sure he doesn't know how to work! You'd wait a long time before you'd see the track of a shovel on the knee of that fella's britches. But you wouldn't have to wait too long to see a hole in the arse of his trousers', said John

'And sure that shouldn't be held against him? He mightn't be too keen to work the land, but he sure as hell knows how to work the head,' quipped Tom. 'Did you hear the stunt he pulled on the Guards in Cashelray?'

'Naw, I didn't,' answered John dismissively, 'I suppose he gave them a wrong name: isn't that what all the so called smart-alecks do, when they get caught.'

'Well he didn't,' answered Tom proudly. 'He used his head quicker than any man I know. There were two Guards on point duty in the town. Says one of them,

' "I see you have no tax?"

"Well, I must be having the devil's own luck; this is me second time to get stopped today", says Snowy.

"Why, were you stopped before?" asked the Guard.

"I was stopped in Williamstown. I was on me way down here to the Medical Hall. I have a sick cow at home," says Snowy. "If I don't get something for her quickly, she'll die on me."

"In that case", says the Guard "you'd better get goin' and look after the cow: but for God's sake get your motor bike taxed."'

'Snowy landed home that evening; and went into McHugh's pub. He met Sergeant Boyle and a few of his cronies and told them the story and him not having been stopped in Williamstown at all. That's the man that has brains for you,' added Tom cheerfully.

'Umn,' sighed John Tarmey, as he wriggled uncomfortably in his chair, 'Sometimes I think it would be easier to eat all you'd see, than believe half all you'd hear.'

Tom and my father laughed heartily as John Tarmey continued his summing up. 'From what I hear, that Sergeant Boyle's afraid of his arse. If he was a proper law man, he'd have taken the licence off Snowy. That'd soon put an end to his trickery.'

Again Tom and my father laughed,

My mother roused me from my dreams and brought me back to reality when she suddenly said,

'John, have you any notion at all of going to bed? Surely to God you must have them lessons done by now? I'll be making some goody* in a minute, would you like some?

'Yes please.' I answered, gathering up my books and pencils, while Tom Farrell stood up to go home. When the goody* was ready she poured it into a tin mug for me and added a spoon of sugar. And having devoured it all, I went off to bed hale and hearty.

* * * *

On Sunday afternoons – particularly during the summer months, I'd be let run up across to Colleen's house so that I could play with Una and Sadie and their brother Kevin. Sometimes Snowy would be there, putting Una and Sadie through their dancing paces, while Colleen accompanied them on the violin.

Colleen was said to be one of the finest fiddle players in the parish and frequently played at house parties. Snowy was stone mad for music and would think up any excuse to start a bit of entertainment.

I was making my way up across the fields to Colleen's house when I heard the motor bike going vroom, vroom, vroom. The side and back of the house was shaded for the most part by trees and hedgerows so I could see nothing. I ran across the last of the boggy fields to reach the house as fast as I could in case Snowy was gone by the time I arrived. I dashed through the little gate leading onto their front street, half expecting to see Snowy on his way to the town. Instead, I saw him circling round the hayfield directly opposite the house and Colleen sitting behind him. They were riding round the newly tramped field as if they hadn't a care in the world.

Soon, Una and Sadie and I were given a tour of the big field. It was beyond my wildest dreams as I sat on the petrol tank while the two girls sat behind their father. We rode bumpily across the field in our short sleeves, as the wind ran soothingly through our hair. It was so exciting driving in and out amid all the dome shaped cocks of hay while Colleen stood close to the gate, rocking baby Kevin to sleep. After a while Snowy dropped us off and dared Colleen to drive the motor bike round the field on her own. I could see Colleen was terrified at the prospects of handling such a monstrous looking machine. But the last thing Colleen wanted was to give in.

'How much will you give me, if I do it?'

Snowy laughed heartily. He thought about the proposition for a moment,

'I'll…I'll give you ten pounds if you ride it non-stop round the field,' he

---

* Goody *(warm milk and bread).*

said with a broad smile.

'Make it twenty,' teased Colleen.

'No! No! It's ten pounds or nothing: you can hump it or lump it!' said Snowy, mischievously.

'Show me the ten pounds. Knowing you; you bastard you mightn't have it.'

Snowy took out his wallet and flashed a brand new ten pound note.

'All right; but I'm only going round once. You have to give me the money the minute I get back.'

'Don't worry your pretty little head about that.,' Laughed Snowy, in his bulging rolled-up shirt sleeves. 'All you have to do is, go right round the field, round all the cocks-a-hay at the end of the field and back to where I'm standing. Do that and I'll see you get your ten pounds.'

After giving her instructions on how to control the bike, she very cautiously threw her leg over the saddle while Snowy adjusted the throttle. And before Colleen knew what was happening the bike took off giddily and she began to scream. But she kept her composure, guiding the machine steadily as she made her way down one side of the big field before slowly circling to make her way back up the other side As Colleen approached us, we could see she was in two minds what to do next. She was too terrified to touch the brakes despite Snowy's explicit instructions. Instead of stopping Colleen flew past us screaming, 'How do you stop it? How do you stop it?'

Snowy was enjoying the spectacle too much, to do anything about it. Instead he stood looking on laughing. When the motor bike came round a second time he shouted, I'm going into the house to make the tea; come in when you're ready.'

Again Colleen went round the field, afraid to touch anything. After pleading for help one last time, she was forced to make a critical decision. As she was unable to stop the motor bike, she deliberately guided it into the nearest cock of hay, where it came to an abrupt halt.

As Colleen picked herself up and dusted herself down, Snowy ran to her side.

'Thanks be to God you had the good sense to stop, I was afraid you'd run out of petrol,'

'Where's my ten pounds?'

'Ah... ha! You didn't bring the bike back, like you were supposed to. That was the deal,' laughed Snowy.

'You lying toad,' she shouted, giving him an almighty clatter across the face. 'You told me you'd give it to me once I circled the field. Now give it to me.'

'Sweetheart, you're good, you're good, I'll grant you that,' laughed Snowy, dismissing her argument. 'All you had to do was ease back the throttle and pull the brake like I told you. But no; you had to go showing off,' he jeered, sarcastically.

And as they both ended up wrestling playfully in the fallen hay, the wallet fell out of Snowy's pocket. Quick as a flash Colleen snatched it and ran towards the house with Snowy in hot pursuit. Suddenly she stopped by the well, screaming at Snowy,

'Stop! Stop you bastard or I'll drop it in the well,' she said, holding the wallet tantalisingly over the bottomless pit that was as deep and as dark as it was dangerous.

Snowy stopped in his tracks, threatening,

'Don't, don't you dare! Don't... you... dare! That's all the money I have.'

Keeping one eye on Snowy she opened the wallet and said,

'Oooh, you lying toad: look all the money you have!'

Quickly peeling off a twenty pound note she again held the wallet over the well that was lined with green scum which was a perfect camouflage for the numerous frogs and other creatures that lay lurking in their imprisoned tomb.

'Give me this twenty and I'll give you back your wallet!'

'But sweetheart that's all I have to me name. I'll give you the ten like we agreed...'.

'Shut up, shut up! And stay where you are! Don't dare come near me or I swear I'll drop it.'

'You wouldn't dare?' teased Snowy as he inched his way closer. Suddenly Colleen tossed the wallet over Snowy's head and took off with her crumpled twenty pound note round the back of the granary which was the other side of the house. Snowy took off after her but she was too quick for him and he gave up. The girls picked up the wallet and ran to meet their father, before giving it back to him, while Colleen watched from a safe distance.

Soon, the two girls and I were racing round the field again, playing games as we hid behind the cocks of hay. After some time we heard Colleen throwing down a challenge to Snowy as he rode round the field. The next thing he was attempting to stand like a circus clown on the saddle while the bike was in motion. He set the motor bike in low gear and quickly stood on the saddle as it rolled gently across the field, before he attempted to balance first on one leg, then the other like a high wire artist. But it was his next feat that took our breath away. Whilst the bike was still in motion, moving slowly across the field, he stood on his head with his two feet high in the air. Then lowering himself onto the bike again he drove at high speed across the field sending us all fleeing for cover. But Snowy wasn't finished. He went and got two wooden stakes and a roll of barbwire and erected a short wire fence in the middle of the field. When he was satisfied it was set at the right height he again rode the motor bike steering it towards the barbwire fence. Approaching the barb wire fence, he stood up on the saddle: and as the bike was about to go under he jumped over the wire and landed on the saddle again. He carried out this feat several times, gradually increasing the speed of the bike each time. By now, people cycling along the road and those out on their Sunday afternoon stroll, stopped to have a gawk. When Snowy saw the crowd gathering he turned his bike for the gate and headed up the gravelled path towards the main road. There he paused for a moment while he looked left and right, then he revved up the engine, going, vroom, vroom, vroom, before taking off down the main road at an almighty rate. We could hear the motor bike roaring as it tore up Woodlawn hill: then backfiring as it slowed down approaching Kilnalag Crossroads where it gave two more farts which made us laugh. The Sunday afternoon strollers who'd stopped to have a look were smiling too; their all seeing eyes taking in every aspect of rural life, in all its summer glory.

It had been a wonderfully exciting day I thought as I reluctantly made my way into Colleen's house to say goodbye. It was time for me to go home. It was getting late. And as I ran down across the boggy fields I stopped briefly to listen to the distant roar of Snowy's bike as it came back from the town. For a few moments I sat on a grassy bank, and recalled with glee every acrobatic move Snowy had made. I decided that one day I too would have a motorbike like his. But instead of doing acrobatics, I'd bring my mother to first Mass. It would be so exciting to pull up outside the church gate and watch her alighting, dressed in her long coat and headscarf. She'd be the envy of the parish, I thought as the rest of the parishioners propped their ancient Raleigh bicycles against the wall. After collecting her again, I'd race home and have five sausages for my breakfast. That would be the nicest part, having five whole sausages for myself. When breakfast was over I'd carry my father down to second Mass. After that I'd change my clothes and while my mother was readying the dinner, I'd do all the jobs around the place. Then I'd put on my good clothes again, have my dinner and drive down to the Ball alley field where I'd give all my friends a spin on the motorbike. Then, John Keaveney, EJ Lyons, and the rest of us would tog out in our maroon and white jerseys and beat the living daylights out of Dunmore or Glenamaddy or whoever we happened to be playing.

But it was the unexpected sound of the Angelus bell that brought me to my senses. I knew it was six o'clock and time for me to be at home. I took off across the fields as fast as my two legs would carry me. I was thankful that there were no cattle to hinder my progress. My mother would be angry if I wasn't home by six, like I said. If I was as much as five minutes late she'd give out to me. Besides, my birthday was only a week away. Therefore it was important to do everything I was told.

Chapter Ten

I'm ten years of age and feel as if I'm king of the castle. There are only three houses left in the village and I'm the only child in it. All the children that were there before I came have grown up and gone away. Margaret Collins has built a new house at the head of the new road. Frank and his brother Malachy and two other men built it. Now Frank has given up his Goldfinches and gone to America while Malachy works as a painter in Galway.

My mother and father bought the gardens and workshop off Margaret for twenty pounds. Now we're converting the workshop into a turf shed by taking out the gable wall that backs onto our garden. My father says it will keep the turf dry during the winter and save us having to reek it in the garden.

Collins's old house has been carted away but the concrete floors are clearly visible. Sometimes I play there by pretending Jackie and I are making cribs and catching birds.

Annie Tobin too has a new house. But the old one is still standing. It's being used to house young cattle and hens and turf. Annie lives on her own because her sons have gone to England and now she has to do all the jobs on her own. She spends ages talking to my mother as we pass by her house, on our way to the well. She's forever talking about her sons. If she doesn't hear from them she worries and if she gets a letter from them, she still worries.

'You know I couldn't sleep a wink for the last fortnight, because I hadn't heard from them in such a long time. And now that I know they're working, I still can't sleep. I'd be afraid they'd fall off them tall buildings they're working on in London. I can't help thinking what happened to poor Peter Cornell, the Lord have Mercy on him; and he only tidying up the yard. And there's his poor father, auld Jim, a bit like mesell after rearing a family: and he still ends up on his own, with no one to look after him.'

'Ah things are not as bad as they seem. Everything will work out, with the help of God. Besides you won't feel until they'll be coming home again.'

'I know, I know, that's what I keep telling mesell. But it's such a long time. I'd give anything, Kate, anything, to have them back with me again. And the funny thing is, when they were here I was always giving out to them. They'd come in from work and throw their dirty clothes round the place and I'd have to go round cleaning up after them. If it wasn't that, I'd be patching their trousers. Somehow I always thought – because their father died young

– that they'd stay at home and work the land: but no, they wanted to be off.'

'But didn't they leave you with a lovely home? Look at the comfort you have now, besides me. I still have to go traipsing up and down to that cursed well, while you have running water.

'But what good is comfort when you've no one to share it with?'

'Well…there is that in it I suppose. Sure I'll probably end up the same way meself. If anything happened to Ned, I'd be lost entirely. I'd be depending on poor John.. And there's no knowing what he'll do when he grows up. But if I have anything to do with it he'll stay at home.'

'That's what I thought when I was rearing mine. But look at the village and the way it's changed. Do you remember the house dances; and all the fun we used to have, with all the music and singing and dancing: and now there's no one to do anything; there's hardly a soul left in the village. I know times were hard Kate; and Lord we were poor, but weren't we happy?'

Listening to Annie I couldn't help but look at Kilby's house. It was indeed a sorry looking sight. No one will fix it now because Kilby will not be coming home, my father said. Mickey Billy's house too was showing signs of decay. There were two holes in the thatched roof that were covered with two sheets of galvanised tin to keep the rain out; and now it looked worse than ever.

But the village's loss is my gain. I have the run of Collins's old gardens. I have the run of the village, and explore every inch of the street from one end to the other. I have the run of the parish and each day I travel further and further afield on errands and I make new discoveries. I call Mr and Mrs O'Brien my mother and father because they look after me and I don't know any different. I try to do what I'm told, but very often I end up doing what I'm not told.

I get up at cock crow every morning and I put on the fire. This is easy because there's an ash hole under the grate and each night before they go to bed, my mother and father bury the coals under the grate, cover them over with ashes and throw a few wet sods on top of them. These sods are always bone dry in the morning, having turned into burning coals during the night. As soon as I get up, I root out the burning coals; put them on the grate, add a few dry sods and in no time at all the fire is ablaze. I fill the kittle from one of two buckets beside the back door and I hang it on the crook over the fire and wait for it to boil. As soon as it's boiled, I'm supposed to raise the kettle and put two eggs into the pea tin, ready for when my mother and father get up. While the eggs are boiling I empty out the piss pot that's under my bed by firing it into the drain at the back of the house, where the street gutter runs down by the overhanging briars, nettles and weeds. But the drain lies dormant because it's blocked somewhere further down and now it stinks to high heaven, especially when the weather's warm. I have to be very careful when emptying out the piss pot in case any of the neighbours see me. I never told my mother but one morning I came within a hair's breath of drowning Mickey Billy's wife

Mary as she walked past our house. I nearly died when I saw how close I came to baptising her. With a neat sidestep, she avoided the contents of the piss pot, then glowered at me, in her filthy rags and oversized wellingtons. Now I hold the piss pot behind my back, whilst I look up and down the street in case anyone's coming. Then I sky the amber liquid down into the drain; rinse the pot in the rain barrel and leave it back under the bed. As well as that, I'm supposed to put out the ashes, sweep the floor, dust the chairs and set the table for the breakfast. But sometimes I forget all this and I sit in front of the fire, daydreaming, as I watch the glowing coals create a magical kaleidoscope of matchstick men, cats and dogs. It's comical to see them all standing at the foot of a mountain staring up at the molten lava that threatens to come pouring down on top of them; thereby destroying the entire valley. But it never happens, because Mrs O'Brien shouts at me from the bedroom,

'John, is the kettle boiled yet?'

'It's nearly,' I shout back, playing for time.

Suddenly she appears out of the bedroom, the rollers still in her hair. She lifts the lukewarm kittle and gives out to me because there's too much water in it and it won't be boiled until kingdom come.

'What sort of a simpleton are you at all, that doesn't know how to put on a fire. Jesus, Mary and Holy St Joseph, will you look at the time. Why didn't you tell me it was that time? You're up this last two hours and you're still not ready for school: instead you're sittin' there all morning... like a...like a... Lúdraman.'

She gives me a clatter across the lug and tells to get ready for school and to get out of her sight because she is sick of the sight of my stupidity.

I scamper out the door as quickly as I can; delighted to be away from her as Una and Sadie and some of the other scholars make their way past our house. Most mornings we meet outside the front door and walk down the road together. But if they hear my mother shouting and giving out to me, they run on down to school. When that happens I have to run down the road as I try to catch up with them. Outside the school we play games while we wait for Mr Feathers, the school principal to arrive, so he can open up.

At the back of the school is a high wall to stop the big lads looking at the girls. But they still manage to climb up, to have a peep every now and again. But if they're caught or reported, Mr Feathers brings them up to the front of the class and wallops them within an inch of their lives.

After school the atmosphere at home is different to what it was in the morning. Very often my mother brings Una and Sadie and the rest of their friends into the house to treat them. She gives them bread and jam and biscuits to tide them over, until they have their dinner at home. Some times Una and Sadie stay with us for the rest of the evening. They have the dinner and tea with us which I really like. Now I've friends to play with. But why they stayed in our house besides anyone else was a mystery so I asked them,

'Why do you sometimes stay in our house after school?'

'We stay because it's our Granny's house and because mammy's in the bog; and there's no one to look after us at home. We can stay here as long as we like; and you can't stop us.'

It's my Granny's house, too,' I replied, confidently.

'Mrs O'Brien is not your Granny! She's your mother,' said Una, with a grimace. 'And if she's your mother, she can't be your Granny, that's what my mother told me.'

I hadn't really thought about that very much, but now that Una had said it, I began to feel uneasy. 'Besides, you don't have a Grandmother or Grandfather like us. All you have is a mother and a father. That means you have to stay here because you have no place to go,' added Sadie as she took a rest against the reek of hay in the garden.

I was very disturbed when she said that. It was probably the first time I realised I was different from everybody else. For as long as I could remember, I felt inferior to the other children in school.

All I wanted was to be like Una and Sadie and everybody else. I wanted so badly to have brothers and sisters and aunts and uncles and grandparents. And now I was afraid Una and Sadie would stop coming to my house, because I wasn't like them.

'And will ye stop coming to my house because I have no Granny?'

'Don't be silly. If we stopped visiting we wouldn't get any bread and jam, or biscuits or sweets or apple pie off Granny. Granny always gives us sweet cake because she likes us. And we still get to have our dinner when we go home.'

It was a fierce blow to my self esteem to think I was the only one in the world who'd nobody belonging to them. It was something I grew more conscious of every single day.

Often on our way down to school we'd meet Mickey Billy's cattle as they grazed idly along the side of the road with no one to look after them. When that happened we'd have to climb over the barbed wire ditch to get past them. Several times the arse of my trousers got caught on the barbed wire fence and left a gaping hole in them. Once or twice I had to go around school all day trying to hide my dignity with my hand. But the big lads pulled my hand away and had a good laugh at me because I was deemed to be one of the boarded out boys who'd no one belonging to them. They said I was only a pauper: that my mother and father put me into a Home because they didn't want me. I was very upset as I didn't know what they meant. I was too ashamed to ask my friends or my mother and father; and I was even more afraid what I might hear.

There were about half a dozen boarded out boys in our school. It didn't matter what we did, the big lads still referred to us as paupers and bastards. I thought about telling my teacher Mrs Patterson, once or twice; but I knew that would only make things worse. On top of that I was considered the teacher's pet because I'd run up the road to get her a sally rod whenever I was asked. I hated it when she asked me to get her a sally rod but what could I do. All I wanted was to be like everybody else.

When I tore my trousers on the barbwire I asked Una and Sadie if they'd go into my house before me so my mother wouldn't be able to see the state of my good trousers. While they were talking I slipped down to my room and changed my clothes. Later when I got my mother gone to the well I put a king-sized safety pin in them to hold them together.

The following morning I had to back out the front door to school in case my mother saw them, but she caught me and threatened to kill me stone dead for having ruined my good trousers. I had to tell her what happened; and how Mickey Billy's wandering cattle were to blame.

My father didn't care what I looked like going to school, so long as I helped him when I came home from school: particularly if the weather was fine and there was hay and turf to be saved. I hated saving the hay because using the rake and fork brought blisters out on my hands. When my father was in the bog I had to help him foot or clamp the turf; and that too was hard.

On my way out the door to school every morning, my mother would warn me, 'Listen here now me buckoo, you're not to be dilly dallying coming home. You have to go to the bog this evening and help Daddy save the turf, while the weather's fine.'

When I'd come home she'd have my dinner on the table and be pouring piping hot tea into a large Lucozade bottle in preparation for my trip to the bog.

'You might as well bring a few sandwiches with you: that's if you can manage them on the bike.'

I was really excited at the thought I was being let cycle all the way to the bog on my mother's bicycle, instead of having to walk. Her bicycle was a lot better than my father's; and much easier to cycle on, because there was no bar on it.

She stood out in the street and held the bicycle for me while I hung the bag with its precious cargo on the handlebars, with my rolled up coat on the carrier.

'Are you sure now you'll be able to manage it: that the bike's not too big for you?' she asked.

'I'll manage! I'll manage. Haven't I cycled on it before?' I said, eagerly; taking control of the bike.

'I know you have. But this is the first time you've had to…'

I'll manage the bike alright,' I insisted, anxious to get on the road.

'Make sure not to spill the tea whatever you do; and if that bag is too awkward for you, you can always walk and you'll still have the bike to cycle home,' she said, thoughtfully.

I convinced her that I'd manage it even though I'd only been cycling a few short months. I knew that the bicycle was ten times too big for me: that the sprocket pin on one of the pedals was worn; that the brakes weren't working properly and that the by-road down by the lake was a nightmare with humps and bumps and stones that would break the cross off an ass. Still, I convinced myself that I was used to the road and could manoeuvre my way around the country every bit as good as Shay Elliott in the Tour de France.

I set off down the road at a nice leisurely pace while under my mother's watchful eye. I knew that once I was out of sight, down by the lake, I could pick up a bit of speed. And I knew once I passed the school and was out on the good road I could really open up and create some sort of a world record.

The bog was about three miles from our house or a mile as the crow flies and if you had the wind at your back, you could really fly. But the bag on the handle bars was proving to be a bit of a problem, as my knee kept hitting off it. Still, if I could avoid hitting it I knew I'd make great time. I tried to cycle up the hill opposite Woodlawn graveyard but with the bag hanging on the handlebars it was too much, so I jumped off and walked.

At the top of the hill I could see the road for miles as I jumped on the bike again and began to pick up speed. And even though I wasn't tall enough to reach the saddle I could still knock a fair auld spin out of it.. I put my head down and crouched over the handlebars like I'd seen them do in, *The Connaught Tribune*. I was a professional cyclist as good as any in the world. I could clearly see the finishing line ahead which was exactly where I'd turn right off the good road and into the bog. I took a quick look round to see where the rest of the imaginary cyclists were. Much to my surprise there was a whole bunch of them, right on my tail, ready to attack. We were taking part in the Tour de France, the greatest cycle race in the world. We were about to enter the famous Champs-Elysee in Paris for the fifth and final lap as we whizzed down the final straight at break neck speed. I was within touching distance of the finishing line when Shay Elliott tried desperately to out sprint me. But I swerved sharply to the right to beat him to the line while turning down the gravelled road into the bog. But as soon as the front wheel hit the gravel it skidded along the road, bounced off a low stone wall and catapulted myself and the bicycle into the middle of next week.

After that awful shock and my incredible win, I picked myself up and counted the cost of my success. The rear wheel of the bike was still spinning, but the front one was badly buckled. My two knees were skinned and bleeding and there was a bump on the back of my head the size of a ping pong ball. The sandwiches were scattered all over the bog, but miraculously the bottle of tea had stayed intact and survived the crash. But I could no longer ride the bike because the front wheel was warped like a hula-hoop and I realized I'd have to abandon my wonderful racing machine. I'd have to leave it on the side of the road and leg it all the way into the bog and walk all the way home. I knew for sure I'd be killed stone dead the minute I set foot inside the front door unless

I could think up an excuse.

But first of all I'd have to deal with the bike. I hid it behind a ditch so no one could steal it. If that happened I knew I was in real trouble. I picked up the slices of bread and cheese that were covered in grit and dirt and wiped them clean on my trousers. I slapped the slices of bread together and put them back into the bag and set off on foot.

Across the vast expanse of brown bog stretching for miles and miles, I could see men everywhere with white handkerchiefs on their heads saving the turf. Further away, I could see women in colourful headscarves carrying picnic baskets to their husbands who wore straw hats to ward of the scorching sun. Right across the bogs, plumes of blue smoke could be seen rising skywards which meant some people were boiling eggs and kettles to make their own tea in the bog. Some times my father too would light a fire but only if the two of us were working there all day long.

By the time I reached the bog where my father was working, I was in a state of panic because I knew I'd have to tell him about the bicycle.

As soon as I was within earshot he stopped working, straightened his back, looked at me and said, smilingly 'Well!'

I said, 'Hello,' and left the bag down on the ground.

He looked at me again and saw my bloodied knees. 'What happened to you?' he asked, a concerned look on his brow,

I felt like crying, but I knew I'd have to be brave.

'There's something wrong with the bike,' I said. 'The front wheel stopped going round and round and I fell off. But I hid the bike behind a ditch so no one could steal it,' I added quickly.

'Ah well…' sighed my father, as he bent down to gather up a few more dry sods, 'so long as you weren't hurt it doesn't matter. You behaved well to hide the bike because a bike like that is valuable. If anything were to happen it, herself would go mad, entirely.' Straightening his back again he asked, 'Was it the brakes do you think? They might have got jammed.'

'I don't know…,' I said looking him in the eye. '…I don't think it was.'

'Well, that's the only conclusion I can come to: unless of course something got caught in the spokes.'

'No Daddy, it wasn't anything like that. The spokes are perfect.'

'Ah well… it can't be so bad so,' he said sounding relieved. 'Maybe it's what it needs a good oiling. Come on, in the name of God and we'll have a sup-a-tay,' he added picking up the bag. My father led the way across the sward to where he sat in the shade of the high turf bank, crowned with purple heather. He divided out the sandwiches which had bits of bog dirt, grit and God knows what else on them and never said a word. We sat there talking, passing the bottle to each other after every second bite, washing the crumpled sandwiches down with slugfuls of warm tea.

Then, as my father lay back and had a refreshing smoke he pointed out the various birds to me. I shielded my eyes and peered into the deep blue sky as the Bog Lark soared higher and higher singing away to its heart content until it suddenly stopped and dived like an arrow down into the bog. Each time it did that other Larks took to the air to continue singing high over the sweet scented heather where Snipes took off with explosive speed at the merest disturbance by a dog or hare; their long bills and white undersides clearly visible. The rapid zigzag nature of their flight as they circled the skies with incredible speed was a joy to behold. Watching them, I thought was the nearest thing to heaven but then my father rose to his feet and we had to start clamping the turf again. It was back breaking work trying to sort out the wet from the dry. We had to make fresh little footing with the wet sods so they would dry while at the same time we had to gather up all the dry turf and build them into clamps so they would season. A few hours later as the day was drawing to a close and the sun was sinking in the west, my father straightened his aching back one last time and said it was time to go home. The very mention of the word home made me ill at the thought of what awaited me when my mother found out I'd destroyed her bicycle.

The two of us began the long walk out to where my father had the wheels of his bicycle set in a shallow drain to protect the tyres from the sweltering heat. I could feel the blood draining from my cheeks at the thought of what my father would say when he saw my mother's bicycle.

When finally we got to the head of the road and I pulled the bicycle out from behind the ditch, his dust laden eyes widened in astonishment, as he gasped, 'Christ Almighty! How did you do that? Did someone run over you?'

I swallowed my Adams apple and said, 'No! It …it just happened. The bike stopped working.'

'Ah! Happened my arse! If you drove over it with a bloody tractor you couldn't do that much damage. How come you're not killed? Are you sure… you're all right?'

'I am. Look!' I said, as I sprang out over the ditch with one bounding leap and landed on the road beside him. But he wasn't impressed. He took hold of the bicycle and tried to wheel it but the front wheel squeaked and wobbled before getting jammed in the fork. In a fit of temper, my father fired the bicycle back in over the ditch again and said,

'Sure that thing's no bloody use, now. I'll have to leave it and pick it up with the horse and cart. And I have more to be doing than coming up here to bring home a wreck like that.'

Recovering from the shock, he helped me up onto the bar of his bicycle. And as he eased himself away from the ditch he said, 'I don't know in the name of God what you're going to say to that woman when you go home. It's a miracle you survived; what ever the hell you did. You must have been going too fast and skidded on the corner?'

I said nothing because my ears were on fire. I held on tightly to the handlebars as the bicycle free wheeled down Woodlawn hill past the graveyard, drawing closer and closer to home.

When we got home it was a great relief to find my mother was not there. She had left a note on the table; she'd gone visiting and had left a pot of goody by the fire for us. While I was heating it up, my father washed his hands outside the back door. When he came in, he poured the goody into a mug for me and added a spoon of sugar. He sat by the fire and ate his straight out of the saucepan. I ate and drank mine as quickly as I could and watched the milk running down my father's stubbled chin that was stained with bog dirt and tobacco. I rushed off to bed so I wouldn't have to tell my mother what happened to her bicycle.

But when I came home from school the following day she was standing inside the front door, waiting for me. She caught me by the hair and dragged me around the room as she let off a powerful jet of steam,

'What in the name of God did you do to my bicycle yesterday?'

I stood looking at her, my mouth half open, unable to speak. Quick as a flash she grabbed me by the hair again and shook me like a rag doll, 'Answer me, will you; you amadawn, before I kill you?'

As I began to cry I said, 'It was an accident.'

An accident! An accident: what kind of an accident?' she bellowed, still holding me by the hair. When I didn't answer her, she shouted again, 'What kind of an accident was it that made kittle-binders of my brand new bicycle? Damn you will you speak up!'

'I tried to stop the bike, but I couldn't,' I cried, feeling that she was going to pulverize me entirely unless I said something, because she still had a powerful grip of my hair, which felt as if the top of my head was about to come away from my skull.

'You tried to stop! You tried to stop! Don't you know you can't stop a jennet when it's going too fast? You were going too fast on that bloody bicycle. I knew I should never have let you up on it, the first day ever.' She let go of my hair and caught me by the scruff of the neck and shook me back and forth before continuing, 'didn't I tell you to take your time: and to go easy on the road. Didn't I tell you that?'

'You did,' I cried.

'And why didn't you do it? Why couldn't you take your time like I told you? Why?'

'Because a dog ran out in front of me,' I lied

'Jesus, Mary and Holy St Joseph, is it a lie you're after telling me?'

'No, it's not!' I said, feeling I had to say something to convince her I wasn't cycling too fast.

'A dog ran out in front of you! What sort of a dog was it?'

'A black one, he shot out in front of me and I couldn't stop because the handle of the brake got caught in the strap of the bag. I couldn't pull the brake… until it was too late.'

She let go of my collar and stood there in front of me, her hands on her broad hips: her fingerprints clearly visible on her flour smudged blue apron. 'And whose dog was it or do you know?'

'I don't know.'

'You don't know! You don't know! You know nothing because you don't want to know. I never in all my life met anyone like you. You know absolutely nothing. You don't even know how to ride a bicycle. *I'll manage, I'll manage!* That's all I could get out of you yesterday when I asked if you'd be able to cycle with a bag. I'll manage. Troth it'll be a long, long time before you'll manage a bicycle again: a long, long time I'm telling you that,' she said, turning round to poke up the fire and to warm my dinner.

'What harm but I was trying to save up a few pounds to buy a radio. But no, I can't even have that much pleasure. Now I have to go and fix that cursed bicycle and I not even having the price of it,' she added, as she began to put my dinner plate on the table.

When she mentioned the word radio it was an awful shock. She had never mentioned the word to me before, ever: not even when I told her John Keaveney said his mother was after buying a radio. Now I felt really bad. If I hadn't broken the bicycle my mother would have been able to buy a radio off Johnny Smyth and I too would have been able to listen to it every day. It would have been like having a friend in the house: one that you could listen to telling stories, with maybe an odd song every now and again. The mere thought of that alone, was enough to make me want to cry. But I didn't because I knew I'd have to be brave.

After my dinner, I tip-toed down into my room to change my clothes, in case she attacked me again. It was such a relief to have weathered the storm, I thought, as I changed my clothes so I could go outside. And as I cleaned out the hens' cabin, it began to dawn on me the cost of my heedlessness in not listening to what she had told me. I was gutted when I realised that because of my behaviour she could no longer afford to buy a radio or a wireless as some of the lads in school called it. I never knew she'd planned to buy a radio. I would have given anything to hear a radio in our house, but now the money would have to go on fixing her bicycle.

The following evening after driving the cows up into the big field beside Colleen's house, I was surprised to see my father coming home from the bog with a small load of turf, with the bicycle on top of it and a shiny new wheel rim which he had bought in Johnny Smyth's garage. A couple of hours later I watched him take the tyre and tube off the old buckled wheel, to fit them on the new one. Then he slotted the wheel back into the fork of the upturned bicycle on the kitchen floor while my mother was up visiting Colleen.

But it was weeks and weeks before I was allowed up on a bicycle again.

Eventually I was allowed to take my father's bicycle on short errands, where I had to warn outlying neighbours about the unexpected arrival of a man from the Department of Agriculture who worked as an enumerator and who wanted to know how many acres of land people had under tillage; as well as the number of cattle, sheep and pigs they had. The O'Briens, when discreetly questioned about a neighbour's stock, would always play down the number by claiming they had lost a cow or two while calving; or that they only had seven or eight head of cattle when they really had ten or twelve. The minute the welfare officer was gone and safely in the house next door I'd be sent on an urgent message to the house under investigation to relay what the O'Briens had said about them.

Back home I'd have to help my father to perform some difficult task, like sculling the cattle. All of our cattle had long horns; particularly the cows. And sometimes in a fight one of the horns would get broken off leaving the animal with a bare stump which my father said was very unsightly if you were trying to sell her. As a result of the horns some farmers sustained serious injuries while tending their cattle. One way of dealing with it was to dehorn the cattle by slipping on a pair of rubber rings. The rings were very tight and had to be slid on as close as possible to the skull. Six weeks later the horns would fall off, leaving a gaping wound either side of the animal's head. To make the job easier, my father began to scull our calves when they were about a year old: just as the horns were beginning to grow. As well as that, our cattle had to be continuously dosed for some aliment or other. A young calf might have a bad dose of scour and unless treated properly would surely die. At the same time a full grown bullock might be eating the tail of another animal. When that happened, the animal doing the damage was referred to as a trimmer and had to be dosed with a bottle of stale urine. First thing in the morning, my father would empty the piss pot into a large whiskey bottle which he'd then seal and leave high up on the shelf in the back kitchen for a few days, until it was rank as he called it. When it was deemed ready, my father would put the trimmer into the stable and tie it to the manger nearest the back wall, which meant it had very little room to move. And it was my job to help him by holding the bottle of medicine. My father would catch hold of the trimmer by inserting his fingers into the animal's nostrils. He'd pull the head alongside its neck forcing the animal to wedge itself up against the wall, where it could not move because it was held in a vicelike grip. Holding its nose firmly with his left hand he'd take the bottle from me and insert the neck of it into the corner of the trimmer's mouth and force the entire contents down its gullet. Very often we'd have to dose the trimmer two or three times, but it always worked.

Another important job I had to do was to help bring the cow to the bull. This was a job we had to do several times a year; depending on how many cows we had and whether or not they kept when serviced. We only had three cows at most and sometimes only two. It was a nightmare bringing a cow to the bull as they didn't like being separated from the herd. A bulling cow or heifer would break all before them in an effort to stay with the herd. As my father and I drove one of our cows to Meehan's bull for the first time, she never stopped trying to break into other cattle along the road. When we were near Meehan's house I had to race ahead, to turn the cow in off the main road and into the yard. Meehan's yard was an enclosed area where a cow couldn't get out, once the gate was closed. As soon as Mr Meehan showed his face he'd ask,

'Which bull will I bring out; the black or the red short horn?'

'I'll stick with the black, I think. She'd a good calf from him the last time, so I'd better stick with him.'

Mr Meehan led the fearsome looking bull into the yard with a heavy chain attached to its flaring nostrils. As soon as he introduced the bull, the cow started rising on him. When the bull tried to do the same thing the cow suddenly turned and began pucking him away with her horns. Mr Meehan was very patient and kept walking the bull round and round while holding an enamel jug in his hand. Eventually the cow grew tired twisting and turning. In an instant the bull rose and did what he was supposed to do. I was fascinated to see the bull's willy plunge into the cow and a stream of white liquid squirt out of it as the cow ran out from under him. Quick as a flash Mr Meehan threw what looked like a jug of water on the bull's willy.

'Isn't she a walking bitch? You think she'd stand. He might have done enough, you'd never know. If she keeps, well and good; if not, you'll have to bring her back again,' said Mr Meehan, before leading the bull back into the stable.

On our way home I questioned my father about the bull's behaviour.

'Why did the bull put his willy into the cow like that?'

'Because that's what a bull does when he's bulling a cow. Don't you remember our cow calving?'

'I do.'

'Well, if that cow hadn't been bulled there would be no calf. A cow has to be bulled before she can have a calf. Sometimes a cow won't keep and will start bulling again three weeks after you've brought her to the bull. If you want a cow to have a calf, you have to keep bringing her to the bull until she keeps. And if the cow keeps, she'll calf eleven months later.'

After considering what he told me and realising that there wasn't an awful lot of difference between what I had between my legs and what the bull had, I asked,

'And where do babies come from?'

'Oh… that's a different job entirely. Where do you think they come from?' asked my father.

'I don't know. Una and Sadie said their mother found baby Kevin under a head of cabbage. But when I asked mammy she said you could find a baby under a bush or a head of cabbage. I've looked everywhere but I still haven't seen any.'

'Ah well, that because there weren't any. When you hear a baby crying that's when you start looking. You could find a baby anywhere but generally it's under a bush or a head of cabbage.'

When we turned in the school road there was a black cow looking at us over a garden gate. She reminded me of the bull.

'And why did Mr Meehan throw water over the bull's willy?' I asked, as our cow walked quietly along the road in front of us. Somehow she seemed quieter, more content than when we were bringing her.

'That wasn't water; that was disinfectant. Meehan was disinfecting the bull's rod. A bull's willy is called a rod. When a bull rises on a cow like that he's serving her or bulling her, which means the same thing. If Mr Meehan didn't disinfect the bull the cow might get a disease and there would be no calf. It's the same as if you went to Dr Roland. He might have to give you an injection to make you better. Then he throws the needle away so the next person won't catch a disease off it'.

'I never knew that.'

'Well, now you know,' said my father, cheerfully.

When we arrived home we turned the cow into the stable for a few hours, to let her settle.

And as I ran contentedly back into the house, little did I realize I was about to hear some extraordinary news, that would take me a long time to appreciate.

Chapter Eleven

My first letter 1957

'There's a letter there for you on the window. It came a while ago, so I suppose you'd better open it,' my mother suggested as soon as I walked through the front door.

She reached across the table to the window sill and handed me the letter. I was very frightened because I didn't know what it meant. I had never had a letter from anyone before and I wondered if I had done something wrong. I knew letters were serious documents that were either from friends in England or America or else some sort of forms that had to be filled in and signed like the dole form my father signed during the winter. When I looked at the address I was really puzzled because it was addressed to: Master Paschal Rodgers, Lakeland, Williamstown, Co. Galway.

Master Paschal Rodgers, I thought. Nobody had ever called me that before and I wondered if it was a joke. As I stood looking at the letter, wondering what to do with it my mother said,

'Open it, can't you… it's all right, it's for you. Your name is on it? Read it out in the name of God until we see what it says.'

I opened the letter and as I did so a small black and white photograph – no bigger than a large sized postage stamp – fell to the ground.. My mother picked it up while I unfolded the letter. I was unable to read it as I was still in a state of shock wondering why anyone would want to write to me.

'Having failed to read a single word, my mother looked at me and said,

'Well Jesus… if that's the best you can do… I don't know why I'm sending you to school? Here…let me read it for you!'

Putting on her reading glasses she began,

Magdalene
Home
College Road
Galway

Dear Paschal,
How are you? I waited so long to find out where you were, living: I can't
believe I've found you. I hope that you are happy and in good health as this
leaves myself at present, thank God. I would like you to write a letter to me and
tell me how you are. Also, I want you to thank Mr and Mrs O'Brien for looking
after you so well. I hope that you'll be able to come in and see me some time.
I'm sending you a photograph of myself that was taken last summer. I've put
an x on the photograph so that you'll know who I am. I hope you like it. Please
send me a photograph of yourself if you have one. If you haven't, please ask
Mrs O'Brien if she could have one taken of you and I will pay her for it.
Paschal dear, I'll be sending you a parcel soon with a few things in it. I hope
that you're good and that you do everything you're told.

God bless you Paschal, and please write soon.

With best wishes
From your mother,
Bridie.

My mother showed me the photograph, saying, 'There you are now. That must
be Bridie in the middle?'

I looked at the picture. It was of a large group of girls dressed in white.
All of them were wearing white caps except the woman who had an x marked
over her head. She had black curly hair. I was still in a state of shock having
received a letter from someone I didn't know. And when my mother didn't
say anything, I didn't say anything. That night after being allowed to stay
up a while, she said it was time to go to bed; that she would close the hens'
cabin herself. I went to bed, but all I could think about was the letter: and that
someone was going to send me a parcel: soon. I'd never had a parcel sent to
me before and I was wondered what could possibly be in it. My mother had
often got parcels from America with skirts and blouses that she wouldn't wear
because they were too gaudy, she said. And now somebody was going to send
me a parcel from Galway. Why would someone send me a parcel when I'd
never received one before, I asked myself?

When I'd forgotten all about it, I came home from school one day, to see
a big brown parcel on the table, addressed to Master Paschal Rodgers. I didn't
know which excited me more, seeing the words Master Paschal Rodgers in big
bold letters or what might be inside the parcel. Everyone in school called me

John, but here I was getting letters and parcels addressed to Master Paschal Rodgers. My mother stood looking at me, hands on her hips,

'Well! Aren't you going to open it?'

I tried untying the knots, but my hands were trembling. My mother took down the scissors that was hanging on the side of the dresser and said,

'Here you are! And don't cut the fingers off yourself!'

I cut the twine and tore open the parcel and discovered a whole load of goodies inside: lucky bags, hankies, pencils, rubbers, socks; a pair of gloves, a jumper and a shirt as well as a beautiful mouth organ. My mother was very pleased and made me try on the maroon coloured jumper which was a bit on the big side. She said it would come in handy for Mass on Sundays, when I was a bit older.

The following day she collared me and put me sitting at the table. She handed me a pen and a writing pad and told me to write a letter to my mother, to thank her for the letter and the parcel.

I look at her questioningly because I'd never written a letter before.

'Well God blast you! Are you not able to write a letter? What are they teaching you in school that you're not able to write a few lines? Here!' she said, pointing to the top right hand corner of the page: 'write your name and address there.'

I made several attempts to do as I was told but had to tear out the pages and start all over again before it was to her liking. Standing, looking over my shoulder like my teacher Mrs Patterson, she said,

'Write, Dear Bridie, over here on the left,' pointing to where I was to write, 'and say, whatever you want to say to her underneath that. Just thank her for the parcel and the few things and sign it from your son, Paschal.'

When I'd finished she said,

'Well God Blast you, could you not have said a little bit more and thanked her for the lucky bags. I thought you liked them.'

'I did!'

'Well why don't you tell her that? Write the letters, PS underneath your name there and tell her how you enjoyed them. Then we'll post it off in the name of God.'

John Paschal Rodgers
Lakeland
Williamstown
Co. Galway.

8th October 1957

Dear Bridie,
Thank you very much for the big parcel. It was wonderful. I liked the socks and

the hankies and the pencils. Goodbye, from your Son

Paschal

P.S. I almost forgot. I would like more lucky bags because our shopkeeper said he was out of luck and that I was lucky that I knew someone that had lots and lots of luck. Goodbye.

My mother read the letter again and put it into an envelope along with a letter of her own. She brought down a stamp she had above in her room, stuck it on the envelope and sent me running to the town to post it. When I got home I asked Mrs O'Brien,

'Mammy, why did I have to sign the letter, from your son?'

'Look, you're far too young to understand anything like that. How many times have I told you, that children should be seen and not heard? You should go down to that room and study your lessons. It would be more in your line instead of going around asking stupid questions.'

I had to go down to my room and pretend I was doing my lessons. It was an awful feeling to be told I was stupid when all I was trying to do was get some answers to a few simple questions. Why was Bridie writing letters to me from Galway when she hadn't written before? And why was she saying she was my mother when the whole world knew Mrs O'Brien was my mother? Or was she? For the first time I began to have niggling doubts. If Bridie was my mother why was she living in Galway?

After thinking about it for a while, I came to the conclusion that Bridie might be a secret grandmother. Most of my friends in school had grandmothers. Some even had great grandmothers. But I couldn't ask Mrs O'Brien about Bridie because I knew she'd give out to me.

Ever since my disastrous trip to the bog, on Mrs O'Brien bicycle, she has been talking non-stop about getting a radio. Nearly every shop in the town had a radio or as some people called it, a wireless.. What the difference was I never knew. I was of the opinion that country people called it a wireless while people in the town called it a radio. I preferred to call it a radio because I thought it sounded better. The priest's housekeeper had a radio. Colleen had a radio. Nan Little had a radio. But it was still a shock for me to come home from school and see a brand new *Pye* radio on the corner of our kitchen table. I was excited at the thought that there would now be something else I could listen to. I was tired listening to Mrs O'Brien, giving out to me every single day. And as I stood and stared at the gleaming mahogany radio, I put my hand on the clear lacquered surface while she turned it on. As I attempted to examine the radio in more detail by twisting a knob she slapped my hand out of the way,

'Don't you dare leave a hand on that radio… or I'll kill you stone dead.'

When she turned the black knob to demonstrate her pride and joy, I could hear some music in the background as it made a crackling hissing sound. She turned it up a bit but the hissing continued. It got so loud you could hardly hear the music.

'Blast it to hell! What's wrong with it? I wonder if it's the battery. According to Johnny Smyth the battery is supposed to last three months. I'll have to ask him to look at it again. Anyway, you'd better eat your dinner.'

'Will it play music like that all the time?'

'I don't know. Sure I'm only after getting it. He brought it up to me an hour ago; and it was working great while he was here, what ever the hell he did to it. There's supposed to be a good programme on, every Saturday night with music and everything. But I'm afraid... if it's going to be crackling like that; I'd be as well off without it.'

'Look!' I said. 'It says, London on the glass... and...... Glas-gow and... BBC Light. Oh! I can see the light there, behind the glass!'

'Look!' shouted Mrs O'Brien, pushing me away, 'Will you stand back from it, in the honour of God before you break it.'

She turned it off altogether and gave it a light dusting with her apron, saying, 'I don't know in the name of God how I'm going to mind it with you. You have your nose stuck in everything.'

On Saturday morning, I was pottering around the house doing the usual jobs like bringing in turf, tidying my bedroom, as well peeling carrots and parsnips for Sunday's dinner while my father was paring the horse's hooves outside the stable door. Mrs O'Brien had gone home to Englishtown to visit her brother Tailor for the day. His real name was Archibald she said, but she never liked it. She preferred to call him Tailor because he was a famous tailor who used to make suits for big shots in Galway. Now he was retired and living in Englishtown – which was her home place – and came down to visit her every now and again. But he wasn't able for the long journey, anymore he said. I loved it when Tailor came to our house, he was so funny. He was always telling stories, but the minute he'd set foot inside the door I'd be sent outside to play. But I'd sneak round the back of our house to the front window, where I could listen.

When my father had finished the horse's hooves and we'd eaten our dinner, which Mrs O'Brien had left for us, he sat down opposite the radio and began twiddling with the knobs. As he did so the radio made a loud crackling noise. He had to turn it off a few times to stop the noise, before carefully turning it on again. I stood beside him listening to the various sounds. Suddenly I could hear a man in a clear distinctive voice say, 'This is the BBC world service.' He then said something about Moscow and London and the Far East. And then my father turned one of the knobs and the thin red line that was behind the glass glided along to the right towards the word Athlone. Suddenly a voice was roaring excitedly, 'It's a try for Ireland. Jackie Kyle has touched down for a magnificent try for Ireland. The ball bobbling about before he managed to control it; after a magnificent pass from Tony O'Reilly. A wonderful try, against the run of play it must be said, but one that should now set up Ireland for a grandstand finish...'

Ireland and England were playing, but every so often the sound would fade away completely. I watched my father's face break into a smile as he held his ear close to the radio. Again, Ireland had the ball and were charging up the field. Again, the voice faded and my father's face dropped like a stone and he sighed deeply. He turned away from the radio in disgust and as he did so the sound came up again, but England were still leading. When the game was over my father and I went about our chores, trying to make up for lost time. Mrs O'Brien was due home in an hour.

'We better shape up if we want to have everything done,' he said.

'Will I feed the hens now or is it too early?'

'I don't care… it's up to yourself. Did you bring in the eggs?' he asked, as he lifted a huge pot of potatoes off the fire and carried the pot outside the back door where he drained off the boiling water.

'I did, but there weren't many, only nine. Mammy said the hens stop laying when the weather's cold. Is that true?'

'I'm afraid it is. If the weather's too cold they won't lay.'

'I'll run out and check in case there are any more.'

As I ran out, my father began to pound the pot of boiled potatoes with the wooden pounder. He added a few scoops of pig meal from the large two cwt bag that sat on a stool in the back kitchen. As soon as he began pounding, half a dozen hens appeared and fought for the few bits of potatoes that flew from the pounder each time he smashed it down on the spuds. When he'd finished pounding, he added a bucket of skim milk and mixed it all up, turning it into a pot of pig swill.

I had returned with three filthy duck eggs I'd found buried in the dirty straw in a corner of the hens' cabin. The ducks were experts at covering their eggs. It was a miracle, they has started laying again, I thought. We hadn't had an egg from them in ages. I washed the duck eggs and put them into the bowl my mother normally used. I couldn't wait to tell Mrs O'Brien about the eggs but then my father took one look at the eggs and shook them close to his ear.

'I'd say they're rotten by the sound of them,' he said, as he proceeded to bring the three eggs out to the garden. He hopped one of the eggs off a stone wall and the stench that followed was so overpowering it was beyond belief. Without further ado, he fired the other two into the hedge, saying, 'Ah, I was thinking, 'twas too good to be true. Ducks don't lay eggs this time of the year. They must have been there God knows how long? It's a great wonder you didn't find them earlier, when you were supposed to clean out the cabin?'

He poured some of the gruel into the pigs' bucket. The rest he kept over for Sunday. It was the only day of the week when we didn't have to boil potatoes for the pigs.

'When are we going to kill a pig?' I asked.

'Ah, I dunno. We might kill one next year; if we can afford it. We'll have to wait and see,' he answered as he removed the big heavy stone that helped to keep the pigs' door shut. He slid back the two strong bolts and opened the door. The minute the two pigs heard us approaching, they started screeching as if they'd never been fed before and jumped at the door trying to force their way out. Already the bottom of the door had been eaten and repaired several times. As soon as the door was opened the two pigs jumped up, trying to get at the bucket. Moving quickly to the right, my father emptied the bucket of gruel into the pigs' trough and the two pigs started gobbling it up. As he turned to close the door one of the pigs suddenly heaved the trough over on its side, spilling the entire contents, 'Serves ye bloody well right! The devil-a-bit-more I'm given ye,' said my father, angrily, annoyed after all the hard work he'd put into mixing the gruel for them.

'Will they not be hungry?'

'I don't care whether they are or not. It's not my fault. Hopefully, I'll be shut of them next week.'

'Are we bringing them to the fair?' I asked excitedly, knowing I'd have a great day in the town if we were.

'We are. But whether we sell them or not is another thing,' said my father as he crossed the garden to where there was an old upturned skillet that had one of its three legs broken. My father left down the bucket and carefully tilted the skillet while he put his hand under it and caught hold of a big white rooster that had been imprisoned all night.

'Why do you always put the chickens under the pot before you kill them?'

'To starve them! You can't go killing a chicken unless it has been fasting twenty four hours, otherwise they'd stink you out of it when you'd go to clean them. Besides, the meat wouldn't taste right. By rights, you're supposed to leave fowl hanging for a few days after you kill them, to tenderise the meat. That's why, when you kill a turkey or a goose for the Christmas, you leave them hanging ten or twelve days.'

I stood watching my father as he held the rooster by the legs with one hand and pulled his neck with the other. When he'd broken its neck, its wings started flapping wildly, signifying that it was about to die. I had seen my father kill chickens several times and was looking forward to the day when I too would have the strength to kill one of them for the dinner. When the rooster was dead, my father sent me into the house for the sharp knife. As soon as he had the knife in his hand, he went over to the hedge and cut off the head. He held the rooster upside down until all the blood had drained away. Then he brought it into the back kitchen and began plucking and cleaning it for Sunday's dinner. Finally, he cut off the two feet which he threw out to the cat; cut off the neck and put it into a jar of vinegar, along with the heart, the liver and the kidneys. Later in the week, Mrs O'Brien would boil the giblets with onions, carrots and parsnips to make soup which I'd have when I'd came home from school.

It was late when Mrs O'Brien came back from Englishtown. I walked up the street to meet her when I saw her cycling in the new road.

'Here, in the name of God; take this bike like a good lad and wheel it into the shed for me. And don't forget to bring in the bag,' she said, handing me her bicycle which she liked to store in Collins's old shed, beside the turf. She took off her gloves and began to untie the silk scarf from around her head.

As I took the bag off the bike, I looked in and saw a sweet cake. a packet of sweets and a pair of trousers. When I brought the bag into the house, Mrs O'Brien gave me some sweets for having done such a good job around the house. Later that night she let me stay up so I could listen to *Céile House* on the radio. First, there was the nine o'clock news which was followed by *Céile House*: a lively programme of music and song. This was followed by *Dear Sir or Madam*, a weekly programme where people wrote letters to the presenter complaining about the government and everything else. After that, it was time for me to go to bed: where thankfully I had something to dream about. It wasn't every day that I was let go to a fair. I could hardly wait for Tuesday. Hopefully we'd sell the pigs and I'd get a new pair of wellingtons as well as the price of a few sweets.

Chapter Twelve

Early on Tuesday morning, I helped my father as he brought our pigs down to the fair. We did this by tying a single rope to one of their hind legs to control them and then we drove them on before us. It was all right while we were walking them down the road but once we were past the school and out on the wide streets the pigs tried to go this way and that and if it wasn't for the rope we'd never have been able to control them.

Already the town was a hive of activity with both sides of the streets being lined with pig laden carts; all part of the great procession that rumbled into town from villages all over the parish and beyond. But farmers living near the town, like the O'Briens traditionally walked their pigs to the fair. When the pigs were sold, they were marked by the buyer and loaded onto lorries, which brought them to bacon factories in Castlebar, Claremorris and Clones.

To get the best possible price, it was important to be out early. The Jobbers liked to compete with each other and as a result worked their way briskly from one end of the town to the other in order to get the best porkers. Very often if a farmer didn't take the price on offer early in the day, he'd live to regret it. On the other hand, it sometimes paid off to hold on to your pigs – especially if they were good – as it would ensure competition from opposing buyers.

After a lack lustre start to the fair, I was minding our two pigs beside Glynn's wall when Tom Farrell came ambling along, his hands tucked under the tail of his jacket, the pipe dangling from the corner of his mouth; looking for all the world like somebody who'd no interest in the fair.

'How are ye gettin' on?' he asked.

'Bad! Bad! I don't know will I be able to sell at all. Sure they're giving me nothing for them,' said my father, a look of resignation on his face. 'I thought you were bringing your two pigs out?'

'I did... and sold them,' said Tom, revelling in the disclosure while scratching the underside of his jaw with the stem of his pipe; his other hand hooked onto the Galluses,* of his trousers.

'Well that's damnable. I was watching out for you and never saw you. And had you any trouble getting shut-a-them?'

'The devil-a-bit,' sniffed Tom, joyously. 'I pulled the wool over the

---

* Galluses *(braces)*

Jobber's eyes as grand as ever you seen.'

'And how did you do that, when and I can't even get a bid? According to some people, the prices are down.'

'They are; and well down!' said Tom as he stuck the pipe back in his gob and tucked his hands under the tail of his jacket again.

'And how did you sell besides any other one: you must have given them away?'

'Faith then I didn't…give them away. I'll tell you how I sold them,' tittered Tom.

'I was making me way out from the house, as grand as ever you seen. I was thinking to meself that if I got thirty four for the pair I'd be happy. I'd even have settled for thirty three or maybe thirty two ten. Though they were plenty good enough to make thirty four, I didn't want to be bringing them home and feeding them for another month. So I'd me mind made up that if I got a middling throw, I'd let them go. I had just turned the pigs out on the road and was facing them for the hill when who did I meet but McGinty or what ever his name is – that big fella from Castlebar.'

'McGinty! McGinty!' exclaimed my father, informatively.

'He looked at the pigs and said, "How much?" sniffed Tom, as he toyed with his pipe. 'I said, thirty six. He looked at me and said, "I'll give you thirty four."

I took off me cap and scratched the side of me head to make believe I was considering it. Then I looked him straight in the eye and said, take them,' tittered Tom, as his ample hairy chest shook with good humour and he cleared the phlegm caught up in his throat. 'He never thought I'd jump. You never saw anyone in all your life marking two pigs as fast. And I'd have settled for thirty three and maybe less,' said Tom, joyfully, as he took the stem out of his pipe and blew into it with enough force to inflate a bicycle tyre.

'I see Sergeant Boyle is wandering round. I wonder will he make it up with Snowy?' said Tom, surveying the scene while taking in the atmosphere of the fair.

'I didn't know they'd fallen out?' said my father, grinding a slice of tobacco into the heel of his hand as farmers all around stood in little clusters trying to wheedle what prices they could out of the Jobbers.

'Didn't they fall out over sweeping the chimney,' said Tom, puffing away contentedly.

'That's the first I heard of it,' said my father indifferently as he began to fill his pipe.'

'Oh they did,' confirmed Tom, as he turned round to face my father. 'Sergeant Boyle asked Snowy would he give him a hand to clean the chimney. He was after buying a new set of brushes in Castleray. That's a hell of a big house he's in; he must have been afraid to tackle it on his own. Seemingly, Snowy told him he'd hold the ladder so he could go up on the roof. Let me see…' said Tom, thoughtfully, pushing the cap to the back of his head. '…it was a week last Friday. I was coming up the town for a few things and didn't I see the head of a sweeping brush sticking up out of Sergeant Boyle's chimney. And said I to meself, he must have Mongan the chimney sweep. And to make it better, the head of the brush was still dancing on top of the chimney when I was going home. Said I to meself, some chimney sweep you are, cleaning the sky. Anyway, as it turned out it was Snowy was inside helping the Sergeant clean the chimney,' chuckled Tom, his shoulders dancing with delight. Snowy kept telling him he needed to add another length on the handle; that the brush wasn't long enough. Snowy wasn't happy until he had the Sergeant on his knees in a lather of sweat trying to clean the chimney; not knowing that the head of the brush was waltzing about ten foot above the chimney; and the neighbours laughing at him. He hasn't spoken to Snowy since,' Chuckled Tom, as he took off his cap and scratched the side of his head before planting it firmly down over his right eyebrow again. 'I'd say you'll see Snowy going to England, shortly. The shillings must be scarce. He doesn't stay too long in the town now, I notice.'

'I wouldn't wonder,' said my father, as a tall Jobber with a brass ferruled cane went round inspecting the pigs. He looked across at our two pigs and without as much as a word he moved on again.

'Well damn and frig them,' says my father, 'I don't think they know what they want.'

'I'll tell you what they'd want …,' said Tom, '…a kick up the arse. What we need is another war. There are too many pigs on the market. It's the same beyond in England. I'd a letter from our John: he says they can't give the pigs away, over there. But if we'd another war…'.

Williamstown fair was often referred to as the birth place of wisdom. Some of these pearls were expressed in jest, some in drunkenness and some in anger: but all were handed down like tasty little morsels from Pake Mitchell's butcher stall. Pake, who plied his trade in the town every fair day, was a stout jovial looking man with a ruddy complexion. As well as that he was well known and respected for the quality of his meat. But when a widow woman stood in front of his stall and began complaining about what he was giving her he was more than ready.

'… Maggie, that's as nice a-bit-meat as you'll get in this town,' he said after trimming the excess fat off a few stewing chops, before throwing them up on the scale. That'll be three and sixpence! How is that?'

'Arrah… is it what you're trying to rob me: and I an auld widow woman? Faith then I won't take them off you Pake; unless you take some of the bones out,'

'Look Misses, when you buy a-farm-a-land, you buy sticks and stones.'

This was a direct hit as the woman was after buying a small farm of land for which she'd paid an outrageous price.

Standing on the street corners were musicians and street singers. They never seemed to get a lot of money but if they showed up in any of the pubs they were generally well received. But my favourite character of a fair day was, Wild Gunning. He was reputed to have been an officer in the Connaught Rangers and served with the British Army in such far flung places as South Africa, Burma and India. Wild Gunning was a gentle giant. Aged around seventy he stood six foot three; and in his hey day was reputed to have been as powerful as an ox. He normally spent his fair days going round the town, marching and saluting as if on parade. With his hob nailed boots, long coat, frayed shirt, stubbled chin and a pair of darting blue eyes, he was indeed a sight to behold. Always on duty in the middle of the road, he'd halt every now and again, to stand at ease. Then he'd shout, Atten-Tion: instantly becoming upright and alert. This was followed by a command: Shoulder Arms. Straight away he'd shoulder his imaginary rifle before giving the order, Right turn: Forward: March and then he'd be off marching to the other end of the town. There, he'd repeat the same exercise as my friends and I laughingly followed him around the town. .

Wild Gunning was known to sleep in two old tar barrels on the side of the road, about a mile from Williamstown on the Dunmore road. At night it was said, he'd put on his coat and, get into one of the barrels, and pull the other one up over his legs.

After a great deal of haggling and support from other farmers including Tom Farrell, my father managed to sell the two pigs for thirty two pounds. But then he had to turn around and buy a pair of Bonhams. The best Bonhams to buy were ten to twelve weeks old. They could be fattened in three months, provided they got good feeding. But like the pigs, good Bonhams were bought early which meant my father had no choice but to buy whatever was left. But the only Bonhams available to him were either two strong barrow Bonhams or light eight week old gilts; neither of which my father really wanted. But he chose the two barrow Bonhams, rather than go home with nothing, as we had plenty of milk and potatoes to give them.

A few days later, I was sent down to Glynn's hardware shop and told to ask for a box of medium sized pig rings. Pigs are notorious animals for rooting. They will soil their bedding no matter how hard you try to keep it clean. They'll gouge deep holes in the floor of their cabin and undermine walls unless they're made of concrete. They'll chew their way through the bottom of a cabin door if its not sheeted with galvanised tin . And if they can't chew their way out, they'll lift the door off its hinges with their hairy snouts, which was why we had to put pig rings on them.

When I came home, Snowy was sitting talking to my father; waiting for me to come home. The minute I left the box on the table Snowy opened it and put one of the rings into the pig ringer which was lying on the table. The ringer was like a pair of pliers, except that the top of it had curved jaws with two different sized slots to accommodate whatever size ring you wanted. My father brought out an old chair we had in the kitchen while Snowy brought out the rings together with a short rope. I was curious to know why my father wanted a chair. There was a small concrete area in front of the pigs' cabin which had an iron gate; this was called the pig sty.

When my father closed the gate, I climbed up on the wall and watched him let out the two Bonhams. He took off his jacket and threw it over the wall. Turning to Snowy he asked,

'Are you ready?'

'Just one second, until I leave this ringer on the wall.' Afraid the loaded ringer might fall into the muck he said to me, 'Here Jack, hold this a minute… and don't let it fall whatever you do.'

'Right,' said Snowy, as he held the rope in his hand. My father grabbed one of the Bonhams by slipping his hand under him. Then he sat on the chair with the pig's hind legs firmly locked between his two thighs while Snowy stood in front of him and wrapped the rope quickly around the Bonham's snout, firmly closing its squealing jaws. Holding the rope, he reached out and took the pig ringer from me. I watched nervously as the pig tried desperately to wriggle free and put up such a fight it made me want to run away. But I knew I had to stay in case Snowy wanted me to hold the ringer for him again. I watched as Snowy sunk the spiked ends of the ring deep into the pig's snout despite its deafening squeal.

'You may as well put on two more while I have him. We don't want to be ringing them again if we can help it,' said my father. 'The last two pigs played hell; they damn near knocked the wall down when the rings fell out,' said my father.

We put three rings on each Bonham and then went into the house to wash our hands. Snowy went home, walking up across the fields, because his motor bike was in the garage, getting fixed, he said.

A week later he came down to our house again; this time to cut the Bonhams. Again I had to help, as my father brought the chair out into the pig sty. Not sure what was going to happen I waited nervously for my father to begin.

'John when I catch the Bonham and sit on the chair I want you to stand behind me and hold his two front feet. You can grab his two feet either side of my shoulder. Do you think you can do that?'

I mumbled yes, only because to say otherwise would be unthinkable. Meanwhile Snowy was busy sorting out the razor blades and the bottle of castor oil which he'd left on the wall.

My father tentatively opened the door of the cabin and grabbed one of the Bonhams and held him in his arms while he sat on the chair. He shouted at me to grab the Bonham's front feet and to be quick about it. I did what I was told

155

and watched nervously as Snowy began the cut out the Bonham's testicles. I thought I'd die listening to the frothy squeals of the Bonham in my ear as he fought like a demon for his freedom. Two or three times, my father shouted at me to hold the Bonham, not to let go. I have to admit, it took a super human effort to hang on because the squealing was unmerciful. I expected the pig to bite my hand off any minute. But he was unable to turn as I held his two feet behind his lugs. The minute Snowy castrated the Bonham, he dressed the wound with castor oil and let him go. And as he stumbled into the cabin, I saw the gaping wounds in his sack, where he had been relieved of his reproductive organs.

Cutting each of the Bonhams only took about two minutes, but to me it was an eternity. It was the most savage experience I'd ever been through and one I did not want to go through again. When it was over, my father praised me for my bravery in holding on. And when I asked him why we had to do it he said,

'If we didn't do that, we'd have ended up rearing two boars. And you can't bring two boars to the fair and sell them as ordinary pigs. No factory would take them. The meat would be too strong; you couldn't eat it. But when they're young like our two Bonhams, you can castrate them and then they'll be all right.'

After that horrible experience I didn't want to have anything to do with killing a pig. John Keaveney had said he hated it when his father killed a pig. Their pig wouldn't stop screaming. I was surprised to hear him say that. I thought John wasn't afraid of anything. Again I asked my mother,

'Are we really going to kill a pig?'

'Ah musha God help you. Isn't it little you have bothering you? It takes four or five months to fatten a pig if you're going to kill it at home And anyway, you can't kill a pig unless there's an R in the month?'

'Why?'

'It's to do with the weather. Fine weather is grand for hay and turf or the like. But if you're killing a pig, it needs to be done around the back end of the year, when there are no flies or midgets around. But... you'd never know,' she added after a moments thought, 'we might kill one later on. We'll have to wait and see.'

Chapter Thirteen

Every morning, before I went to school, it was my job to dust the chairs, the dresser, the radio and the pictures. But now that I was on holidays it didn't really matter. I could do the dusting after my breakfast; whenever I had the time. And it was on one of those mornings, after my mother came down from the well, that she decided to turn on the radio; but there was no sound.

'Jesus Mary and Joseph; what's wrong with me radio? Did you do something to it?' she asked, as I topped up the turf basket with two buckets of turf.

'No. Is it not working?'

'Ah working me backside! You must have done something to it. It was perfect yesterday evening and now I can't knock a meg out of it,' she said, looking angrily at me, as the dimple on her chin took on a life of its own.

'I didn't go near it! I dusted it this morning, the same as I do every morning,' I pleaded, innocently.

'Are you sure you didn't break it or something? I know you. You have your nose stuck in everything. Tell the truth and shame the devil!' she ranted, with a look that clearly told me I was under suspicion.

'No.' I croaked, trying to hide the guilt I felt for having twiddled with the knobs in an effort to get the sound back after it stopped working.

The following day Johnny Smyth was asked to come out to have a look at the radio.

'Look, young fella, I'm up to me two eyes. I'm on me way to Cork to pick up a person. Tell Mrs O'Brien I'll call out tomorrow…if I have the time.'

Johnny could be very cranky when children went into his shop for a penny worth of sweets and they weren't too sure about what to buy in order to get the best value. Johnny would look at them as they stared goggle eyed at the delicious array of sweet jars, on the knee high counter. While they were trying to make their minds up, Johnny would scowl,

'Ah come on, come on, I haven't all day!'

When he came to our house and took one look at the back of our radio I knew he wasn't impressed. I could see he was in a cantankerous mood as he scowled at Mrs O'Brien,

'Christ Almighty Misses, how can it work; when the battery's flat? Didn't I tell you when you bought it, that that battery will only last three months?

You have to keep them charged. I'd safely say you have it ran into the ground. What sort of people are ye at all that ye can't keep an eye on the battery: and I after warning ye …!'

'Arrah damn and blast you to hell, is it what you think I have the radio on, night, noon and morning? I haven't turned the bloody thing on three times since I bought it,' retorted Mrs O'Brien as she stood, hands on her hips, afacing Johnny.

'Ah but sure Misses, that's worse again! Radios were meant to be used. If you don't use them, they can seize up altogether.'

'Well by God there's no fear of your tongue seizing up. Can you fix the bloody thing or not, that's all I want to know? If you can't, it's no use to me. You can take it away with you. I'm sorry now I bought it off you, after all the trouble it's given me.'

After taking the wet battery out of the radio Johnny made for the door, muttering to himself,

'Isn't it shocking! There's no pleasing some people!' Then turning round he said aloud 'Let one of ye call in this evening and I'll give ye a new battery: and see how ye get on with it.'

A few days later the Berlin Philharmonic orchestra could be heard reciting Handel's Messiah on RTÉ radio as Mrs O'Brien sat knitting contentedly beside the fire. And as the tempo of the music increased she suddenly stood up and chased out a hen from under the table before turning it down. From that day, the radio was on virtually non-stop. When Mrs O'Brien didn't want to hear it, she turned it down and when she wanted to hear Dear Sir or Madam – which was her favourite Saturday night programme – she simply turned it up. Only when she was going to bed or leaving the house for a few hours did she turn it off altogether. On Sunday afternoons, my father and I would sit listening to Mícheál O'hEither's match commentary. Mícheál – or Michael as he was known – was a wonderful match commentator. He'd have us sitting on the edge of our seat with anticipation – particularly if Galway were playing.

After that it was my job to walk down to Johnny's garage with the wet battery every three months. It was a heavy cumbersome block, about the same size as a car battery. Made entirely of glass, it stood on its end and had a wire handle. Whenever I'd go into the garage, I'd see scores of batteries lined up on the floor, waiting to be charged. John Keaveney said the batteries were full of acid and would burn the legs off you if you weren't careful. But despite getting the battery charged every three months, the valve still went and the radio had to be sent away to Dublin..

Some people had fancy radios: like Nan Little whose radio was supposed to have been brought from America. Nan had a little country shop attached to her house which was about a mile away from our house, on the Glenamaddy road. The shop was in a room on the left hand side as you went in the front door to the kitchen. Sometimes my mother would send me off to Nan's with a can of buttermilk.

If the radio was on when I went in, Nan would stand up on a chair and turn it off, saying, 'John'een a grá, I'm sick listening to that auld bugger. Tell me have you any news?'

When I'd tell her I hadn't, she'd smile and say, 'Well thanks be to God for that: because no news is good news.'

No matter how often I'd go to Nan's, she'd always give me something nice for myself. As soon as I'd set foot inside the door she'd go into the shop and bring out a few penny bars or a bar of chocolate, whispering, as she made me sit down on the tattered well worn settee, 'There you are now a grá'een, that's for yourself, and don't tell anyone.'

Nan looked as if she had never washed herself. Her wrinkled features were crinkled with layers of powder that could have been applied yesterday or the day before. She was small in stature and the spitting image of a china doll. She had a pile of blond ringlets that were bound into a hive of multicoloured hair curlers perched on top of her head. And she had two blond ringlets that hung down either side of her chubby face that made her look girlish in an attractive sort of a way. For some reason she had a great grá* for American blouses and wore several different colours at the same time.

Over her blouse, she wore an Aran cardigan that was always dripping with gem encrusted broaches that seemed to match her brown framed glasses and pearl ear rings which adorned her ever smiling face. Around her waist, she wore a three quarter length red flannel skirt beneath a dirty polka dot apron. Underpinning her colourful attire was a pair of brown laddered stockings and black high heeled shoes that looked as if they had been made by a blacksmith.

If by chance she had no sweets left – which often happened – she'd make me a cup of tea and give me a thick slice of sweet cake. The problem with Nan's china cups was, they sometimes had traces of lipstick and thumb prints all over them and I'd cringe at the prospects of having to drink from one as she handed it smilingly to me.

If Nan heard the church bell ringing in Williamstown while I was there, she'd switch on the radio to catch the six o'clock news. Nan's radio took pride of place on the long decorative mantelpiece, high up over the fireplace. Underneath the mantelpiece, the arched fireplace itself was festooned with hundreds of sea shells as they formed little fields and paddocks from the largest right down to the smallest, each a different shade of green, with zigzag lines of sea shells depicting the stone walls which were synonymous with much of the rural landscape round her house. She said her brother Paddy in America had collected the sea shells in Salthill, when he was home on holidays.

The little walls and fields were about the only thing in Nan's house not

---

* Grá *(a liking or a love for).*

touched by human hands, everything else in the house had been painted a hundred times over, in gaudy colours including the main chimney breast which was painted green white and gold, the colours of the Irish flag. The small eight day clock and statue of Our Lady – standing each side of the radio – were painted a dark blue as was every flower vase and urn on the window sill and sideboard.

Ancient picture frames, that looked if they might have originated in Noah's ark – were painted blue and gold as were the pictures of the Sacred Heart and Pope John XXIII hanging either side of the back window. There was a basin and jug on a wooden washstand in the corner and they too were painted, blue.

Nan sold groceries as well as an array of sweets which she could never keep in stock as every child in the parish and its mother came to shop in Nan's. She sold cigarettes by the packet, in fives, tens and twenties. She sold *Clarke's Walnut* plug tobacco and an array of pipe lids for the discerning pipe smoker. To say she sold sweets and minerals would be an injustice. In truth she gave them away. She sold boxes of *Rinso* for washing clothes, balls of Blue for whitening them; and Drummer Dye for changing the colour of whatever shirt, sweater or blouse you wanted. She sold pig rings and poultry rings as well as mouse traps and boot polish.

Visitors to our house would often ask how Nan made a living. It was said people from afar would go into her shop when they could get nothing on tick elsewhere. She had a slate hanging on the wall behind the counter. She was supposed to write down people's names and what they owed. In turn they were supposed to pay her when they sold cattle, sheep or pigs. It was said half the people in the parish owed her money, yet she never refused anyone. A lot of young people used to visit Nan's house, at night, for a game of cards. But before going home they'd cadge a few cigarettes off her. Most of her borrowers, however, ended up going to England, America or Australia because there was no work for them in Ireland. But when Christmas came and seasonal greetings started to arrive, Nan's Christmas cards would be bulging with money, as a thank you, for favours she had done.

If I was in Nan's house and Tommy the post came and handed her a letter she'd insist on shoving a pack of ten *Players* or *Woodbines* into his pocket as a thank you for having brought news from afar. And as Tommy closed the front gate behind him, Nan would tear open the envelope, smiling contentedly while I'd sit on the well worn settee, watching the glasses slide down her wrinkled nose as she read the letter, firmly holding the crisp twenty dollar bill in her hand. Doing her damndest to hide the tears welling up in her eyes, she'd laugh half heartily, rest her wrinkled jewelled hand on my knee and say, 'Ah musha, John'een a grá, but Patrick was a trickster: the greatest trickster under the rising sun. You didn't know him... did you? Sure you didn't a grá'een. Well he'd come in here late at night don't you know, gasping for a smoke, by-the-way. Then he'd give a cigarette to one of the girls, so he could walk her home. Lord, but he was a rogue.'

All I could do was smile at Nan, as she shook her blond ringlets in my face. I never met or knew the man she was referring too, yet I always felt I knew him better than I knew Nan herself.

'Ah John'een, Patrick was the grandest fella that ever stood in shoe leather. He had the rosiest cheeks you ever saw and a smile to die for', she'd beam, remembering him fondly. 'I cried me eyes out the morning the poor devil'een came into the shop, to say goodbye: and he going to America. And signs are on him, he's doing well in New York. He tells me he's going to join the police. Patrick never misses a Christmas or an Easter that he doesn't sent me a few dollars, the poor creature,' she'd whisper emotionally. 'The Lord God be good to him…and keep him safe where ever he goes.' Then she'd wipe away the tears with the sleeve of her cardigan, turn round and throw a few lumps of coal on the fire. And with her blackened hand, she'd scratch the side of her nose, go into the shop and serve some customer a crusted loaf; while I contemplated whether to attack the second penny bar or bring it home to Mrs O'Brien.

Nan's shop was also known as the turkey station. When I first starting visiting Nan's, I used to see women going in and out with turkeys under their arms, but I never knew why. I thought they were bringing them as gifts. Nan had lots of turkeys in her back garden, but there was always one big turkey in the front garden, giving a majestic display of its prowess.

We only ever had one turkey at home and it was a pet in that you could walk up to it in the garden and stroke its feathers. When it first started laying, Mrs O'Brien collared me and said, 'John, will you give me a hand to catch the turkey until I bring her up to Nan's.'

She grabbed hold of the turkey in the garden while I held a Hessian bag. She tied the turkey's legs together, put her into the bag with her head sticking out and tied the bag on the carrier of the bike. Then the two of us set off walking. Mrs O'Brien wheeled the bicycle, while it was my job to keep an eye on the turkey, in case she flew away.

'Why are you bringing the turkey to Nan's?' I asked, as we went along the road.

'Ah… why do you think? So, that Nan's turkey cock can do a job on her! I like to keep a turkey hen so I can rear a few turkeys for the Christmas. I don't want to keep a turkey cock because they'd eat too much. Besides I'd be damned minding them. It's a lot easier to bring a hen to the turkey station.'

When we arrived, Nan was in the middle of making a sandwich. Straight away she left down the knife to help Mrs O'Brien take the hen out of the bag and put her in the garden for the cock to deal with. But all the hen would do was fight with Nan's turkey cock. Our turkey hen tried her best to tear ribbons out of the cock with her sharp claws but the cock was too skilful and dodged her every move.

Looking at me, Nan said, smilingly.

'John'een I'm thinking I'll have to put manners on that turkey of yours.'

I didn't know what she meant as I followed her into the house while Mrs O'Brien kept an eye on the turkey.. Nan took down a pair of U pins, about eight inches long that were hanging on the mantelpiece. she caught hold of our turkey hen and slipped the pins over her wings and pinned her to the ground, thereby insuring the hen would sit for the cock whether she liked it or not. The turkey cock began by parading its colourful body in all his majestic glory, before mounting the hen and treading her swiftly. Once the turkey hen was securely back in the bag Nan hung the u-pins back up on the mantelpiece, a look of satisfaction on her face as she said,

'Now John'een, that's another job done. And that ye may have lots of turkeys for the Christmas.'

Without batting an eyelid, Nan finished making her sandwich and handed me a thick slice of sweet cake and a cup of tea. A minute later she did the same for Mrs O'Brien, while we both cringed at the state of the cups. We said nothing but gulped down what she had given us. We wouldn't dream of showing disrespect because Nan was such a kind hearted person.

'Ah, you can't beat the drop-a-tay,' said Mrs O'Brien.

I nearly laughed out loud as Nan turned round and said, 'Would you like another sup, just to warm it up, a grá'een?'

'Oh good God, no: I've enough, Nan! I can hardly finish what I have.'

'Well there's plenty more in the pot; don't be short a grá'een: and be thankful you have the health to enjoy it.'

'Well that's as sure as your there. If we couldn't enjoy a drop-a-tay, I don't know what we'd do.'

'That and a good squeeze,' smiled Nan, with a glint in her eye. 'We won't feel it now, until the carnival? Lord isn't it happy for ye… livin' near the town, where ye can hear the music every night? You'll go for a night or two, I suppose?' queried Nan teasingly, looking at Mrs O'Brien.

'Arrah…what would I be doing at a dance and I hardly able to wag?'

'Ah musha…I suppose no more than meself it isn't any younger or better looking you're getting,' replied Nan, sweeping the crumbs off the table into her fist and out the back door to the birds. Turning round she continued, 'But what about poor John'een there, you'll have to let him go a night or two, to look at the girls?' suggested Nan, humorously as she threw back the blond ringlets from around her rouge tinted cheeks.

'Troth then Nan, he'll not be goin' anywhere. Soon enough he'll be goin' places and looking at girls. And if I have my way, he'll have little or nothing to do with them by the time I'm finished rearing 'im. These bloody carnivals are a pure humbug, if you ask me. It's just an excuse to get hold of people's hard earned money. I'll tell you one thing, if the people around here had any sense, they'd stay at home.'

'Ah musha Kate... weren't we young ourselves, once. Sure the young wans have to look forward to something?' said Nan sympathetically. And in a more sombre tone she said, 'I believe Harry Ryan's going all out this year? He tells me this year's carnival is going to be bigger and better than ever.

'So I believe! But look at the money he'll make... That's if he doesn't get too big for his shoes and go broke,' replied Mrs O'Brien, as she handed me her empty cup and bread plate and urged me to leave them up on the table along with my own. 'Thanks Nan; that was a lovely.'

'Musha Kate you're very welcome: very welcome a grá. But doesn't the poor creature deserve to make a few bob: the same as everyone else. Anyone with fifteen children deserves a break. Are you sure you won't have another supeen-a-tay, a grá,' asked Nan, turning her attention to me.'

'No thanks,'

The only problem with Nan's tea – apart from the state of her cups – was that it was left stewing by the fire all day and tasted like treacle.

'Tell me, what do you think of Fr Keaveney? Isn't he a lovely man,' said Nan, resting her backside on the corner of the settee.

'Well Lord, but he's a gentleman compared that auld Fr Murphy. I couldn't imagine Fr Keaveney reaching into your shopping bag if he caught you bringing home a few bottles-a-porter from the town. And as for Nora Keeffe – his housekeeper – I think she's the grandest person. I sent John down a week ago with a can of butter milk, for to make her feel welcome and dammy but, but didn't she give him a bar of chocolate for himself and put two oranges and another bar into the sweet can and told him to say thanks very much to Mrs O'Brien.'

After that, they spent ages discussing the people of the parish. I had grown restless by the time Mrs O'Brien stood up to go home. Again we walked all the way back to our house with me keeping an eye on the turkey. Mrs O'Brien was terrified anything would happen it.

'But the turkey is tied,' I explained, as we turned in the new road. 'How could anything happen?'

'That's what you think. Turkeys are very temperamental: they're easily frightened. Sometimes they can just drop dead on you. So you have to be careful how you handle them. I brought a turkey to Nan years ago and she dropped dead, and I bringing her home on the carrier of the bike. Nan said she must have got a fright. Turkeys like to see where they're going and that's why you should always leave their heads out of the bag if you're bringing them anywhere.

Every once in a while, Mrs O'Brien would send me running to Nan's, with a pound of fresh butter; and to get a few things in the shop. A few weeks after our visit to the turkey station I walked in the front door of Nan's house – which was always open – but there was no one there. A large rooster was roaming about the kitchen pecking the breadcrumbs from under the table. He carried on pecking and didn't take the slightest bit of notice of as I sat down. I then saw the back door was open so I ventured out to see where Nan was. I could hear her talking to herself as she struggled with a turkey cock in one of the cabins. When she saw me she said,

'John'een, I'm trying to put manners on this fella. I've to put rings on their feet so I'll know them. Would you ever keep an eye on the shop like a good lad'een. If anyone calls, tell me. I'll be in, in a minute.'

When I went back in, there were two roosters fighting in the kitchen. My first instinct was to shoo them out, but I was so taken by the spectacle I decided to watch them. Round and round the floor they went attacking each other with outstretched claws and razor sharp bills. Every so often the two Rhode Island Reds would pause briefly, eyeing each other up: their ruffled feathers standing on the backs of their necks, their bright red combs swollen with exertion as once again they attacked each other, viciously. And when one of them managed to sink his beak into the colourful plumage of his opponent, all hell broke loose as they attacked each other with their fearsome talons, tearing strips off each other. They were edging ever closer to Nan's large brown tea pot, brewing on the hearth stone. It looked like a fight to the death, as once again the two roosters stood momentarily facing each other. Soon they began bobbing and weaving again like two prize fighters before the two of them in a mad frenzy up-kittled Nan's teapot and sent scalding hot tea all over the floor. Before I'd time to do anything, Nan came in and walloped the two cocks out the front door, saying, 'Bad cess to the pair-a-ye. Ye've destroyed me-supeen-a-tay, and I lookin' forward to it.'

By the time our turkey finished hatching, she had ten chicks; one for every egg she had under her. Mrs O'Brien was very pleased and knew that with proper care she'd have at least half a dozen turkeys for sale by Christmas and still have one or two left over for ourselves. As soon as they were reared, she planned to give one to Nan for services rendered. It meant Nan could keep the turkey for breeding or sell it on to someone. Mrs O'Brien said, knowing Nan, she'll do neither. She'd probably put the turkey up as a prize on card playing night, where every farmer in the village would make it their business to be there, hell bent on winning the turkey for Christmas

But all of that was still a long way off: anything could happen, I thought. Of more immediate concern to me was, The Williamstown Carnival. The very mention of the word evoked dreams of endless pleasure; and debate amongst the people on a scale I'd never ever witnessed before.

Chapter Fourteen

Every year, the people of Williamstown organised a summer carnival as a money-making exercise. Sometimes it was the local farming organisation that ran it on behalf of the local community. Other times it was run by one of the many prominent businessmen in the town who decided to run a carnival for their own benefit.

Entertainment played a huge part in people's every day lives. But nothing in the parish created a buzz quite like the summer carnival. Williamstown Carnival was known far and wide for its outstanding entertainment. It had become so successful that it once held three carnivals the same year, one after the other: all of them run by different organisations. But no one was deemed better at organising a carnival than Harry Ryan; and so the opposition fell by the wayside.

The carnivals were held in mid-summer when people were home on holidays from America, England and Australia. I had never been to a carnival and was hankering to go because I'd heard so many stories about swinging boats, chair-o-planes and bumping cars. By all accounts the excitement would begin once the amusements arrived in the town, to be set up in the square for the duration of the carnival. In a field close to the town, a huge white marquee would be set up, with dances every other night for two whole weeks. All of it organised by Harry Ryan. As well as being a shopkeeper, he was a garage owner, an egg merchant, a travel agent, an undertaker, an auctioneer, a peace commissioner, and a hackney driver. And to supplement his income further he ran a carnival every year.

There was a parochial hall in the town where concerts and plays and dances were occasionally held, around Christmas and Easter. And from time to time, there were house dances here, there and everywhere throughout the parish. But all of them, paled into insignificance when it came to Williamstown Carnival. House dances were frequented by local people, but when it came to the carnival, people came from miles around. Holiday makers arranged their annual visits to coincide with the carnival. Ireland's leading show bands would be booked well in advance. Weeks before the carnival, posters would be posted on every lamp post and notable tree trunk throughout the parish. All of this I learned from listening to Tommy the postman.

I was feeding the hens in the garden when I caught first sight of Harry Ryan's incredible poster. Harry was driving as the car cruised by our house on its way into the village. On the roof of the car he'd erected a huge double sign that you could read from the back or front. The caption read; **Win a Free trip to New York.** *Williamstown Carnival, from July 15th to July 30th, is offering you the trip of a lifetime. Why not come along and dance the night away with Ireland's leading show bands: The Dixie's, Johnny Flynn, the Rhythm Stars, the Premier Aces and many more. Spot prizes galore.*

Harry Ryan's carnival was the talk of the town. The free trip to New York was discussed by everyone coming into our house and there was a fierce debate about whether you had to attend every night in order to qualify for the prize: the lucky winner to be announced on the final night. There were raffle tickets galore in every shop in town and country.

A week before the carnival, Harry Ryan had two cars touring the country with loud speakers as well as signs promoting the carnival on the outskirts of the neighbouring towns. And on the Sunday morning of the opening night he had a car outside the church after Mass urging people to come along; to dance the night away with the lady of their dreams. A huge white marquee had already been erected in Glynn's field beside the school. Loudspeakers had been fitted on poles all around the marquee, so the music could be heard all over the parish.

Like everybody else I couldn't wait for the carnival to begin. Every day, my mind was in turmoil trying to figure out a way I'd be let go: despite the fact that Mrs O'Brien had already told me I was too young to go: still, I lived in hope. Coming home from second Mass, my heart was pounding in my chest at the sight of swinging boats and bumping cars being tried and tested in Williamstown square. There were men on ladders frantically erecting banners and speakers and lights.

By the time our tea came round, I'd almost lost the will to live. I'd given up all hope that I'd ever be let go. Mrs O'Brien hadn't opened her mouth once or said one solitary word about the carnival. And what really broke my heart entirely was that EJ Lyons was going – because he had told me after Mass. John Keaveney, thought he might be let go. Fatso Fannon would certainly be there, because his parents let him go everywhere.

As soon as the carnival music started, I hung around the front door listening. I didn't want to be too far away in case Mrs O'Brien decided to let me go. But there was no mention of the amusements even though I gave her ample opportunity by telling her I could hear the music. In desperation I sat by the fire while she sat across from me darning my socks.

'I can still hear the music, sitting here,' I said.

'Well…I hope you're not expecting to be let go, because you're not going. It's no place for the likes of you. I might consider letting you go for a few minutes next week: that's if you behave yourself and have all the jobs done.

And anyway, I haven't money to be throwing away on swinging boats and the like. 'Tis far from swinging boats I was reared let me tell you. How do you think people managed before swinging boats were thought of? How?'

I didn't say anything. My mouth was dry. I was lost for words. My heart ached like it had never ached before. After looking forward to the carnival for so long, it took a super human effort to hold back the tears. 'Maybe next Sunday evening…the two of us will go down to have a look. We'll wait and see,' she added, sensing my disappointment. But I didn't want to go down to the amusements with my mother. I wanted to go on my own: to be with my friends.

Accepting my fate, I made my way nonchalantly outside and began kicking a ball against the gable end of the house but my heart wasn't in it. Turning my back to the gable wall, I sat on the ground listening to the tempo of the music as it echoed over the warm landscape like some magical dream. It was as if I was being transported to distant lands where I'd never been before. The words, hauntingly beautiful were accompanied by the rhythmical beat of drums, saxophones and trombones. I tried to visualise what the amusements might have been like but it was the words of the song that brought a tear to my eye because I could not be there to see the amusements for the first time.

> *I left my heart… in San Francisco,*
> *High on a hill… in San Francisco.*

The following day the carnival was the talk of the parish; and how many people were there. Tommy the postman arrived in the late afternoon and threw himself down in the corner where he took out his half empty pack and lit a fag. I took my time sweeping the floor in the back kitchen because I wanted to take in every word before I was forced to go back out again

'…I believe 'twas the biggest crowd ever seen at a carnival in Williamstown. Sergeant Boyle was telling me he never saw anything like it. He said he'd put the figure at the dance, somewhere between nine hundred and a thousand.'

'God Almighty, where did they come from?' asked Mrs O'Brien.

'I believe they came from all over,' said Tommy as he leant back and drew refreshingly on his cigarette. 'There were people there from Kilkerrin, Newbridge and Castleplunkett: even as far away as Roscommon. And what harm, but they're running a carnival of their own above in Newbridge this week and they say there's no one at all going to it. This free trip to New York has gone to people's heads. But two weeks dancing will test the best of them, let me tell you that. Where are people supposed to get money, Kate? That's what I'd like to know?'

'Well, where is right. I wonder who'll win the trip to New York or is it for real, do you think?'

'Oh it's for real all right. They say Harry Ryan had to apply to the court for a licence. So everything must be above board.'

'But how in the name of God can he afford it. He was supposed to be broke after the last carnival.'

'Arrah not at all! That Harry Ryan is as cute as a bloody fox. He wouldn't be paying for that trip to New York at all. He'd wangle that out of *Aer Lingus* and make believe he was paying for it himself.'

'Well I wouldn't wonder a bit. You know he's fit for anything.'

'Anything! Anything! But he may thank his wife Margaret. I don't know in the name of God how she does it. She has a line of washing out first thing every morning. Fifteen nappies I counted the other morning, and they say she's expecting again.'

'So I believe. The poor creature hasn't time to draw her breath,' said Mrs O'Brien as she handed Tommy a mug of tea and a piece of rhubarb tart. 'Here now, enjoy this and you can have more if you want.'

'No, no! This will be fine now, thanks.'

'And she never gets to go outside the front door from one end of the year to the other; except maybe to come to our little do once a year. Very often we have to start eating without her, it's that late when she comes. But what can one do? She has to wait until *himself* closes the shop and by then it's near eleven o'clock.'

'Ah musha, if she had any sense she'd have hung a bloody sock on it long ago, or else locked *himself* in the other room. She should give herself a break, for a year at least. This will be what, her sixteenth?'

'Her sixteenth!, Where in the name of God do they sleep? Seventeen people in a house that you couldn't swing a cat in!'

By the middle of the week, the ongoing carnival was still the main topic of conversation. If I was anywhere near the house and saw the postman coming, I'd make sure to push the cat off the window so I could sit and listen. And though a few visitors might call to the house from time to time, nobody could carry news quite like Tommy. After listening to his analysis of the carnival for a few minutes there was a dramatic change of subject.

'Tell me did you hear anything about the priest's hens?' asked Tommy.

'The priest's hens! Is it Fr Keaveney, you're talking about?' asked Mrs O'Brien.

'Yes. I'm only askin' because I've a feeling you know nothing about it; and I'd hate you to hear the news from some other one.'

'Hear what?' asked Mrs O'Brien, a quiver in her voice.

'I don't know how to say this to you now Kate, but I think your son-in-law has been a bold boy: he might be in a spot of bother.'

'Jesus, Mary and St Joseph, is it Snowy you're talking about? Don't tell me he's in trouble?'

'Now, now, don't say anything, don't let on I told you. I don't want to be the conveyor of bad news: but there's little point in you not knowing when the whole town seems to know. I'm only telling you because I know yourself and Nora Keeffe are great friends: and that you give her a drop'een-a-buttermilk every now and again.'

'But what have the priest's hens got to do with it, asked Mrs O'Brien, a croak in her voice.

'I'll tell you what it has to do: Snowy is supposed to have stolen the priest's hens – what few he had – so he could get a few shillings to drink during the carnival. That same bloody carnival that has the people robbed: because they can't afford to go in the first place: now have you got it!'

'Oh Glory be to God Almighty, Tommy; is that true?'

'As true as my name is Tommy; and that's true enough! He's supposed to have gone into the priest's garden the other night after the pubs closed. He took the five or six hens that were roosting on a bush at the back of the house. The following morning he sold them to one of the lads in Henry Naughton's, for three shillings-a-piece: and Henry only living across the road from the priest's house. Now, there's cheek for you.'

'Oh Jesus Tommy… He never took Nora's hens, did he?' gasped Mrs O'Brien.

'He did. He bloody well did.'

'Oh, I'll never be the better of this. Wait until *himself* hears it. How are we going to live it down? How am I ever going to face Nora Keeffe again: and she so good to us?'

'Wait, Wait! Hang on a minute now, all's not lost. Wait' till you hear the full story…'.

'Jesus, Mary and Joseph, don't say there's more?'

'There is! There is! There's always more. There's always a sting in the tail. Only in this case it might have a happy ending. You know Kate, how some of them priests are supposed to have extraordinary powers? They can put a curse on you if they feel like it. Well in my humble opinion, if any man has that power, it's Fr Keaveney. Though I'm not saying he'd put a curse on a person – he doesn't strike me as that sort of a man – but he has the power, nonetheless… which in this case seemingly, he's put to his own good use…'.

'A curse?' echoed Mrs O'Brien, in a barely audible voice.

'Wait… wait till you hear what happened, The following morning when Fr Keaveney found out his hens were missing he had a right good look round the garden, as you do: and having found no trace nor tidings of a fox, a hen, or a feather, he went straight down to the barracks and reported it to Sergeant Boyle. Naturally Sergeant Boyle being an intelligent man and all that, went straight up to Naughton's, to see did he know anything. But Henry wasn't there; he was gone to the railway station with a-load-a-hens bound for Dublin. But as luck would have it, he still had a few hens running round the yard. Later that evening didn't the priest's hens fly over the gate, cross the road and back into their own garden. Henry could hardly believe his eyes. He ran after them but couldn't catch them. He told Mossy in the yard what was after happening. And it was then Mossy told Henry how he'd paid Snowy eighteen shilling that morning for six black hens.'

'Oh Tommy I'll have to sit down before me legs go from under me,' sighed Mrs O'Brien wearily. 'I wish to the Lord God Almighty Tommy, that he'd go back to England and stay there. Colleen will die when she hears this. Maybe she knows already, but she never opened her mouth to me. Then again we'd be the last to know: thanks be-to-the-Great-God-Almighty that you had the good sense to tell me. I'd hate to be going round and people looking at me sideways; and I not knowing a thing. And what's going to happen now, I wonder? Will he be summonsed do you think?'

'Oh I'd say so. I'd say so. You know *himself* and Sergeant Boyle aren't great, since the cleaning of the chimney? If you ask me, Boyle will have it in for him. The chickens could come home to roost yet, in more ways than one, if you'll pardon the expression, Kate.'

'Well that's as sure as you're sitting there; and that's sure enough. And no more than a story you'd think Snowy would have done the decent thing and helped him clean the cursed chimney; instead of acting the jennet. It'll come back to haunt him yet, wait till you see,' said Mrs O'Brien.

'He'll be bloody lucky if he doesn't get jail. Stealing the priest's hens could be classed as a very serious crime, in the eyes of a judge. I'm thinking Snowy will have his work cut out. He'll have to use all his guile and wisdom to get out of this one, Kate' said Tommy.

* * * *

The following day I had to run to the town for a message and I saw all the amusements on the square. My heart ached that I could not even see them in action. Everything was locked up but I still managed to steal a look in at the bumping cars. Some of the cars were red, some were blue and some were green, each one a different shape and colour. I liked the red one which was of a little boy with a lovely smile. Some of the other cars were of laughing girls and one was of a boy with a sour puss. When I'd finished looking at them I ran up as far as Glynn's field where the Marquee was set up, but it was closed. All I could see were men trying to stretch the big canvas tent, reinforcing it on the ground.

When Tommy the postman called again on Friday he said the crowd on Thursday night was bigger than Tuesday night's, but was still smaller than Sunday night's. I couldn't wait for the weekend to come round. I worked hard around the house and tried to keep out of trouble so that I'd be let go to the Carnival. But there was always the nagging fear that something would go wrong. I recalled the times I was left minding the chickens and my ill fated trip to the bog on Mrs O'Brien's bicycle. I couldn't afford another setback like that;

it was too painful, I thought. I was greatly relieved when Sunday afternoon came round without any major hiccup. Around eight o'clock my mother called me into the house after my father had gone rambling for the night

'Your father said maybe I should let you down to the amusements for a while. Would you like that?' she asked, as she straightened out the sleeve of a red cardigan she was knitting. I could scarcely believe my ears.

'I would,' I answered.

'Well you better wash your hands and face and comb your hair and put on your good shoes.'

When I was ready, she said,

'Here you are now, there's nine pence for you. You can have two goes on the swinging boats or whatever and get yourself an ice cream in Johnny's.'

By now the music could be clearly heard in the village. I couldn't wait to go down the town and was praying fervently that John Keaveney or EJ Lyons would be there to go on the swinging boats with me. If they weren't, then I didn't know who I'd let on the swinging boats with me.

'It's a quarter to nine now and you're to be back here by ten o'clock; before it gets too dark. Do you hear that?'

'I do.'

'And remember to have manners and keep well away from them trick-a-the-loops that hang around the square. Be sure to say please and thank you when you're going on them things and let me not hear a single word of complaint about you. And whatever you do hold onto the swings and don't go too high. I don't want you landing on top of your head. And if it wasn't for your father the devil-a-out-that-front-door I'd let you go. But seeing as you were good all week, I'll let you go this time. I thought I'd take a walk down meself along with you; but I'm not up to it. And remember, you'll not be let go again; so make the best of it. And, like I said, be back here by ten o'clock.'

I nodded in agreement as she combed my hair and straightened my shirt collar before escorting me out onto the street, where she stood listening to the music. I walked slowly down the road, knowing she was watching my every step. But as soon as I turned the first corner I ran as fast as I could and almost collided with a woman on a bicycle as she made her way into the village.

When I arrived in the square I found the place was a sea of colour with red, white and blue lights flashing everywhere. And when I heard the sound of the bumping cars as they bumped and bounced and crashed into each other and saw the creaking swinging boats swinging right up to the sky I was delirious with excitement. I stood for a second not knowing which way to run. There was so much to see and so many people enjoying themselves I didn't know where to begin. I ran over to the bumping cars where most of my school friends were. I spotted John Keaveney standing on the platform that ran around the arena. And Fatso Fannon was there, but I didn't want to go in the bumping cars with him. It was John Keaveney's second night he told me. He was there on opening night and knew which cars were the best. There were six cars altogether. Some of them were getting stuck and wouldn't move at all no matter how hard the driver tried unless the man taking the money gave them a good shove. Then all of a sudden they'd start to roar around the track as the poles connecting the cars to the wire meshed ceiling ignited and started showering sparks overhead like sheets of forked lightening, as they sped around. Then another car would stop and the attendant would hop from the rear of one bumping car to another in an effort to get it going again. There was a green car which John said was the best of the lot, so we agreed to go for a drive in that; though I would have preferred the red one which was number five. When time was up and the cars stopped there was a mad scramble to get into the cars before somebody else. If you didn't get there in time you just had to wait until the next turn: that's what happened to John and me. We were too slow off the platform. By the time we reached the green car, two lads had reached it from the other side and we ended up shouting, trying our best to push each other out of the way. But the other two lads succeeded because one of them had got his hands on the steering wheel first. By the time we turned round to jump into another car it was too late. The big lads all round the arena laughed at us but we didn't care. Though we were embarrassed we were determined to get into the green car the next time. When the time was up we sprinted across the arena to the green car which was on the far side. Again we were beaten to it and had to walk away.

Having failed to get into a car the second time, the big lads began to make fun of us, so John and I decided to give the cars a miss for a while. Instead, we made our way over to the swinging boats. We were just in time as there was one boat still empty. John paid the attendant while I climbed in and secured the boat. When all the boats were full, the fairground attendant freed them by dropping one end of a long wooden plank which he had lifted up earlier to slow down the boats; and to stop them when the three minutes were up. The minute John Keaveney jumped in he took charge of the rope and began pulling on it. Soon we were sailing majestically up into the air. As he pulled harder and harder we sailed higher and higher: so high I was afraid the boat would sail right over the top. I told Keaveney to slow down but he just laughed and kept on pulling the rope for all he was worth. We screamed with absolute fear and excitement as the boat went so high it tottered for a brief moment and threatened to go right over the top. I was relieved when the attendant finally lifted the long wooden plank to slow us down and we were able to jump out again. We ran across to the bumping cars once more and after a few failed attempts we managed to jump into the red car, number five, which was my favourite. I was so happy to have got the red one, because it reminded me of EJ Lyons.

It was an incredible feeling to be sitting there behind the wheel, waiting for the off. Before we knew what was happening, our car started vibrating and moving backwards before it shot forward and began colliding with every other car. I wrestled frantically with the wheel and shouted at Keaveney to leave it alone as he tried to steer it one way while I tried to steer it the other. I wanted the car to go in a proper circle so I could get a good long spin out of it. Then who did I see driving the green car, the one with the sour puss, but Fatso Fannon. Keaveney and I nearly died laughing as I made straight for him. But as I did so another car hit me and spun me around and I had to start all over again. John was stone mad to steer and kept shouting at me to turn this way and that and to push harder on the pedal. I roared back that he had handled the boat so I was entitled to drive the bloody car. Suddenly a path opened up in front of me and I cut right across the middle of the arena and crashed straight into Fatso Fannon's car with such force I was almost thrown out of my seat; and that to me was hilarious. I'd rammed Fatso's car up against the safety barrier and now he couldn't move at all. John and I laughed our heads off as we watched him plead with the attendant to help get the car going again while we cruised around bumping into this one and that one. By the time the attendant prised Fatso's car away from the barrier, we had already gone around three times. Then the three minute alarm sounded and the cars ground to a halt. Fatso Fannon started complaining that he hadn't had a chance to drive at all which we thought was hilarious because the attendant wouldn't listen. Instead he ran round the arena collecting all the three penny fares he could before the cars started up again. Now that I only had three pence left while Keaveney had sixpence, we had a fierce argument about how best to spend it. I wanted to spend it on the bumping cars but Keaveney wanted to go on the chair-o-planes. Eventually we decided we'd spend his sixpence on the bumping cars and I'd get a three penny ice cream which we'd both share.

After that, we had a quick look at the rifle range and other stalls before deciding to go up as far as the Marquee where the dance was being held. There was a small red hut out in front where people paid to go in to the dance. As soon as they got their tickets they went straight in. There were two loudspeakers high up in front of the marquee. The sound of the music was so hypnotic it made us want to go inside to have a look. As people were going into the dance two men held the canvas flap open for them. We could see the band playing on the stage at the far end of the marquee and people dancing on the floor. Some of the girls wore fancy ball gowns that swung up around their waists as they danced. We inched our way closer to get a better view but the men shouted at us,

'Hey! Stay away! Ye're not supposed to be in around here.'

We didn't want to get in trouble so we ran down to the town again. Though the town was lit up, I could see it was getting dark as more and more people began pouring into town. Most of them were cycling in twos and threes, and fours. But a lot of the women – particularly the younger ones – preferred to walk; linking each other in twos as the made their way along, either side of the road, while the men preferred to race each other on their Raleigh bikes such

173

was their excitement to get there first.

There were four cars parked outside the church near Fr Keaveney's house. And having had a good look at them I decided it was time to go home. John had arranged to meet his father outside McHugh's pub which was on the corner of the square. He wanted me to stay with him but I told him I was going home: that I might see him again, the following Sunday night.

When I got home, Mrs O'Brien started giving out to me for being late. I told her I had no way of knowing the time; that that was why I was late. She asked were there many in the town and when I told her all about the amusements and the amount of people I'd seen she seemed happy enough. She gave me a mug of Goody* and left the rest by the fire for my father. I was so happy going to bed knowing I'd crashed into Fatso Fannon's car, putting him out of the race. I thought it was the most exciting night I'd ever had; and I just couldn't wait to go again

On Monday, I met Una and Sadie and they informed me that they were being let go to the amusements on Tuesday night. I was disappointed to hear they were being let go because they were a lot younger than me. Still, they were mad to know all about the amusements. I told them everything I knew and advised them as best I could.

The following Sunday night – the last night of the carnival – Mrs O'Brien knew I was expecting to be let go, as she sat weighing me while knitting beside the fire.

'I suppose you're expecting to be let go to the carnival again, are you?'

I didn't know what to say as I sat across from her, so I said nothing.

'Well, you can put any ideas you have out of your head, because you're not going. It was alright last week to let you go for an hour or so. You know you're too young to be hanging around the town like a corner boy. It's no place for the likes of you. Besides, I'm not made of money. 'Tis far from amusements I was reared and it didn't do me a-bit-a-harm.'

I wanted to cry when she said those horrible words, *you can put any ideas you have out of your head, because you're not going.* She had just read my mind. It was like a dagger to my heart. And because I hadn't been let go the first night, I was full sure she'd let me go the last night, but no.

When Tommy the postman called on Monday I was soon sent out to play. I knew instinctively that that she didn't want me to hear anything. Quick as a flash I ran round the back of the house and tip-toed up to the front window. I was just in time to hear Tommy saying,

'Well, by all accounts Mrs O'Brien, it was the biggest crowd that was ever seen at a carnival in the West of Ireland. There were eleven hundred people there, they tell me.'

---

* Goody *(warm milk and bread).*

'So I believe. I met Annie up the street, a while ago. She was after coming from the town and she told me 'twas packed: and that Harry Ryan's brother, Michael won the free trip to New York.'

'Well be damn but, he did, he did. And now they're saying it was all a fix. But that's humbug. Pure humbug! Isn't the man as entitled as anybody else to win it? Just because he's Harry's brother shouldn't be held against him. Sergeant Boyle and Guard McMillan were standing there watching when the draw took place. Some young lady from Castlerea pulled the winning ticket. Just because Michael was on the door every single night shouldn't bar him from winning. I hope that himself and the wife have the good sense to go to America: and eff the begrudgers.'

'Well yes, I hope so. Wasn't she over there for years?' said Mrs O'Brien.

'She was! She was! Wasn't that where she met Michael? And a nicer person you couldn't ask to meet in a day's walk. And wouldn't it be a grand thing for the two of them to go over again; and have a bit of a holiday for themselves?'

'Well it would, surely. But sure there's no satisfying some people.'

'Look, Mrs O'Brien, some people would begrudge you the steam of their piss, so they would. The steam of their piss! They'd be afraid you'd bottle it as a cure for arthritis. That's what has this bloody country ruined. Begrudgery! And I believe Doctor Roland is in trouble again,' said Tommy, tactfully changing the line of his conversation.

'Again?' asked Mrs O'Brien.

'Be damn but yes, again. He's a great doctor; but a terrible man to deal with. He'll be goin' on until he's struck off the register: and striking off he'd want after what he said to poor Mrs Higgins.'

'Is it Mrs Higgins in Kilnalag?'

'Yes! The very woman! He must have been bad after the drink. They said he was in McHugh's pub the night before and was footless. Anyway it seems there was a fierce crowd in the dispensary the following morning. There were three or four from Kilnalag: John Divilly and auld Mrs Higgins and a couple more. Roland passed in and never as much as said, good morning, kiss me arse or a thing. The first one to go in was John Divilly, the poor creature. John has had trouble with his bowels for years. Anyway when Roland finished with him he slid open the hatch and shouted, "Next?" in that gruff voice of his. That was alright until another patient from Kilnalag came out. They all happened to be sittin' together in the waiting room. The next bloody thing Roland sticks his head out the hatch and shouts, "Is there any other fucker from Kilnalag who can't shite?"

'Oh mother of God Tommy did he say that?'

'He did then! He did then! Mrs McCormack and Josephine Flynn from Briarfort got up and walked out. And could you blame them?'

'Oh Tommy, that was terrible. If it was me I think I'd die. He'll be reported:

he'll be shifted, wait till you see?'

'Reported? Sure what good is it? Aren't them-shower-a-tricksters above in Galway – the Health Board – every bit as bad? They know what he's like. But they're afraid to open their mouths. They think the sun shines out of his arse. And he is good, I'll grant you that – if he'd stay off the drink.'

'Arrah… but sure he won't! How many times was he near kilt? How many times did he crash the car?'

'Killed? You couldn't kill him: you'd have to shoot him.'

The conversation flowed as they discussed this one and that one. And it wasn't until my mother told Tommy that she was expecting Tailor on Sunday that I had anything at all to look forward to. I was over the moon when I heard about Tailor. He now only came to visit us once a year; when the days were good and long. I hadn't seen him for a long time and was looking forward to seeing him again.

'…You know he wasn't well there for a while,' continued Mrs O'Brien.

'So you were telling me.'

'The cycling takes a lot out of him. Besides he says there's nothing but cars on the road now. They'd mow you down like a scythe. It's not like one time where you'd have the road to yourself. That's why I hate going home meself: because there's no knowing when you might meet a car or a lorry?'

It wasn't until Saturday afternoon that Mrs O'Brien informed me that Tailor was coming; but I didn't let on I knew. I'd just finished my dinner when she said.

'In the name of God, John'een would you ever go out and pull them cursed weeds in front of the house: they're starting to grow again. I can't bear the sight of them. Tailor is coming tomorrow and I'd like to have the place looking middlin'. And when you have that done you might tie a string on the lavatory door so he can close it. I hung some pieces of newspaper there yesterday, so don't touch them in case he needs them.'

I liked Tailor because he was always telling stories. As well as that he always brought either a cake, a packet of biscuits or some sweets. He generally came for a few hours on a Sunday afternoon. But if the weather turned bad and he couldn't go home, he'd sleep in the armchair and cycle home the following morning.

When I'd finished pulling the weeds, she handed me the hedge clippers and said, 'You might try and do something with that hedge a grá. You're stronger than I am. I'm not able to cut it any more. See what you can do with it. And you might shove the branches under the hedge down the garden. Because if I'm not mistaken; there are one or two hens laying out, in Collin's old garden.'

I tried cutting the overgrown branches on what was anything but a hedge. At one end, beside the road, was a small tree that produced long cone shaped purple flowers in early July. At the other end, beside the grain store, was a rose bush that produced pink roses in June and July. But in between the two was an overgrown wild hedge that produced tiny pink flowers during the summer and white berries in autumn. I loved picking the berries and squirting the spit into Una and Sadie's ear whenever we were playing.

'I don't think that auld hedge-clippers is much good,' said Mrs O'Brien as she watched my pathetic attempts at hacking the lopsided hedge.

She took the clippers off me and tried cutting the branches but they were too strong. 'Ah, blast it to hell, this auld thing wouldn't cut newspaper. Would you ever go into the back kitchen and bring out the saw until I see if we can cut these branches. And while you're at it, bring out the scissors so I can cut a few roses.'

I brought out the saw and between breaking and cutting and hacking off bits of branches we managed to tidy up the hedge,, making it look more presentable. I dragged the branches through the narrow gate, between the grain store and the house, into the garden and stuffed them under the hedge with a hay fork. When I saw a path in the nettles at the very bottom of our garden, close to the hedge, I followed it across to the far side of what was Collin's old garden. There I saw a brown hen nesting in the weeds. She started gluggering like a clocker as I inched my foot closer. Suddenly she flew at my foot as I tried to push her off the nest to see if there were any eggs under her. Instead I found she had a clutch of day old chicks and I ran excitedly into the house to tell Mrs O'Brien. She was delighted. She found an old shoe box and together we went down the garden to where the hen was hatching. She put the chickens into the box while the clocker tried to fight her off. The clocker followed the chirping chicks all the way across the garden and up to the front of the house. We had to build a make shift pen for them beside the hens' cabin with bits of boards and net wire to stop them wandering all over the place. We knew if we weren't careful the rats or weasels might get them.

I was out playing football when I saw Tailor coming down the street, with his bicycle. He'd got off at the head of the village and was slowly walking down. Fortunately Mickey Billy's geese were not out so I ran up to meet him. He was a short stout little man with a cheerful expression. He wore a black trilby hat, a dark three piece suit with a gold watch chain across his waist and a pair of black shoes with a shine on them like a hound's tooth As I approached him, he took out the watch and checked it before slipping it back into his waistcoat pocket.

'Hello John. How are you?' he said, smiling.

'I'm fine, thanks.'

'Is that yeer cat, I see sittin' on the winda?'

'It is. And we have another cat and she has four kittens. Well... she's not really our cat; she's Annie Tobin's. But she had the kittens in our stable. Our cat sits on the window all day, because he likes the sun.'

'I think I'll bring yeer cat home, because there isn't a decent cat in our village. Besides, I have a mouse under me bed that needs catching badly. They say if you have a good cat no mouse will dart-in your door.'

'But that's our cat! You can't have him. He's great for catching rats. He caught a rat the other day and brought it into the house so we could see it.'

'Oooh, I don't want that sort of a cat: if he's going to bring rats into the house! And there's me thinking I'd put him sittin' on the bar of me bike and bring him home..'

'But the rat was dead. He was only showing it to us.'

I knew Tailor was only joking and that he wouldn't really take our cat. But because he was such a nice looking cat a lot of people had asked if they could have him, but we always said no.

'Do you like cats?' I asked, as the cat jumped down off my bedroom window and Tailor propped his bicycle beneath the window sill..

'Oh I love cats and dogs… but I hate liars,' replied Tailor as Mrs O'Brien appeared at the door.

'Musha, you're welcome and you made great time, altogether. I didn't think you'd be here for another hour. You must have left early?'

'I left after second Mass. I skipped out of the church before the priest had time to ask me my sins. He'd love to hear my sins but I don't have anything worth tellin'.

'Oh Lord God Almighty; do you hear who's talking?' said Mrs O'Brien, cheerfully.

I smiled when I heard Tailor say, but I hate liars. Mrs O'Brien was always saying to me when she suspected me of telling lies, '*You can catch a mouse, you can catch a thief, but you can't catch a liar.*'

Sometimes she accused Tailor of being the greatest liar in the world because he loved telling stories about people with quare names. Names like, Whistler Keaveney, Tom Pat Ned, Mouse Nee, Blackie Staggers and Harry White. When he started telling stories I loved listening to him. Once I knew he was coming I made sure to have all the jobs done so I could spend more time listening. I hung around, just outside the front door. Harry White was one of my favourite characters and now Tailor was talking about him. He sounded so exciting I would have given anything to have seen Harry.

'…Ah sure he's not right in the head, the poor auld devil. Wait until you hear what he did a couple of weeks ago. 'Twas the fair day in Glan: he was drinking all day and arguing with people. Eventually, they threw him out of Daddy Quinn's pub because he had enough drank. But the bould Harry wouldn't hear of: no more porter. And the next bloody thing didn't he, ups-with-the-fist and drove it straight through the winda. He was that badly cut, the neighbour brought him to the doctor: they were afraid he'd bleed to death…'

'Jesus, Mary and Holy St Joseph, is it again? Didn't he do the same thing a few months ago?'

'He did! But sure he's as thick as an ass. Only this time people said, he cut his hand to let out the porter; he'd that much drank.'

'Oh Sacred Heart… he must have near cut the hand off himself!'

'But wait until you hear! He stayed away from the town for a few days and 'twas rumoured he was in a bad way: that he wasn't well. But well or not he was sittin' in front of the house when who did he see going into the village, but Blackie Staggers, driving the hearse. Blackie was going in to drop off a coffin at Mouse Mee's house because auld Mrs Mouse had died that morning…'

'Is that the same Mouse that came home from America?'

'Sure damn it, there's only the one Mouse in it! You're thinking of the Mrs Mouse that moved out to Patch, she's a first cousin,'

'Oh yes. Now I have you.'

'Anyway, Blackie pulls up alongside Harry, winds down the winda and says; "begod Harry, according to some people in the town you're dead. There's a fierce rumour going round Quinn's pub this morning that you got a bad turn last night and passed away."

"Oh, that's what some of them 'effers in Quinn's pub would like to hear alright. But I can tell you I'm far from dead. They'll have to put up with me another while, I'm thinkin'. Is there any chance you'd give me a lift into the town on your way back? I could do with a loaf-a-bread."

"There's every chance", says Blackie. "I'm just going in to drop off this coffin. I'll be back in a few minutes and you can have a lift in along with me."

Sure enough, when Blackie comes out, Harry's waiting for him at the gate. But before he gets into the hearse he says to Blackie, "you know I was thinking about what you said earlier; about me being dead and all that. Is there any chance I could get into the back of the hearse? I'd love to give the effers, in Quinn's pub, something to talk about."

"I don't care what you do. You can sit on the roof for all I care," says Blackie.

"Right," says Harry; and with that didn't he climb into the back of the hearse and Blackie drove at a snail's pace all the way into the town. People stopped on the side of the road and started blessing themselves when they saw the corpse with the two hobnail boots stuck up against the back window and him lying flat out: the rosary beads in his hands and they joined across his chest.'

'Ah… I don't believe you!' said Mrs O'Brien.

'That God may come down and strike me dead this minute. And didn't Blackie slow the hearse down entirely when he saw Whistler Keaveney coming out of Daddy Quinn's pub. Blackie wound down the winda and shouted, "Now Whistler, is it true or not?" pointing to the corpse in the back of the hearse. "I have to keep going. I'm bringing him to Galway for a post mortem."

Whistler stood with his mouth open, took off his hat and hurriedly made a sign of the cross before dashing into Quinn's to inform all and sundry that Harry was dead: that he'd seen the corpse on its way to the hospital.'

'Ah you're not serious, you're having me on? You know something you're the greatest liar under the Sun?'

'All right: all right! If you don't believe me, hop on your bicycle and go up to Daddy Quinn's and you'll find out whether 'tis the truth or not.' said Tailor.

'And what happened then?' asked Mrs O'Brien.

'Blackie pulled up outside the town and let Harry out-a-the-hearse. Harry turned round and sneaked back into the town and went straight to Daddy Quinn's.. He stood at the door for a minute. Sure the customers nearly fainted when they saw him. He said, "I've come back to haunt ye: ye miserable shower-a-bastards."'

'Ah well look it… I don't know what to say!' said Mrs O'Brien

'Talk about banter and cráic. And to crown it all didn't Daddy's Quinn's wife Peggy, give Harry a pint; and all he was after putting her through? But faith she wouldn't give him more than one. "Off with you now, you scut, out-of-me-sight," she said.'

'And how is he getting on since, I wonder?'

'Dammy if I know! I haven't heard a cricket since, except that Blackie was threatened with the sack for allowing Harry into the back of the hearse and him with the dirtiest pair of boots in Ireland on him.'

Shortly before Tailor was due to go home, Mrs O'Brien called me and gave me an old shopping bag saying, 'Would you ever run down to the field and pull a decent bunch of carrots and onions and a few nice sized beetroots and put them into this bag for Tailor. And you can leave them beside the bike when you come back.'

When I came back and left them beside the bike I overheard Mrs O'Brien talking about Bridie and myself.

'…Oh his mother is very good to him and sends him a parcel three or four times a year.. And as for writing; sure the Lord save us, you couldn't keep up to her. She writes to him every single week. '

'What does she do or what does she look like?'

'That I couldn't tell you: though wait a minute. What am I saying: I've a photograph of her here on the window sill, some place. As far as I know she works in the Laundry.'

For a while there discussed the photograph then Mrs O'Brien, said,

'What harm but she has me damned, asking me to bring him in so she can see him. It's all very fine bringing him in, I'd be afraid she'd want to keep him.'

'She would too… but then again she mightn't be let. The nuns are very strict, in them places I believe. They probably wouldn't allow her to see him. Wasn't it the nuns that brought him out to you? So they'd hardly go changing the goalposts now?'

'Oh it was. And I pray to the Lord they keep her there. I'd be afraid of my life she'd land down here on top of us and bring him up to Galway. He's a great help; and it would be nice if he stayed at home and worked the land when he's finished school: because as you know we're not getting any younger. We'll need someone to look after us in our old age. But sure, there's no knowing what he'll do. And though he's still very young, he has a mind of his own. He knows exactly what he wants. Football; that's all he ever thinks about. He's at it morning noon and night. I've tried my best to stop him, but 'tis no use. That's all they play in school, so I suppose it's hard to blame him. And as for shoes or wellingtons, sure you couldn't keep him shod. He has them flittered in no time. I don't know how many times I caught him kicking tin cans round the garden.'

'Ah sure none of us knows what's going to happen. But I'd be inclined to think he's a man for the land.'

'Well I hope you're right,' sighed Mrs O'Brien. 'We'll just have to wait and see. I must go out and see where he is.'

I darted round to the back of the house and started shooing the hens, making believe I was chasing them away.

'Joooohn?' she shouted, at the top of her voice.

'Yes,' I replied as I came running.

'Oh Good, I thought you were still down the field! Are them the biggest onions you could get?' she asked, checking the vegetables in the bag. 'How many onions did you give him? One, two, three…six,' she counted, 'Would you ever run down again and bring up another three or four; and make sure they're good and big because he likes onions.'

I ran down to the field again, intrigued that they'd been talking about me. I didn't know what to make of their conversation. The most surprising thing was they were referring to Bridie as my mother. And for the umpteenth time I asked myself was Bridie my mother as well as Mrs O'Brien. She must be, I thought, because in her letters she always said, from your mother, Bridie. But then a major problem arose. How could I go and see Bridie when I didn't know where she lived? I knew she lived in Galway, somewhere. But that was a city. And how would I get there when I had no money and didn't know where her house was? I had often thought about asking Mrs O'Brien if we could go up and see her; or better still, why could she not come down and see us like Tailor. But I knew if I opened my mouth I'd get a right ticking off: children should be seen and not heard. Go down to your room and do your lessons, it would be more in your line than going around asking stupid questions that don't concern you. That's exactly what she'd say.

Lying in bed that night I couldn't get the gist of their conversation out of my head.

If what they were saying was true and Bridie wanted to keep me in Galway; I thought that would be brilliant. And having carefully analysed it, I came to the conclusion that Bridie lived in a house, something like Nora Keeffe's. Nora had lots of nice furniture with pictures and flowers and blessed statues. And she always had apples and oranges and bananas on the table whenever I brought her buttermilk. As well as that, she had loads of chocolate bars and always put one or two into the can, for me to bring home to Mrs O'Brien. So Bridie must be like her, I thought. How else could she send me parcels and sweets for my birthday and other occasions, whereas Mrs O'Brien never sent a parcel to anyone because she couldn't afford it. Mrs O'Brien often bought me an ice cream and sweets but she never bought lucky bags or anything fancy like them.

But when I thought again about what Tailor and Mrs O'Brien had said I was even more confused. What did Taylor mean, *changing the goalposts now? The nuns are very strict*. And why does Bridie say in her letters that the nuns treat her very well?

Unable to solve the mystery of my two mothers, I tried to put the subject out of my head. The problem was, it just wouldn't go away.

Chapter Fifteen

Apart from watching and waiting for a parcel from Bridie, sport was my one great passion. I'd spend hours every evening playing football. And on Thursday evening I'd be sent running to the town to buy *The Connaught Tribune*. As soon as I'd arrive home, I'd start reading it. I loved reading about the Galway football team and their forwards Sean Purcell and Frank Stockwell and the way they could score.

I also loved reading about other famous sportsmen: men like El Cordobés, the greatest matador in the world. And if I wasn't reading about him, it was about Shay Elliott in the Tour De France and I'd sit there at the table dreaming that one day I too would be a great cyclist. But Mrs O'Brien would soon put a stop to my daydreaming by giving me some job to do. Very often I'd have to go and round up the cattle and transfer them to a new field of grass. And if the weather was very dry, I'd have to let them out of the field every day and drive them as far as the lake so they could get a drink of water. The jobs were always straight forward and easy. Yet the easier the jobs, the more likely I was to make a hames of them. And driving the cattle down by the lake and into the field we called *Górt Mór*, was one of them.

I was three quarters of the way down when I met Mickey Billy's cattle grazing along the side of the road with no one to look after them. Had I seen Mickey Billy's cattle in time I might have been able to do something about it, but it was too late now. The minute the two herds met they went to battle straight away. It was a frightening experience. The two herds were locked in fearsome combat and I had no idea how to separate them. Mickey Billy's herd were greater in number, therefore it was going to be very difficult to get through. For a split second, I stood rooted to the ground, not knowing what to do. I was terrified our in-calf cows would be injured and I'd get the blame if anything happened. I knew I had to drive our cattle through come what may and the only way to do that was to stay close behind, to wallop them on.. But I didn't feel like walloping our cattle as they had done nothing wrong. Already Mickey Billy's cattle were forcing ours back, so I boldly stepped forward, walloping one of our bullocks in an effort to force it through. Suddenly Mickey Billy's herd forced one of our cows back on top of me and I was knocked to the ground. Before I knew what was happening, I was being trampled into the ground, with death defying horns grappling each other, inched from my body. Instinctively, I rolled myself into a ball in an effort to protect myself. For all of two or three minutes, the cattle fought a relentless duel as I tried to avoid their hooves and horns. I was convinced that sooner or later one of their powerful horns would go straight through my body. Several times their hooves skidded off my body as they inched their way forward, almost falling on top of me. This was even more terrifying as I knew I'd be killed stone dead if one of the cows slipped and fell on me. For what seemed like an eternity, I rolled this way and that in the rising dust and dirt to avoid being trampled to death as Mickey Billy's herd finally pushed my cattle back up the road. Recovering from my ordeal, I dusted myself down and ran after the cattle before they could make their way home. I knew my mother would go mad if she saw the cattle coming back home again and of course I'd get the blame.

At the end of the narrow road, the cattle turned in off the road opposite the lake to where they could graze on herbs and wild grass There, I was able to separate the two herds before driving our cattle down the road into Górt Mór. I ran home quickly so I could wash myself and get ready for school. When I told Mrs O'Brien what happened she praised me and said I was lucky I wasn't killed. But she insisted I take off my shirt so she could have a look at me.

'Jesus Mary and Holy St Joseph, you're black and blue. How in the name of God is it, you weren't killed? You know I have a good mind to go down to Castlerea and have a lawyer's letter sent to Mickey Billy for letting his cattle out on the road; to kill and maim all before them. People are sick and tired of them on the road every day. Are you sure you're alright? For all you know, you might have broken something? I don't like the look of that bruise on your shoulder', she said examining me closer.

'It's alright, it's not sore,' I protested, though I flinched when she touched my right shoulder blade.

'I ran home and it wasn't a bit sore. It was sore at first, but it's alright now,' I said, eagerly, wanting to go to school.

'Are you sure?

'I am!'

'Maybe I should bring you to the doctor.'

'No! I'm all right,' I protested again.

'I know you're mad to go to school. But if your shoulder gets too sore or you feel sick or anything like that, be sure to tell the teacher and come straight home and I'll bring you down to the doctor.'

I ran out the door because I was already late for school. I'd heard the rest of the scholars passing while I was washing and changing my clothes. But that didn't stop me dreaming as I made my way down to school. I stood on the road reliving those horrible moments when I was almost gored to death. I knew I was destined to be a matador in sunny Spain. After what I'd been through, I could have taken on the most dangerous bull in the world. And there on the dusty road I practised; how as a famous matador, I'd twirl my cape this way and that, neatly side stepping my way out of danger. And after teasing the bull for about the hundredth time, I'd plunge my gleaming sword straight between its broad shoulder blades as the crowd rose to their feet to give me a standing ovation and I in turn would bow my head, slowly, in appreciation.

In school, I couldn't wait to tell my friends how I had taken on a herd of wild cattle, single handed; and won. And what was more I had the marks to prove it. All that day I could think of little else: how I'd been almost trampled to death and had come through unscathed.

When I came home I thought very seriously about writing to the King of Spain, offering myself as a fearless matador to rival El Cordobés; the legendary bullfighter. But then I thought Mrs O'Brien might not like the idea; and besides I'd have to write to Bridie and tell her how I was going away to become a matador: and she might not like the idea either. And when I thought about it more seriously, I realized it would be a terrible thing to have to refuse the King of Spain if he ever wrote back and said, yes, El John Paschal, we would love you to be our new matador. Let me know when you're coming and I will arrange to meet you.

But my mother wasn't long knocking that dream out of my head when she said,

'When you finish your dinner, I want you to leave on your good clothes so you can go to the town for me. I'm having a-bit-of-a-party on Sunday night; so I'd like you to get me a few things.'

She reached across the table to the window sill and handed me a long list she had already made out.

'Who's coming to the party?' I asked eagerly, thinking the party might be for me.

'Ah musha who do you think? A few friends of mine: what few I have. Nurse Finnegan and Mrs McMillan... the few women that were here last year! Isn't it great how you've forgotten about them already; and all the sweets and chocolates they brought you?'

'Oh yeah, I remember. And you made a swan out-a-the-butter. I didn't know they were coming again,' I said excitedly.

'Well now you know. Look, I've five score of eggs there in the basket ready for you to bring down to Harry Ryan. And with eggs four and sixpence a score, you should have more than enough to pay for what I need. Make sure you go easy when you're carrying them and rest yourself going down the road. Harry Ryan should have everything I want: if he hasn't we'll have to try and get them elsewhere.'

I looked at the list and was amazed at all she was getting: a pound of tea, two pounds of sugar, a pound of tomatoes, a pound of cooked ham, a bottle of salad cream, a bottle of *HP* sauce, a large Swiss roll, a packet of strawberry jelly, a packet of *Bird's custard*, a large tin of peaches, a packet of Mikado biscuits, a two pound pot of blackcurrant jam, a bottle of sherry, a bar of carbolic soap, *The Connaught Tribune*, five herrings and a half a quarter of tobacco. I was excited at the thought that when I'd come home, my mother would make a bowl of sherry trifle and I'd be given the job of stirring it. . With any bit-a-luck, I'd be able to dip my finger in and taste it before it set. I loved sherry trifle and would eat and drink the entire bowl if I got the chance. But I was hoping I wouldn't have to gut the fish. That was one job I didn't like. Sometimes, I'd have to stand watching Mrs O'Brien pulling the guts out of the herrings. It was my job to call the cat and give the guts to her by throwing them under a bush, down the garden.

'Now whatever you do, don't lose the change, because that's all I have to my name. Make sure you put the money into your pocket. There are no holes in them good trousers, so you've no excuse.' She lifted the egg basket off the chair and left it down beside me on the floor. Then she escorted me out to the street saying, 'Don't lose that list whatever you do; and make sure to mind yourself and watch where you're going. And when you come home I'll have something nice to eat,' she said affectionately.

I made my way slowly down by the lake, happy in the knowledge that something nice awaited me on my return. I looked back to see if anyone was following me, but there was no one else on the road. I had to change hands several times as the basket was heavy. I stopped for a moment to wipe my sweating brow and to savour the delights of Mother-Nature; as across the far side of the shimmering lake I could hear iron clad cart wheels rumbling along the main road and female voices shouting in anger as they tried rounding up errant stock. And somewhere far, far away I could hear dogs yelping as all around me I could see small birds twittering on nearby branches, their sweet notes overshadowed by the chirping sounds of thrush and blackbird, as bumble bees zigzagged their way speedily through the autumn haze. And as I picked up my basket once more, I couldn't help but admire the numerous fields with their stacks of golden corn as dragon flies flew low over the dusty road before flying across fields and hedgerows.

Lackadaisically, I wandered on with my heavy basket trying to make up my mind whether I wanted to spend Sunday evening listening to the visitors or playing football in the ball alley field. I didn't like listening to people anymore because it wasn't half as exciting as playing football with my friends.

Now that I was getting bigger, I was sometimes allowed to play with the big lads in the ball alley field on the edge of the town, across the road from where the new church was being built. While I was trying to figure out how best to approach Mrs O'Brien, I thought I heard the distant boom of an aeroplane somewhere in the summer sky. I looked up at the broad expanse of infinity to see if I could detect where exactly it was. But the sky was so vast, so blue and so high up it was almost impossible to detect anything. Eventually I spotted the plane emerging from a snow white cloud. It was but a tiny speck, sparkling like a precious jewel far, far away and I began to wonder how it ever managed to get up there. It was so hard to imagine people sitting there contentedly, going all the way to America and I thought I wouldn't like to be up there because the plane might never come down … *crash*!.

In what seemed like a blinding flash, I lost all control of my senses. My knees crashed to the ground, my chin hopped off a stone and I saw a multitude of stars pass before me as the basket of eggs exploded before my very eyes. By the time I'd refocused my vision my stomach was ready to heave at the sight before me. It was the most sickening sight I'd ever seen. I couldn't believe what had happened to me. I'd tripped on a stone because I wasn't watching where I was going. My big toe was bleeding. I knew instantly the minute I'd get home I'd be killed stone dead. I was eleven and a half years of age and nothing like this was ever supposed to happen, again. It was one thing to break a china cup; they could be replaced, but eggs! To make matters worse it was the biggest basket I ever carried. I wanted to run away because I knew what it would be like to go home and face my mother. I stood in shock looking at the gooey mess on the road and I wanted to die. It was littered with slime and eggshells and egg yolks mixed with grit and cow dung. Then a strange thought struck me. It was the exact same spot, the scene of my dice with death and the cattle earlier in the day. Recovering from the shock I realized I couldn't just stand there; I had to try and gather up the eggs before anyone saw me. I gathered what eggs I could and placed them gently in the basket. On closer inspection, I was relieved to discover a number of eggs which only a hint of a crack in them. I put them into the basket, making sure to turn the cracked side down so that Harry Ryan wouldn't notice them. To finish the job off, I added a score or more that had only a small dent in the shell. I knew our eggs were bound for Dublin, London, Paris, Istanbul and beyond. And I prayed with all my heart that no one in London or Paris or Istanbul would notice or complain if their hard boiled eggs happened to have a dent in the shell. After all, it was what was inside that mattered, I thought. Then to my horror, I realized I'd forgotten to count them. For a moment I considered taking them all out again. I'd pile them on the side of the road where I'd count them, but then I thought better of it. I had no idea how many eggs were in the basket or how many eggs I'd broken. Now I'd no choice but to carry on. But before leaving, I decided to nudge the broken eggs into the side of the road, where despite my bleeding dust covered toe, I trampled them into the ground so no one would ever know I had crash landed there. Now my two feet were yellow, the slime and egg yolks having squirted up between my toes; and in a vain effort to remove the evidence I wiped my feet on the grass but they were still dirty.

With a lighter basket and a heavier heart I walked on into town to face Harry Ryan. It was a dreadful nightmare watching Harry taking the soiled eggs out of the basket one by one. When he had finished he turned to me and said,

'A bad day at the office I guess,'

I felt awful. I handed him the list that Mrs O'Brien had given me. He left it on the counter and began lining the dirty basket with sheets of newspaper; then he studied the list and began putting things into the basket. He said he was out of *HP* sauce and was sorry he had no Swiss roll on account of the strike. I followed him out the back door of the shop to fetch five good herrings. When we went outside there was a cat feasting on the herrings which were in a large wooden box, left up on a barrel. He chased it away and rummaged down through the box to choose five good herring; shooing bluebottles out of the way as he did so. He wrapped the herrings in newspaper and shoved them into the basket along with everything else including the docket. Turning for the door I plucked up the courage to ask him how many eggs I had because I knew I'd be asked, the minute I went home.

'Young man, I haven't the foggiest. I'll have to go through them all again. No doubt the Missus will have enough to make me a decent omelette,' he said smiling, as he held the shop door open for me. 'It was a pleasure doing business with you Mr Rodgers. Call soon again.'

I made my way home, as slowly as I possibly could. I was dreading every step that brought me nearer the house. I was trying to think up all kinds of excuses to give Mrs O'Brien. But I had no idea what I was going to say. I felt like Our Lord must have felt when he fell three times on his way to Calvary.

Soon I was within sight of the house and as I rounded the last corner I could see Mrs O'Brien white washing the back kitchen in readiness for the visitors. As I drew near the house she turned and half heartedly smiled at me, asking,

'Well, how did you get on? Did you manage to get everything I asked?'

I didn't say anything because the words wouldn't come out of my mouth. She looked at me for a split second, then the soiled basket and her face dropped like a stone. She screamed like a stuck pig and made a lunge for me with the brush, but I ran into the house, with her hot on my heels,

'Jeeeeesus, Mary and Joseph, don't say you fell, again?' I half threw the basket up on the chair as she made a bee line for me. I ran screaming around the kitchen but she grabbed me by the scruff of the neck and wheeled me around the floor as she walloped me with the paint brush right down on top of the head.

Wallop! 'What in the name of God,' Wallop! 'did you do with my fine basket of eggs?' Wallop! 'I declare to God Almighty I'll go mad this day,' Wallop! 'after I spending half the day washing and counting those bloody eggs.' And when the brush went flying she went, Thump!, across my shoulder with her clinched fist, 'Merciful God Almighty what am I going to do with you?' she ranted, as she snatched the wet dish cloth off the table and started walloping me across the face with it. 'You must be the thickest lad in Ireland. You must have the feet of an ass; after I warning you', Wallop! 'time and again to go easy and watch where you were going. Those eggs were all I had in this world and now you've gone and destroyed them.' She stopped to draw her breath for a moment as the colour drained from her cheeks. Standing there gasping, she asked, 'How many eggs did you break?'

'I don't know.' I cried.

She hit me with the dishcloth again and again as the tears ran down my cheeks. I felt each lash of the dishcloth as it stung my face. She stopped the onslaught for a moment while she stamped her foot on the ground and sneered at me, 'You don't know! You don't know, because you're as thick as an ass.' Again she asked, 'How many eggs did you break? Answer me before I break every bone in your body.'

'A lot', I cried, as I began to feel the terrible weight of guilt for what I had done. Looking up at the sky like an eejit, when I should have been watching where I was going and walking meekly down the road like St Patrick who walked thousands of miles all over Ireland; and never fell once.

'A lot', she sneered, still holding the wet cloth over her shoulder, ready to land another blow. 'How many? I asked you.'

'I don't know,' I replied, shivering with the fear that if she really knew how many were destroyed, she'd finish me off altogether.

She grabbed me viciously by the hair while she brought down the weight of the wet cloth across my shoulders again and again until I was a shivering nervous wreck. Thump!, went her clinched fist across my shoulder, again. 'You don't know!' Thump! 'You don't know! I'll bet Harry Ryan knows! How many eggs did you give him or do you know?'

'I don't know. I asked him but he wouldn't tell me,' I sobbed pitifully.

'That the Lord God Almighty may protect me and save me from all harm,' but you're a right Pleota,* ' she snapped. 'It was a bad day I ever laid my two eyes on you. You have me heart broke every single day I get up out-a-me-bed: to think, what you did to my beautiful basket of eggs, after they going up in price. And I trying to save every penny I could, so we could get the electric light.'

Then she began emptying the basket.

'Where's the Swiss roll? Don't say you came home without it,' she said, 'or I'll kill you…and I waiting to make the sherry trifle.'

'Harry Ryan, said there was a strike on… he hopes to have them… next week,' I mumbled, trying to hold back the tears at the thought that she'd start walloping me again.

'Ah, next-week-me-backside,' she replied angrily. Then realising she wouldn't be able to make the sherry trifle, she stopped emptying the basket, looked at me in astonishment and said,

'Is it what he has no Swiss rolls left? Is that what you're trying to tell me?

---

* Pleota *(softie)*.

'Yes. 'They might have some in Johnny's,' I suggested, hopefully,'

'And God Blast you to hell! Why didn't you go into Johnny's, when you knew Harry Ryan had none? Why?' she asked, standing there looking at me, the dimple on her chin, twitching, with splatters of whitewash all over her face: her coiled plaited hair tucked under an old headscarf.

'Because…I… I had no money.'

'You had no money! But you have money for sweets and the devil knows what when it suits you! And there's me thinking that I'd have a few bob left over after all the shopping: but no, you had to go and break every egg I ever had and now I don't know whether I'm coming or going. Go down there to that rotten room and change your clothes and go outside and finish that back kitchen: that's if you're able to do anything.'

I quickly changed and went outside and finished white washing the back kitchen. It was a great relief to be outside. But I knew she'd have it in for me for weeks and weeks. And I was so looking forward to Sunday's party and my chance to go playing football in the ball alley field. Now I wasn't sure whether the party would go ahead or not.

By the time Sunday came around, I'd resigned myself to the fact that I'd have to stand listening outside my bedroom window while everybody else was enjoying themselves. After what happened I daren't mention anything about wanting to go down to the ball alley field.

My father had already gone rambling when Delia Tully, the first of the visitors, came cycling in along the new road. As soon as I spotted her, I rushed into the house to tell Mrs O'Brien. Then I hung around outside watching and waiting for the others to arrive while Mrs O'Brien entertained Delia.

'… I don't know-in-God's-earth, where I'd be without him. He milks the cows before he goes to school and when he comes home he cleans out the stables and everything for me. You know he can turn his hand to anything and is a great one entirely to send on a message.'

'Lord, aren't you lucky? I wish I'd a little lad'een like that. There's me; and my three girls beyond in New York and I hardly able to walk. If only I'd someone like John Paschal, I'd be elected. How old is he now?'

'He'll be twelve now come May. You don't feel them growing?'

'I was thinking that. I can see he's growing all the time. You won't feel until he's reared. Then the two of ye can sit back in yeer old age and he'll take care-a-ye.'

'Well… that's what I'd be hoping anyway. But sure there's no knowing what he'll do. He'll be sittin' his primary exam next year or the year after. And if he passes that, I'll have to let him go to Castlerea for a year I suppose. The Government are threatening to keep them in school a bit longer. And if he goes to Castlerea I won't see him at all, be the time he gets home in the evenings and everything.'

Next to arrive was Mrs MacMillan. She came walking up by the lake, like she always did when ever she was visiting. Soon Nurse Finnegan and Mrs Lowry came cycling together in along the new road. I could hear them all laughing and joking while waiting for Mrs Ryan to arrive. When it seemed as if they would have to go ahead and start eating without her, Harry Ryan's car pulled into the street. Holding a brown paper bag she got out of the car as Harry turned to her and said, 'Enjoy yourself sweetheart. I'll be back for you in an hour or so.'

Because Mrs Ryan had such a big family to look after she wasn't able to stay more than an hour. As soon as the hour was up, Harry was back to collect her. The visitors said it was a shame she had to leave early; she was such a good natured person. She deserved a night to herself because no man or woman ever went without while she stood in the shop, despite the fact she had sixteen mouths of her own to feed.

As soon as the party was over, I was called into the house, to sit down and have whatever I wanted. I had a great feed of chicken and ham with spring onions, tomatoes and fresh garden lettuce. I had a piece of cake and a bowl of sherry trifle and I washed it down with two cups of tea. My father did likewise when he came home while my mother and I did the washing up.

During these annual events, we always treated ourselves to the best of everything, the same as the visitors. But the thing I enjoyed most was studying my mother's butter sculpture. When ever she had a party in the house, she'd go to great lengths to set the scene. Covering the table with an Irish linen cloth she'd set the table for six, using her best china along with her prized Newbridge cutlery and Waterford crystal glasses. But pride of place always went to her unique butter sculptures which best illustrated her unique talents as a butter maker. In the middle of the table, she'd stand her Belleek butter dish with her exquisite creation. Sometimes she'd make a basket of eggs, illustrating the intricate basket work, right down to the smallest detail. Again she had sculpted a swan and cygnets which were my favourite. The swan sat gracefully, her head slightly inclined, keeping an eye on her flock as they brought up the rear. I couldn't take my eyes off them and was delighted that nobody had touched them. And the more I thought about it, the more I realised that nobody in their right mind would dream of plunging a knife into such a beautiful piece of work. Instead, the visitors had sampled the butter from one of the smaller dishes. These contained little blobs of butter in the form of sea shells my mother had made as an added attraction.

When we had everything washed and dried, we put the presents of cakes and sweets and chocolates into the bottom half of the dresser where I was told not to touch them. But the following day I was called in from the garden and given a piece of cake and a bar of chocolate after Mrs O'Brien had had her afternoon nap.

A few days later, after I'd come home from school, I was told there was a letter on the window for me. It was from Bridie. I tore it open and took out the letter along with a small black and white photograph showing a large group of women. Again, Bridie had put x on the photograph identifying herself as the tall thin lady in the middle. She looked very frail compared to some of her friends who though not as tall were more amply proportioned. I read the letter, which was the same as all her letters. How was I getting on? Was I behaving myself? And when was I going in to see her? When Bridie first started writing to me, her letters were neat and tidy with not a single word out of place. Now a lot of her letters had words and whole sentences blacked out. When I asked my mother why Bridie was scribbling out so many words and making such a mess of her letters, she said,

'Maybe she's not as smart as you think! Some day, me bucko, you'll learn that you have to live with someone to know them. If you were living with her now, instead of me, you mightn't think half as much of her. Look, when you finish your tea I think you should write her a letter. I don't think you wrote at all, last week, did you?' she asked looking seriously at me as she sat relaxing by the fire which was something she seldom did as she was always either knitting or sewing.

I said nothing as I tried to recall when I'd last written to Bridie. As far as I was concerned, I was always writing because Mrs O'Brien was always telling me to write.

'Let Bridie not think that I'm stopping you, because I'm not. If she only knew how you have me heart broke night, noon and morning, she might think long and hard about writing to you at all,' she said, giving me a disgruntled look.

I went down to my room and sat at the table asking myself why I had to write to Bridie every week. I hated writing letters the best of times but I particularly hated being told when to write. Wasn't it enough to write and thank Bridie when she sent me a parcel, I thought? I never had to write and thank people in England or America when they wrote or sent parcels, so why did I have to keep writing to Bridie?

To help keep the peace, I wrote a letter to Bridie, which was little more than a note and showed it to Mrs O'Brien. She gave it her approval by handing me the money to post it. Seeing she was pleased with the letter, I asked,

'Why do I have to keep writing to Bridie, when I don't have to write to anybody else …in America …or…England?'

'Ah, because she's your mother, that's why!' she said, clinching her fists with indignation

The way that Mrs O'Brien had said, 'Ah because she's your mother,' made me feel very uncomfortable. My mind was starting to go blank again. It didn't make sense.

'How…how… can I have two mothers?' I brazenly blurted out, despite my reservations.

'Look! Will you stop asking stupid questions like a good lad? If you must know its a long story. You're too young to understand the ways of the world. Besides, I'm sick and tired telling you that children should be seen and not heard. How many times have I told you that? How many?' she reiterated, stamping her foot, like a bull ready to charge.

'A lot,' I answered meekly. I was deeply hurt that she would not give me a simple answer. 'Why don't you run down and post that cursed letter and not be annoying me!' she said, giving me a look that told me more than I needed to know: don't ask any more questions.

I ran to the town and posted the letter, but I couldn't help thinking how crazy it was that people wouldn't tell me anything. I thought about asking my mother what a bastard was, but I knew there was no point when she wouldn't even explain to me who Bridie was. It was terrible to think that nobody in the world could help me. Fatso Fannon called me a pauper every single day of the week and a little bastard if I managed to score a goal or a point against him. One day I asked John Keaveney if he knew what a pauper was and he said he didn't. He said he thought it was a person with no money. Yet when I had a few coppers and bought sweets, the big lads still called me a pauper and a mean bastard because I wouldn't share.

After a while I began to develop my own theory. I thought being a pauper might be the same as being an eejit. Everybody in school knew what an eejit was – a person who knew nothing: and I was beginning to feel like an eejit, because I knew nothing. I didn't know who Bridie was. I didn't know why I had two mothers when the whole world only had one. I didn't know what a pauper was. I didn't know what a bastard was. And to make matters worse my father had called me a-son-of-bitch because I hadn't told him one of our calves was passing red water. I didn't know red water could kill a cow or a calf and I felt really bad when the calf died two days later. Had I told my mother or father in time, they could have saved the calf they said. I began to think then, that I must be really stupid because there were so many things in life I didn't know and trying to find the answers was killing me.

I was living in the hope when I'd go into Mr Feather's class I'd learn all the answers. Once you were in his class, you were considered one of the big boys. All of us in third class were due to go into him next year. He was the new principal of our school and was supposed to be very strict. Nobody knew for sure what he was really like. Some of the lads in the fourth and fifth classes said he was a tyrant. But the lads in the sixth class said they'd soon put manners on him. It was hard to know what to believe. The only thing we could do, was wait until it was our turn to go into Mr Feather's class; but the omens as far as we were concerned were not good: not good at all.

Chapter Sixteen

If it wasn't for EJ Lyons, I didn't know what I'd do. I liked EJ. He was great fun altogether. Everyone liked him, except, The Chicken. The Chicken was our new teacher. His real name was Mr Feathers but we sometimes called him The Chicken behind his back. We thought it was hilarious for someone to have a name like Feathers. Some of the bigger lads would skit amongst themselves and say, 'Good morning Mr Feathers,' as he opened up the school, while laughing at the absurdity of it all.

Entering the classroom each morning, our new teacher looked very business like in his dark three piece suit, with a gold watch dangling from his waistcoat pocket. He'd leave his black briefcase down beside his desk, take off his jacket and hang it on the back of the chair. He had black elastic bands on his arms to hold up his shirt sleeves which matched his gold studded black tie. He wore gold framed glasses, which he polished meticulously before starting in the morning and very often repeated the exercise throughout the day. When he removed his glasses, it left a red imprint on his nose which we found amusing. It was as if some woman with horrible lipstick had kissed the bridge of his nose. His sleek black hair was so well oiled it was set like jelly.

Mr Feathers was very strict and loved nothing more than using the rod, which he liked to call the cane. John Keaveney didn't like him because he was always picking on him. EJ Lyons didn't like him because he was always walloping him. I couldn't make up my mind whether I liked him or not because he hadn't done anything to me, but I was inclined to agree with my friends that he was a bit like Pontius Pilate. EJ claimed he looked like Pilate in our Catechism book. Besides, he'd give us an awful lot of homework to do and expect those interested in serving Mass to learn Latin in Mrs Patterson's class as well. Only pupils in the fourth and fifth classes were chosen to serve Mass. All of us wanted to serve Mass but we couldn't unless we were chosen. There were sixteen pupils in our class but only three of us were picked. John Keaveney, Eamon Finnegan and myself plus five others from fifth class. EJ Lyons said,

'Lads, I'm glad I wasn't picked. It's a relief to know I won't have to be wracking me brains learning auld rubbish that no one can understand. I'd rather be listening to the bird'eens in our back garden: that way I might learn something.'

All EJ wanted was to learn how to imitate birds and animals. Most days he spent his lunch break chirping away like a bird, demonstrating his extraordinary talent. I have to admit he was good, very good and getting better every single day.

One day, Mr Feathers came down to EJ in a fit of temper. He asked him to stand up and put out his hand because he was continuously talking. Very reluctantly EJ got to his feet.

'Why do you want me to put out my hand, Sir?' asked EJ, with a sly grin.

'Let me show you,' said Mr Feathers, angrily as he grabbed EJ's left hand and held it out forcefully. Three times he brought the weight of the cane down. We could hear the whistle of the cane as it swished through the air before it warped itself bow-like across EJ's short chubby fingers.

'Now you know why I wanted you to hold out your hand.'

'I do, but it's a bit late… I thought you wanted to give me a few bob,' gasped EJ as he locked his painful hand under his arm to ease the severity of the pain.

There was a sharp intake of breath all around at EJ's brazen response. We knew instantly that The Chicken – as we called Mr Feathers on the QT – would not take too kindly to back chat. But inwardly, we were willing the show to go on.

We could see The Chicken's blood pressure rising as his gills suddenly turned crimson and he caught hold of EJ's other hand with such viciousness we thought he would pull it from his shoulder. 'Awe' cried EJ in response, as The Chicken prepared to give him a few more slaps.

'Don't you ever… answer me like that again, or I declare to God I'll come down on you so heavy, you won't know what hit you,' shouted The Chicken as he pushed EJ into his seat.

EJ never batted an eyelid, except to bury his hands under his arms to stem the pain which was clearly etched on his face. And as Mr Feathers went and sat behind his desk clearly exasperated, John Keaveney whispered aside,

'I think you ruffled his feathers.'

We were sniggered so much we buried our heads in our hands because we thought our sides would burst.

Sometimes during class, Mr Feathers would give us a few hard sums to do; then he'd slip quietly out the door and down the corridor to visit a young lady who was in the girls' class. It was obvious he liked talking to her and she liked talking to him. Occasionally, she'd come up to our classroom where the two of them would sit side by side resting their backsides on the heavy framed fire screen, whispering, while we pretended to be doing our lessons.

As soon as The Chicken had flown the roost as EJ was fond of saying, he'd stand on the desk and give a loud whistle as a signal for hostilities to begin. We'd throw books and pencils at each and start carving our initials on the desk. Occasionally, we'd borrow the answers to our sums, from those that knew them and everyone was happy. It was a great feeling to know we'd get all our sums right for once in our life. Later, we'd sit smiling contentedly; having been told that after weeks of trying the teacher had finally managed to knock something into our thick skulls.

The very minute the teacher was out of the room, EJ would start imitating every living thing. He'd sneak up behind you and go snork, snork, snork, right into your ear. Eamon Finnegan was forever asking him to imitate the blackbird, the thrush and the crow. No matter what we asked EJ to do, he could do it. We'd listen spellbound as he went through his daily routine. By far the loveliest sound was the song of the blackbird. When called upon to do it, he'd slip his two little fingers into the corners of his mouth and give us the distinctive mating call of the blackbird; followed by the mystical sound of another blackbird responding, somewhere in the distant forest.

But I knew EJ was skating on thin ice, because if Mr Feathers ever caught him, he'd have his guts for garters. And so it came about that early one day, The Chicken hurriedly left the classroom, to visit his female friend. But then he came back unexpectedly and caught us all jig-acting. He demanded to know who was doing all the whistling, but no one responded. He paced over and back across the room to no avail.

'Fine,' he said, 'if that is the way you want it. You can all stay in this afternoon. And here you'll stay until somebody owns up and tells me who was whistling.'

Once three o'clock came, he stood at the head of the class once more demanding to know who'd been whistling in his absence. Again nobody said a word. Nobody would shop EJ or give him away. For about fifteen minutes we sat in total silence, watching the clock slowly go, tick-tock, tick-tock, tick-tock: a quarter past three. All you could hear in the room apart from the clock was a bumble bee trying to get out the window. In desperation, he said,

'I'm still waiting. I'm not leaving here today until somebody tells me who's been whistling. And if that means we have to spend the night here, then so be it.'

Unexpectedly, EJ put up his hand and gave us all a fright. We thought he was about to own up. The teacher raised his spectacled brow in glorious anticipation,

'Yes,'

'Well sir…,' said EJ, like a spider inviting a fly to dinner, 'I can't stay here tonight.'

'Well that's too bad, sighed The Chicken. 'What's so important, that you can't spend the night with us?'

'I have no pyjamas.'

The room reverberated with suppressed fits of laughter. The Chicken scowled at EJ, clearly annoyed that he'd been upstaged.

'If you've nothing better to say, sit down,' he growled.

Again there was total silence. And with nobody offering to shed any light on the culprit, the teacher tried coaxing us into submission.

'Eamon Finnegan, you look like somebody who'd like to get something off your chest. What can you tell me?'

Eamon hesitated for a moment before dragging his long thin frame into an upright position. 'Nothing Sir, I was reading my composition.'

That seemed to annoy The Chicken even more as he looked at Eamon contemptuously and barked. 'You were reading your composition, is that what you're trying to tell me? Liar! While everybody else was creating mayhem… you were reading your composition is that it?'

'Yes', muttered Eamon, half heartedly, after a momentary tremble.

'Aren't you the dedicated scholar? Hear no evil, see no evil. Sit down, you simpleton …before I lose my temper. The rest of you might think you've got away with it this time: but remember, I'll be watching you from now on. And when I finally catch the culprit, he'll wish he'd never set foot inside this room.'

Glancing at his watch once more he uttered that welcoming phrase, 'Dull amach,' which meant we were free to go. We ran out the door and down the corridor like a marauding pack of laughing Hyenas. Screaming and jostling and laughing our heads off. Bursting out into the school yard, EJ shouted, 'Up she flew.'

'And the cock flattened her,' replied John Keaveney deliriously. Not to be outdone I added my penny halfpenny worth, 'That Chicken sure takes some licking.'

For once I had an excuse for being late home from school. I couldn't wait to tell Mrs O'Brien what had delayed me. But as I rounded the last bend, I got an awful shock. There was a lorry parked on the street right beside our house. Two men were unloading timber, and rolls of asphalt and bundles of slates. I figured we must be going to put a new roof on our house. I was delirious with excitement at the prospect we would soon have a house to rival any house in the parish. Mrs O'Brien hardly noticed me as I entered the front door. She was too busy putting things away. She was putting away the good china and leaving it above in her room under the bed. I asked her why she was hiding it.

'I'm not hiding it. I'm minding it. We're putting a new roof on the house. If I don't put everything away, it'll be destroyed. In a few days, the place will look like a pig sty. And if it rains before we get a chance to put the new roof on, things will be ruined entirely.'

A few days later I was surprised to see the state of our house. It was like nothing I could ever have imagined. All the old thatch had been pulled down and lay in a pile all along the front and back of the house. But it was what lay beneath the old thatch that really surprised me. The builders were throwing down big lumps of soot blackened sods and boughs of old trees, bent and twisted beneath the thatch. Underneath the boughs, I could see part of the ceiling which was covered with a thick layer of soot. After the builders had finished working for the day, my father began clearing away the rubble from the front of the house with the horse and cart. I asked him why everything on the roof was so black and why there were lumps of clay beneath the thatch.

'Everything's black, because when this house was first built, it didn't have any ceilings,' he began. 'That time there used to be a lot of chimney fires: and sometimes the thatch would catch fire and you'd end up with smoke and soot everywhere. It's only a few years ago we put in the ceilings, to stop the dust falling down.'

'But where did all the clay come from?'

'Ah... they were scraws that were put across the branches of the trees – or boughs if you like – for to hold the thatch,' he said, leaning on the shovel, to draw his breath.

'I remember when this house was built, I was about the same age as you are now, maybe a biteen younger, we used to live in that shed where the cows are now, but there was no chimney in them times, except a hole in the roof. The house was too small so my father decided to build a new house... and this is where he built it.'

'And where's your father now?'

'Ah... he's dead!' he replied, causally, lighting his pipe. 'He died long ago,' he added thoughtfully, as he drew vigorously on his pipe in an effort to keep it alight. When he was satisfied it would keep going he stuck the pipe into the corner of his mouth and continued talking. 'My father and a few of his friends drew all the stones from Knock-a-Danial quarry with the horse and cart. Then forty men from the village came together and built the house in one day. It was the first and only house around here to have been built like that. Of course, everything was ready for them, the stones, the mortar, the timber, even the scraws or clay sods you're talking about. They were cut there at the back of the house. I remember they were piled up here in the front street, the same as that lorry-load-a-stuff is now. And when the walls were build and the ribs and rafters were in place they turned the scraws upside down and laid them out on the roof like mats. All my father and I had to do after that was thatch the roof. If you didn't have scraws on the roof, you wouldn't be able to thatch the roof because you'd have nothing to stick the scallops into. I don't know how many times it's been thatched since, but as you can see, the old roof was beginning to sag. The problem is, the more you thatch an old house the heavier the roof gets. Sooner or later it starts to sag and then it holds the rain.'

My mother came round the back of the house with the sweeping brush and began sweeping up. She made me scoop up the dirt with the shovel while my father emptied the cart in a corner of the field.

While the re-roofing was going on my mother was forever cleaning and sweeping as dust and dirt from the ceiling formed little pyramids all over the house. Even the beds had to be covered with old sheets to keep the dirt off them. Only the back kitchen, which had a flat roof, was free from falling debris. It was the only safe place in the house to have a cup of tea. And that was where I had my dinner every day when I arrived home from school.

When I saw the workmen laying the foundation of a room opposite our front door I asked Mrs O'Brien,

'Are we going to have a new toilet?'

'Ah bad cess to yourself and your toilet: isn't the bottom of the garden good enough for you? What I want is a hall in front of the house with a big window, to give us-a-bit-a-daylight.' Continuing to make a cake in the back kitchen, she added, as she shook a bit more flour on the brown soda cake, 'and if I could see my way, I'd like a nice little table and sideboard in it to show off my geraniums. You know we're having two new doors put in; one at the front and one at the back. There's no sense in having two half doors in front of the house now that we're building on a new hall. And with any bit-a-luck, we'll be able to get the electric light when we have the house finished. And another thing, I'm getting rid-a-them ducks and geese after this. They're too dirty. They have the place destroyed, scutterin' everywhere. If I was shut-a-them, I'd be able to keep the place clean and tidy and not be up to me elbows in muck every other day. If I could just do that, I think I'd die happy. We'd have a house as nice as anyone in the parish. I think it's the least I deserve, after thirty years scrimping and saving.'

I was over the moon when she said that. Not only would we have a nice house but we'd be as rich as everyone else in the parish, I thought, with a radio and electric light and everything.

Already, there were gangs of workmen erecting poles in fields and gardens everywhere. They started off by erecting poles on the side of the main road. They were followed by other gangs erecting poles into villages prepared to sign up for the light; and ours was one of them.

Meanwhile, the work on our house was going on so long I hated coming home from school. Mrs O'Brien was constantly giving out to me, to try and keep the house clean. But it was almost impossible: particularly when the men took out the front door and began building the new hall. Most of the time the front and back doors were opened which created back-drafts down the chimney. Some days the draft was so bad the smoke drifted back down the chimney in waves, almost choking us. And if we turned our back at all, a hen or two would sneak into the house and scutter all over the floor and I'd have to sweep it up.

Every night the builders had to spread a tarpaulin sheet over the roof to keep out the rain until the job was finished. Some days it was too wet to do anything and they'd go off home: other days when it was fine they wouldn't come at all, because they were too busy elsewhere. But when Paddy the builder turned up again, Mrs O'Brien was ready and waiting.

'Paddy, in the honour of God, will you stay and finish the bloody house, once and for all. I'm sick and tired of you coming here when you feel like it. Or is some other one's house more important, that's what I'd like to know?'

Paddy who was helping put the last of the slates round the chimney shouted down to Mrs O'Brien, as she stood on the street in front of the house, hands on her hips, looking up at him,

'Oh Begod Mam, there's no one more important than you. The weather is the problem Missus. I wouldn't like to leave anyone's house open to the elements. Another day or two now… and we'll be gone out of your sight.'

'Well thanks be to God for that; because not one penny more will you get off me until you have everything finished. Besides I'm sick and tired cleaning up after ye,' she said, as she turned to go into the house.

She was so proud of her new hall she went and bought a mahogany sideboard, a mahogany coat hanger and a half moon table off Harry Ryan. Then she went into Geraghty's drapery shop and bought lace curtains for all the windows. Soon she had the best china in the house on display in the glass-fronted sideboard, which give her more room on the dresser. Rummaging in the wardrobe she found a linen place mat to put on the new table to display her favourite geranium. The geranium was a blue and white flowering plant called, *Splish Splash* that had come from her home place. And to round it all off as it were, she stood an old framed photograph of her father and mother in Victorian dress, on the sideboard opposite the front door.

When at last the heavy rain came I lay in bed as it lashed down on the roof creating a terrible noise. I was terrified the rain would come down through the ceiling, but it never did.

A few weeks later, the electrician who had a new shop in town came and wired up the house, while a group of men dug a hole beside the hens' cabin and erected the last of the ESB poles into the village.

There was fierce excitement in the village in the run up to the power being switched on. Under the guidance and supervision of an ESB official, Mrs O'Brien switched on the light as people from adjoining villages came to see it working for themselves before they'd consider signing up for it. It was a proud moment for Mrs O'Brien when she pressed down the black switch inside the hall door and the light came on and she received a round of applause. It was incredible to see the light reach into every corner of the room like nothing we had ever seen before.

From that day on I could read my books with ease and even do my lessons in bed if I'd wanted to. I no longer had to sit under the lamp at the table while my father struggled to read the newspaper by the fire. The old table lamp was put back up on the mantelpiece in Mrs O'Brien's room opposite the good lamp that was rarely used.

By now the whole countryside was being connected. The electrical shop in the town displayed a vast array of light bulbs, two and three-pin plugs, sockets and switches. Mrs O'Brien brought me with her when she went to buy a white lampshade for the front hall. Inside the shop were scores of lampshades, bedside lamps, radios, electric irons and electric kettles. The shopkeeper asked her to consider buying a sacred heart lamp that would stay lighting twenty four hours a day. But she said,

'Arrah… Sacred Heart lamp how are you! 'Tis far from Sacred Heart lamps I was reared!' The ordinary light is plenty good enough and will do me, while I'm in it. And if it wasn't for John'een here and him trying to do his lessons, the devil-a-electric-light I'd bother with. Besides, I didn't want to be the odd one out when the rest of the village was willing to sign up for it. But if it was again, a toilet in the house is what I'd have gone for, instead of the light. It seems I could have got the light anytime. But *himself* wouldn't hear of building on a toilet. He'd have had to dig a big hole in the garden…to build some sort of a tank for it to work; and he wouldn't hear of it..'

'And haven't you an outdoor toilet? Isn't that good enough? Many is the house in the parish that hasn't even got that. What do you want a toilet for? They say you have to sweep them every day and buy rolls-a-toilet-paper… and that's more money. What you need Missus is a nice little electric iron and not be killing yourself reddening that heavy iron of yours, in the fire. Here, let me show you,' said the grey haired shopkeeper as he took an electric iron off the shelf.

'Arrah is it what you think I'm made-a-money? How am I supposed to pay the electric bill, when I get it: and I not having two pennies to rub together?' said Mrs O'Brien as she stepped back from the counter in case she'd be forced to buy.' Look, will you leave that bloody thing back where you got it and not be tempting me. I'll take that shade I was looking at instead; that's all I came in to buy. I'm not buying another thing because I'm broke. Maybe when we sell a few cattle, I'll think about it.'

'Suit yourself Missus. You know you're more than welcome. When you come in again, I'll give you the best deal in the house.'

Holding the door open for Mrs O'Brien he smiled and said, 'How's Snowy...I mean Máirtín? How is he getting on? I hear he's going to England, Friday.'

'Is he? Well I never heard a word,' replied Mrs O'Brien.

'Oh I don't know! I'm only saying what I heard. Some people would tell you anything.'

'Well that's as sure as you're there!' replied Mrs O'Brien, an edge to her voice, as the shopkeeper closed the door after her.

When she'd safely turned in the school road, she mumbled to herself.

'Lord isn't it great how some people seem to know everything.'

After thinking about Snowy and his motorbike which I'd not seen on the road for a long time, I casually asked,

'Is he really going to England?'

'Ah don't ask me! Isn't it great how you too have your nose stuck in everything?'

It was obvious something was bothering Mrs O'Brien. What it was I had no idea. But I didn't have long to wait, to find out.

Chapter Seventeen

We were just in the door, when Tommy the postman called. Mrs O'Brien put on the kettle while I changed my clothes and went outside to listen. It was a while before Tommy came around to talking about Snowy and when he did I inched my ear that little bit closer. Since we'd added on the new hall, I'd found it increasingly difficult to hear what was being said in the kitchen.

'And I believe Snowy's going to England?'

'He is... thanks-be-to-the-Great-God! At least he won't be able to get up to any mischief... I hope. You know he had me heart broke because there was no knowing what he'd say or do next,' said Mrs O'Brien

'Well, I can understand that Kate. But you must remember, underneath it all, he's a good-hearted creature.'

'I know! But there's nothing good-hearted about having to replace Fr Keaveney's hens. I suppose you heard the case was settled?'

'Well, bedamn but I didn't, Kate. I didn't. I knew Sergeant Boyle was anxious to bring him to court and all that. Then again, I said to meself, maybe 'tis only a rumour. Every day I go out, I hear a different story. But I didn't hear the case was settled. I didn't hear that now,' replied Tommy.

'Well, I'll tell you what happened,' said Mrs O'Brien, setting the table. 'But for the love of God keep it to yourself. '

'Look! Anything you say under the roof of this house will not pass my lips, I can assure you!'

'Indeed I know that a grá, I'm only just saying, because I'd like to keep the gossip mongers wondering. The thing is Tommy, you couldn't be up to Snowy; he has a fierce way with him...'

'I know, I know, I only wished I had his talent.'

'Well Tommy, 'twas like this; he knew he'd get a summons and have to go to court: and that it would be all over the papers. So, what did he do but go down to Henry Naughton and tell him he was going to England; that he'd send him the eighteen shillings he got for the hens. But faith Henry said, 'Snowy you don't owe me a penny: but you owe me six hens. Now, I don't want you giving me the priest's hens again, because they wouldn't stay with me when they were here; they must have known I was a sinner. But if you can bring me six good hens, then I'll forget all about it.'

The next bloody thing didn't Snowy appear outside the door there and ask if I'd give him six hens. He told me he'd fix me up as soon as he went over to England. Anyway, to make a long story short, I gave him the hens and he brought them down to Henry Naughton's and everything seemed honky dory until yesterday. Colleen came running down and told me how Sergeant Boyle had landed above with a summons for Snowy to appear in court, in three weeks time. Snowy met him in the street and started laughing as Sergeant Boyle held out the summons. God forgive me Tommy but I enjoyed it when Colleen told me what he said.'

'I could well imagine...,' said Tommy, enjoying the story.

'Looking at Sergeant Boyle, he said, "burn the bloody thing, burn it, because I won't be in Court. Henry Naughton won't be in court; and I doubt very much if the parish priest will be in court, unless it's to anoint either yourself or the judge."

"Now look here Snowy," says Sergeant Boyle, "less of your auld codology. You've a serious case to answer. You stole six hens belonging to Fr Keaveney and I intend to see that you pay for them."

"Pay", laughed Snowy, "for what? I didn't steal any hens: It's what I borrowed them. Obviously they didn't like their new surroundings and flew home again."

Sergeant Boyle didn't know what to do when Snowy suddenly turned and went back into the house. The Sergeant tried handing the summons to Colleen, but faith she said it had nothing at all to do with her. So off he went with his tail between his legs. And where did he go but down to Fr Keaveney's; Nora was telling me yesterday. She was in the parlour and overheard everything that was said. And cheeky enough of Sergeant Boyle didn't he try talking Fr Keaveney into giving evidence in court, but faith Fr Keaveney wouldn't. He said, "I think Sergeant, we should let bygones be bygones. I know that Snowy can be rash at times, but his heart is in the right place. If anything he's performed a miracle which could be verified in Rome, as well as in any court of law. He allegedly stole six hens belonging to me and sold them to Henry Naughton... for eighteen shilling. And yet, I have the same six hens; Henry Naughton has six hens and if that doesn't constitute some sort of a miracle then I don't know what does. If I could perform a miracle like that, I think I'd be a Bishop."

There was nothing more the Sergeant could do, said Nora, because Fr Keaveney wouldn't hear of it. So hopefully, that's the end of it.'

'Well Lord God Almighty,' chuckled Tommy, 'but it would take Snowy. I knew he'd pull some stroke, some stroke. The man's a genius, I'm telling you! You should be proud of him?'

'Ah stop your goin' on, will you! You're worse than himself: he thinks the sun shines out of his arse. Here, will you have a piece of apple tart?'

'The smallest bit, Kate: the smallest bit. And then I'll be hitting the road.' After a lengthy pause, he added, 'I must say your house is looking well. I was looking at it coming down the street. That hall looks lovely.'

'Do you like it?' she asked: though I knew what she was really looking forward to.

She couldn't wait to show off the house to Delia Tully and the rest of her friends. But the first ones to see it were the men working with the thresher.

For days I'd been listening to the hypnotic sound of threshing machines as they wound their way through the surrounding villages. It was the most magical sound I'd ever heard. From early morning until late at night all you could hear was Wooo... woo-woo, Wooo...woo-woo, Wooo...woo-woo. At one point there were three threshing machines vying for business as they worked their way through the countryside. But it was Martin Flannigan's machine which entered Lakeland first. Therefore he was entitled to thresh the whole village which consisted of about forty houses, spread over a wide area.

My father had asked me to give him a hand manning the bags at the rear of the threshing machine, which was due to reach us either Friday or Saturday, depending on how he got on everywhere else and how many mechanical breakdowns he had. Up until now my father had been threshing the corn with a flail, which was a slow boring process that went on for days. I couldn't wait to see this gigantic machine working in our haggard. I'd already seen it passing along the road and it looked like a giant wooden box on wheels, half as big as a house. It had three giant fangs protruding from one end, which John Keaveney had said looked like a Chinese dragon with its mouth open. The mouth was supposed to spew out the straw after the sheaves of corn had been fed into a hole on top of the thresher. I just couldn't wait to see it working in our garden because if the sound was anything to go by then it must be some sight, I thought.

Sure enough, there was fierce excitement as Martin Flannigan struggled to manoeuvre the threshing machine round the back of our house with the aid of his tractor. He couldn't pull it in the gate without touching the back corner of our newly reconstructed house. Instead, my father and Tom Farrell had to take down the gate, remove the gateposts and knock a bit of the wall beside where we emptied out the piss pots each morning.

'Ned, I thought you told me I could sail a ship through this gate?' remarked Martin Flannigan, in growing frustration.

'Well... I thought so,' replied my father, embarrassingly, as he looked at Martin's frantic efforts to avoid getting caught on the eaves of the house.

'You'd be lucky to bring in a donkey never mind a friggin' ship,' shouted, Martin, peevishly, trying to be heard above the roar of the engine.

'Ah blasted to hell haven't you enough room now? So get on with it,' sniffed Tom Farrell angrily as he lifted his peaked cap and scratched the back of his head, as Martin sat up on the tractor for about the fifth time and finally pulled the machine into the haggard.

The thresher was placed midway between the four giant stacks of corn – two on either side. Martin unhooked the threshing machine, spragged the wheels and drove the tractor forward five or six yards. After a little manoeuvring he connected a fan belt from the drive shaft of the tractor to a rotary wheel on the side of the thresher. When he was satisfied everything was in order, he hopped up on the tractor again and took the strain of the belt before again hopping off to spragg the wheels once more. As soon as everything was ready, he revved up the tractor and the main fan belt started to glide along and it in turn started the threshing machine which had half a dozen wheels and fan belts spinning at lightening speed on the right hand side. And they in turn seemingly, drove the internal organs of the thresher at incredible speed. Finally, before commencing, Martin eased back the throttle a little, setting the engine at a steady pace.

One man had already climbed onto the stack of barley with his hay fork. He began to throw the sheaves, two at a time, down on top of the thresher, where two men stood with knives, ready to cut the ties while a third man stood in a shallow box and fed the loose sheaves into the feeder, where they were gobbled up faster than a snake swallowing a spider. Soon the machine was groaning like a monster: Wooo…woo-woo, Wooo…woo-woo, Wooo…woo-woo. Two men with hayforks stood in front of the thresher as the fangs spat out straw as if it was vomiting. The straw was spewing out so fast, it almost obliterated the men as they gathered it all up in great big forkfuls, before firing it into the making of a new reek of straw. I looked around and saw several cats sitting on their tails, waiting for the mice to appear. My father meanwhile shouted into my ear,

'Hand me one of those sacks and get a move on.'

I handed him a sack which he hooked on straightaway, ensuring all six grain shoots were catered for. The grain was cascading down five of the shoots at an unbelievable rate, while the sixth barely did anything as it spat out a mixture of inferior grain and foreign seedlings. As soon as one sack was filled, my father closed off the shoot by sliding down a metal plate, before unhooking the sack of corn and hooking on another empty sack. Each time he did it, he heaved the sack up onto Tom Farrell's shoulder. Tom ran with the sack into the grain store, where we had two wooden bins ready and waiting. He emptied the sacks into the bins and came back out with the empties. When the bins were full, the sacks had to be securely tied and stacked on top of the bins; right up to the ceiling. While my father was unhooking and frantically tying the sacks, it was my job to keep an eye on the shoots, making sure the bags didn't overflow. As soon as one was filled I had to shout at my father. In between, I had to check the sacks we'd borrowed to make sure there were no holes in them. I loved watching the corn pouring into the sacks. Sometimes two or more sacks had to be unhooked at the same time and there was instant panic as the grain shoots overflowed and spilled on the ground. Every once in a while Martin Flannigan would shovel away the chaff building up beneath the vibrating thresher, to ensure the smooth running of the machine.

All of a sudden there was a roar of excitement and I glanced around the side of the thresher to see a big rat land on Martin's shoulder after it had been flicked off a stack by one of the workmen. Quick as a flash, a man speared the fleeing rat by pinning it to the ground. And with a deft flick of the prong he fired the wounded rat across the garden where it tried to run away but was pounced on by one of the cats before being dragged off triumphantly.

Nearing the bottom of the stacks I could see they were alive with mice. There were fleeing everywhere: big ones, small ones, grey ones black ones; even the cats couldn't keep up with them.

After almost two hours the threshing was finished. I could hardly believe our four stacks of corn had been converted into two reeks of straw, oats and barley.

Once the threshing was done, my father told the workmen their tea was ready. And while Tom Farrell and my father helped Martin Flannigan free the thresher from the mountain of chaff some of the men went up to Mickey Billy's to ensure everything was in order. Mickey Billy's oats should have been threshed before ours as the thresher came down through the village, but he wasn't ready, he said.

After a lot of twisting and turning, Martin Flannigan managed to pull the thresher out onto the street, narrowly avoiding the gable end of our house. But it took a lot of persuading on my father's part to get Martin to have something to eat in our house. My mother had everything laid out on the table; brown and white bread, ham and tomatoes, hard boiled eggs and cheese, as well as two large teapots, brewing on the hearth stone. People sat wherever they could and gobbled up everything in sight. One man said hunger was a great sauce and that one should eat whatever was in front of them because there was no knowing when they'd get the next bite: it all depended on the driver. Some of the men laughed. They said they didn't think Flannigan had a belly on him at all because he'd never ask to stop working. It was only the grace of God that he had stopped now; so they could all have a break. Flannigan laughed too as he said,

'Tis all right for ye. Ye can spend all day sittin' on yeer arses because ye can afford it. Not like me! I can't afford to sit around. I have to work for a living.'

This response drew peals of laughter as some of the workmen raised their mugs to signify they wanted more tea. Mrs O'Brien and Colleen were kept busy making tea and resetting the table as men drifted in and out of the house in relays.

Only six people could sit at our table at any one time and they had to eat up quickly to let others sit down Altogether I counted seventeen men. They were from all over the village and beyond and I knew that my father would have to go and help each one of them in turn.

Because we now had plenty of oats and barley, it was my job to help my father bring a bag of oats and barley to the mill. We'd be no sooner in the door from the mill than Mrs O'Brien would have a cake of oaten bread baking on the open fire. The cake was flat and about the same size as a dinner plate. After she had half cooked it, she'd finish it off by roasting it on the open hearth. And every single morning she'd give me a rock solid piece of oaten bread to bring with me to school. And if John Keaveney or EJ Lyons or Eamon Finnegan didn't have any, I'd break off a chunk and give it to them because they'd always give me some, when they had it.

For a long time it had been rumoured that The Chicken was leaving our school. Keaveney and EJ swore he was being shifted, because he was useless. But each Monday, to our horror, we found he was still in command. He continued to treat us the way he always did, by belting the living daylights out of us. He wrote a composition on the board and asked us to copy it down. It was something we were good at. So EJ, John, Eamon and I decided to have a race, to see who could finish it first. EJ won, but only just, John was second and I was third. When I looked up, I saw the teacher was watching us. He'd caught us talking. With his hands behind his back, he very slowly made his way down, between fourth and fifth classes. Working from the back, he began checking everyone's copy book. When he saw my writing he pulled my ear and said,

'You call that writing, do you? You haven't even bothered to copy down what I wrote. You just scribbled it, didn't you? Now, start and do it all over again and this time, do it right. Otherwise, I'll come down on you like a ton of bricks,'

I quickly turned over a new page and began copying it while The Chicken moved on and looked over EJ Lyons writing. He stood beside EJ; hands behind his back, and said,

'Mr Lyons, do you realise I can't make out one single word.' Tapping his finger on EJ's copy book, he added, 'That there is indistinguishable. It's like something you'd expect to find in an Egyptian cave. Have you any idea what you might find in an Egyptian cave?'

When EJ didn't answer, he caught him by the lug and again asked,

'Have you any idea, Mr Lyons, what you'd expect to find in an Egyptian cave?'

EJ squealed, 'How can I answer…when you're pulling the lug off me?'

'Less of your auld guff,' snapped The Chicken as he rapped EJ viciously across the head with his bare knuckle. EJ cowered in his desk pretending to be more afraid of the teacher than he really was.

'It might interest you to know, that early Egyptian caves were for a long time, shrouded in mystery. That's because they bore an indistinguishable scrawl that very few people could understand. These early symbols or drawings were known as hieroglyphs. They dated back to the time of the Pharaohs who once ruled Egypt. And that Mr Lyons is what your scrawl looks like.'

EJ, still cowering in his seat said nothing.

'Did you hear what I said?' growled The Chicken; again tapping his finger on EJ's copy book. '…That there, is indistinguishable – I cannot read it. I'd need to hire someone like that English explorer, Lord Carnarvon, who discovered Tutankhamen's tomb, to decipher it. Unfortunately, he died of a mosquito bite: so I have to try and decipher it, but I can't. Why is that?'

When EJ did not reply, The Chicken ranted,

'Why is it I cannot read your writing? Yet, if I look up at the blackboard…' he indicated with his hand, '… I can clearly read it? Why is that?'

After a deathly silence, EJ, looked at The Chicken and quipped, 'Sure every monkey can read his own writing.'

The Chicken strode briskly to his desk, picked up the cane and began flexing it with such venom we began to fear for EJ's life.

'Would you be so kind as to come up here, where everybody can see you?'

EJ very reluctantly stood up and made his way to the front of the class.

'Now would you be so good as to raise your hand?'

Very bravely, EJ raised his hand, but it wasn't quite high enough. So The Chicken lifted it up ever so carefully with the cane until it was straight and true. Taking a step back The Chicken brought the cane down with all the force he could muster, only EJ's hand wasn't where it should be by the time he brought the cane down. The Chicken was furious. He very quickly grabbed EJ's hand and forcibly gave him three wallops as an oily lock of hair fell across his temple. When he'd finished he grabbed him by the scruff of the neck and threw him towards his seat with a vengeance,

'There! Let that be a lesson to you and don't you ever speak to me like that again.'

The Chicken went behind his desk and made believe he was polishing his glasses. He had worked himself into such a frenzy the sweat rolled down his forehead. In an effort to recover his composure, he blew out his cheeks and mopped his wrinkled brow before putting on his glasses again. Then standing up he wiped the entire composition clean off the board with four clear swipes of the duster before slapping it down on the ledge. Facing us once more and never for a moment taking his eyes of EJ he said, 'First thing tomorrow morning I'm going to ask you to read out today's composition: so you had better learn it.'

Just then the eleven o'clock bell sounded. He looked at his watch and said, 'Dull Amach.'

Out in the school yard, John Keaveney and I had a great time making fun of EJ. John crept up and pinched EJ's ear saying it was a mosquito bite while I drew a picture of a cave on the school wall with a monkey in it. I put EJ's initials on the monkey and showed it to him. When EJ saw it, he hit me in the mouth and there was blood everywhere. Later he said he was sorry, that he didn't really mean it and we all ended up laughing before it was time to go back in again.

Every day during our lunch break we played football in the school yard. We now had proper goal posts but very often the ball ended up being kicked over the school wall where it rolled down the town and we never saw it again: not even when we finished school.

When that happened, we had to try and make a football of our own. We'd go through all the cloakrooms until we found an old coat, then we'd roll it up into a tight ball, tied it with a bit of twine and play with it until lunch break was over.

One afternoon as we were about to start our hated algebra class, there was a gentle knock on the door. The Chicken answered it and spoke to somebody for a few minutes. We could not see who it was even though there was glass in the door. Then The Chicken came in followed by a man carrying a hold-all and wearing a pinstriped suit. He was not unlike our teacher except that he was taller. As the man left his hold-all on the desk The Chicken told us to leave down our pencils and to pay attention for a few minutes.

'Good afternoon boys…,' the man began, nervously twiddling his thumbs. '…I hope that you're all well and that you're not too busy with your lessons.' Hesitating for a moment and drawing a deep breath he continued. 'Have any of you boys ever heard of Lyons tea?'

There was total silence in the classroom as he looked at everyone, trying hopefully to find a response but there was none. None of us in class knew what he was on about as we looked questioningly at each other.

'Lyon's are the third largest importer and distributor of tea in Ireland: surely some of you know that?' Again there was total silence as our teacher began to look uncomfortable with his back to the blackboard; his arms neatly folded as he swayed from side to side. 'Does anyone here drink tea?' asked the man with a smile. Suddenly we all put up our hand

'Aaaah! I thought so!'

The man went on to tell us the history of Lyon's tea and the various brands being blended in their new warehouse in Dublin.

'In the coming weeks, Lyons tea will be available in every town in Ireland. And as part of our promotion I'm giving away a wonderful prize of a two pound pack of Lyons special blend tea, to the first person who can name any one of the three countries where they grow tea?.'

On hearing this, my heart began to pound. The evening before, I'd been rummaging through an old suitcase that once belonged to Colleen, which was hid under the bed in my parent's bedroom. In it I found an old *Where in the World* book, which I'd put into my school bag without telling anyone. I wanted to show John Keaveney the lovely pictures that were in it.

The book was under my desk. I knew the answer was only a finger tip away. I very quietly reached under my desk and took it our while keeping eye on Mr Feathers.

'Well, can anybody tell me where they grow tea?' queried the man.

One of the older pupils put up his hand and said, 'England.'.

'No. I'm afraid not. You'll have to try again. It's a wonderful prize to be giving away. Just think what your mother will say when you go home with a two pound pack of Lyons tea.'

In desperation I turned another page and there it was before my eyes, a map of Ceylon with a picture of a girl plucking the leaves in a plantation, a wicker basket on her back. I closed the book and slid it back silently under my desk and raised my hand.

The man looked at me; his eyebrows raised, his mouth open,

'Yes?

'Ceylon, Sir,'

The man's face broke into a smile. 'Correct! Ceylon is the right answer. It's one of the three countries where tea comes from: the other two countries being China and Japan. And what's your name?'

'John, sir.'

'Well done John and congratulations. If you'd like to come up here, I'll give you your prize,'

I went up and the man shook my hand and handed me the red two pound pack of Lyons special blend tea as my teacher Mr Feathers looked on, proudly.

As I sat back in my desk the man said, 'You'd be surprised how many schools I go to and they don't know the answer. But I'm happy to say, your school is right up there with the best of them. Your teacher, Mr Feathers is obviously doing an excellent job; you should be very proud of him. I'll leave you now to get on with your lessons. And on behalf of Lyons I'd like to thank you and your teacher for giving up your time. All you have you to do now when you go home is tell your mother about our wonderful product. It's called, Lyons tea.'

After that the man had a few words with the teacher while everybody in our class looked at me questioningly; wanting to know how I knew the answer. After a brief conversation, Mr Feathers escorted the man to the door. I could hardly believe what had happened; being saved from a horrid algebra class to winning a packet of tea in the space of half an hour. It was like a dream I thought, but it wasn't. I had a two pound packet of tea in my schoolbag to prove it. I couldn't wait to get home, to show it to my mother.

I ran all the way home, but was surprised when I saw Ryan's hackney car outside our house. Harry was talking to my mother and father and I got the impression that something was wrong. I had no idea what it was, but something was definitely up I thought as I reached the house. Harry was behind the wheel as he said, 'Right folks…that's all we can do for now. I'll see you in the morning.'

When Harry was gone, I showed my mother and father the packet of tea I'd won. My mother said I behaved well to know the answer; that it was a blessing she wasn't wasting her time sending me to school. My father asked me how I knew the answer. I told him I'd read it a long time ago in one of the Far East magazines, Nora Keeffe had given us. Then my mother said, as I sat eating my dinner while my father had gone outside

'You saw Harry Ryan's car I'm sure? He was here to make arrangements for Kilby's funeral. He died early this morning. Your father has to go to Ballinasloe tomorrow afternoon to pick up the remains. He'll be brought to the chapel tomorrow evening. We were wondering if you'd be able to ring the bell. You know Kilby has nobody belonging to him and it would be a nice thing if somebody could ring the bell. You'll be serving Mass in another couple of weeks, so I'm sure Fr Keaveney wouldn't mind. Would you be able to do it do you think?'

I was in an awful dilemma. I didn't know what to say. My first instinct was to say yes. It was so out of this world I thought to be asked to ring the bell for Kilby's funeral.

Even since I'd arrived in Lakeland, I had heard a lot about Kilby but I had never laid eyes on him: and yet it seemed as if he was part of the family. Every so often, my father would hire Ryan's hackney car to go up and see him, in Ballinasloe mental hospital. I remembered as a child having to mind the house while Mrs O'Brien went to the corpse house when Kilby's wife passed away. She had spent the entire evening in the corpse house while I was supposed to look after the house and I ended up smothering the chickens. Shortly after that, Kilby was sent to Ballinasloe never to return.

Now, Mrs O'Brien wanted me to ring the bell for his funeral. The only problem was would I be able to pull the rope. The bell was situated in the grounds of the church. The bell stood on its own, high up in the belfry under a line of tall Beech trees that grew all along the back of the church grounds. I had often seen men ringing the bell for Mass and for the Angelus and it always seemed like a Herculean task to me. So how was I going to do it if they found it so hard?

'Well…' said Mrs O'Brien, standing looking at me, hands on her hips, '…are you going to ring the bell or not…that's if Fr Keaveney will let you?'

I nodded my head as I downed the last spud on my plate, 'Yeah,'

'Well you don't sound very enthusiastic…I must say. Take care would you go out of your way to help. That's the problem with people nowadays, nobody wants to do anything.'

She stood looking out the kitchen window for a few minutes, her arms folded, in a pensive mood. And having come to some decision she turned and said, 'Look, you might as well run down, like a good lad, and ask Fr Keaveney's if it's all right to ring the bell for Kilby's funeral. If he's not there and Nora Keefe answers the door, tell her I sent you down to ask Fr Keaveney if you could ring the bell as the funeral is coming in tomorrow evening. Here, I'll give you a supeen-a-milk to bring down with you; it might sweeten her,' she said, going out to the back kitchen.

Ever since Fr Keaveney and his housekeeper Nora Keefe came to Williamstown, Mrs O'Brien has been great with them. Now and again she'd send me down with a little can of butter milk, to make the bread.

When I rang the priest's bell, Nora Keefe answered the door. I told her my story and she went and got Fr Keaveney. He was a big powerful man with a gigantic belly, and as he stood at the door, hands behind his back, he smiled and said,

'Well, now do you see... it's a great honour to be asked. What time is the funeral... do you know?'

'I...I...don't know,' I answered. I hadn't thought of that and my mother hadn't said what time. 'Daddy is bringing Kilby from Ballinasloe and Mammy said I'd have to wait out at the top of the school road. Then when I'd see the hearse coming I've have to start ringing the bell,' I added quickly, reaffirming my desire to ring the bell.

'Well ...if it's around seven o'clock, I'll be ready and waiting. You can go ahead and ring the bell. Tell your father I'll meet the funeral whatever time it comes in.'

I ran home and told my mother. She was delighted.

'Well at least that's another job out of the way. I'd hate anything to go wrong now.'

I stood in the kitchen looking at her; wondering what she meant. What could possibly go wrong now? Wasn't the man dead?'

Chapter Eighteen

The following evening, I waited patiently round the house until it was time for me to ring the bell. Mrs O'Brien too was getting ready but she sent me on ahead in case the hearse came in early. I was at the head of the school road by half past six, waiting and watching as people began to gather outside the church. I stood looking up the Glenamaddy road for an hour or more but still there was no sign of the funeral. Some people round the church began to drift into Glynn's pub out of the cold. It was a quarter to eight and pitch dark and if it wasn't for the street lights I didn't think I'd be able to make my way into the church grounds. I'd already seen Fr Keaveney go in and out of the church a few times while looking impatiently in my direction for signs of the hearse. Finally around eight o'clock the hearse came into view.

I raced into the church grounds remembering what Mrs O'Brien had told me. I was to ring the bell slowly, six times; followed by a pause, another six; a pause and finally another six. Eighteen rings altogether. I caught hold of the heavy rope and looked up at the huge bronze bell hanging way up in the belfry but all I could see was the ghostly outline of the bell against the night sky. I pulled on the rope half-heartedly wondering how I was going to make it go nice and slow, but nothing happened. I pulled again with all my might but still there was no sound. In desperation, I jumped on the rope and pulled for all I was worth. This time I thought I saw the bell moving, silhouetted against the night sky but still there was no sound as my feet hit the ground. While I was trying to figure out what was happening, the rope suddenly hoisted me into the air and I got such a fright thinking it was going to pull me all the way to the top I let go of the rope and landed on my arse with an almighty *thud*, just as the first bell rang out. Inspired by the sound, I jumped onto the rope like a trapeze artist and wrapped my legs around it like a chimpanzee. I pulled on the rope again in case the bell stopped ringing and before I knew what was happening I was in full motion. The rope was pulling me up and I was pulling it down to ring out loud and clear. It was like magic. With the booming sound of each peel ringing in my ears, I counted four and pulled harder than ever to make sure the whole parish could hear the bell for Kilby's funeral. The sensation of dangling on the rope was better than any swinging boat I was ever on as the rope hoisted me up into the air before landing me back down again with a heavy thud. For no reason at all, the bell began to ring on the double like it was celebration time on New Year's Eve. I counted five: five and a half. Six: six and a half. Seven: seven and three quarters, eight. There was no stopping the bell now. Mystified by the double ringing I looked up and saw both sides of the bell strike the ball in quick succession. I clung desperately onto the rope in an effort to slow it down but I couldn't hold it. I let the rope run through my hands and as it did so I could feel the searing heat on my palms. I looked down towards the church entrance and saw Kilby's remains being carried shoulder high into the church followed by the congregation. Still counting, I let the bell ring of its own accord as it began to get slower and slower until it reached number twelve or was it thirteen and when it seemed as if it was about to stop ringing I pulled again with all my might and it gave another resounding peal. It was at that point I learned how to ring the bell, properly. All it needed was a good pull, then let it up and down unaided. And as the rope went up again for the second time, I pulled it once more to reach my target. Eighteen rings I counted, with half a dozen smaller ones thrown in for good measure.

Walking away from the sacred ground, I felt a great sense of holiness. I had done what no one in my school had ever done before. I had rung the bell for a funeral. And not just any old funeral, but Kilby's funeral: a man whom my father had agreed to bury over a pint of porter in some pub in Ballinasloe. And I for my part had agreed to ring the bell for his funeral when no one else in the parish was prepared to do it.

I hung around outside the church until the funeral was over; wondering if anybody else was dead; praying silently that I'd be chosen to ring the bell again the following day. After a while people started coming out of the church and I saw Mrs O'Brien with some of the neighbours. I went quickly towards her, seeking words of approval. Instead she glowered at me and I knew enough to turn and walk away. But as soon as she'd said good bye to Annie Tobin outside our house and we were safely inside our front door, she turned despairingly towards me, still dressed in her headscarf and long black coat,

'Well Jesus, Mary and Joseph... but that was some job you did on the bell. I thought I told you, going out that door, to take your time and to give it six rings like you'd hear at a proper funeral...,' she shouted, stamping her foot on the ground. 'That bell was... Jesus...like nothing I ever heard before...' Seeing the dimple on her quivering chin, I headed for the safety of the front door. '...you'll have us disgraced entirely...get out of my sight you amadawn before I kill you. And you supposed to be an altar boy: some altar boy you're going to make!'

I stood outside the front door in the dark, afraid to show myself. After a few minutes, when I figured she'd calmed down a bit, I sneaked back into the house to get the flash lamp. I went outside and closed the hens in order to redeem myself while Mrs O'Brien fixed up the fire and got the supper ready. Then, I decided to go down to my room, to study my Latin, just to be on the safe side; especially after what Mrs O'Brien had said: *Some altar boy, you're going to make.*

* * * *

For months, Mrs Patterson had been teaching us Latin. Now we were ready to serve our first Mass. Certain boys were chosen to serve Mass because they were deemed to be good Catholics: but the way Mrs O'Brien was going on about me, I wasn't sure if I was up to the job. When a priest said Mass in the church there were generally two or three altar boys serving with him. But sometimes there might be as many as six required. If it was a High Mass for some well known member of the community, then there might be as many as a dozen priests concelebrating. During that Mass, six altar boys were needed to light the two dozen candles on the tall brass candelabras on the main altar as well as the numerous small candles on the two side altars. The altar boys had to bring water and wine to the various priests concelebrating the Mass as well as finger bowls and towels for them to wash and dry their hands. While the priests were giving out Holy Communion, the altar boys had to carry a Communion plate in front of them as they went along the altar rails. When High Mass was over, they had to carry the incense and thurible and holy water as well as a large crucifix for the purification of the body before it was removed from the church, for the burial.

Mrs O'Brien had already sent me to the dressmaker to be measured up for a new red *soutane,* together with a white *surplice.* The only reason I wanted to become an altar boy at all was that I'd be in a position to get little gifts of money every now and again. If I was lucky enough to be serving Mass when a couple were getting married or a child was being baptized or somebody was having the stations in the house, then I might be given a few coppers as a thank you gift. The older altar boys had often told of their extraordinary good fortune while serving Mass, particularly during the house stations. Mass in the house was a major event that took place in spring and autumn. House Masses were revered by people living in the villages and these Masses were always referred to as, *The Stations.*

While I sat in my bedroom thinking about my impending career as a new altar boy, Mrs O'Brien was thinking about something entirely different. She called me out of the room and said, 'Tomorrow morning before you go to school, I'd like you to bring me down three or four buckets of water from the well... so I can wash and scald that auld bath. Daddy will be at the funeral; and knowing him he won't come home until he's well oiled. Tom Farrell is coming on Saturday to kill one of the pigs, so the two of us will have to have everything ready.'

'Are we really going to kill a pig?' I asked excitedly.

'We are...thanks-be-to-God. I thought I'd never see the day when we'd have a bit of black pudding again.'

'And what are we going to do with the other one?'

'Well Lord, how stupid can you get? We'll sell it of course. What else would we do with it? You don't think we were going to keep feeding them forever, do you, and they eating us out of house and home? The least we deserve is to have a nice bit-a-bacon; and with any bit-a-luck, we'll get a good price for the other one when we sell it.'

Tom Farrell arrived early and started sharpening the long knifes he brought with him. My mother was in the kitchen boiling pots of water, while my father and I went out into the pigs' cabin to catch one of the pigs. Normally we'd have two pigs ready for the fair, every three or four months. Then my father would buy another pair of eight to ten week old Bonhams for around ten or eleven pounds and we'd start rearing two pigs all over again. We'd feed them potatoes and pig meal with gallons of skim-milk; and to make sure they were ready for the fair, we'd add a fistful of oats for the last two weeks to harden up the bacon When a jobber was buying a pig the first thing he'd do was assess the quality of the bacon by pressing his thumb down on a pig's back. If a pig was rock hard, like a board, then it was considered good quality bacon. But if a pig was soft to the touch then the bacon was considered fat and inferior and not worth near as much. So, instead of feeding and selling pigs all the time my mother decided it was time we killed a pig. Bacon was getting too expensive she said.

The minute my father caught hold of the pig, Tom Farrell slipped a rope around its hind leg and walked it across the garden towards the horse cart. There, Tom quickly knocked the pig to the ground by pulling one of its hind legs from under it. My father and I held the pig, while Tom expertly tied its front and back legs together. Then he tied another rope round the pig's snout and closed its mouth but it didn't stop it screaming. It only seemed to make it worse. They lifted the pig up onto the cart where they tied it down on its side, leaving the head and shoulder hanging slightly over the side of the cart, but the pig still managed to put up a fight in an effort to free itself. Meanwhile, Mrs O'Brien brought out two buckets of boiling water as well as an empty bucket, which she left beside the cart. Quick as a flash Tom seized the empty bucket and plunged the knife straight into the pigs breast and up into its heart. Warm blood spurted out onto his wrist and into the bucket while the pig screamed unmercifully and I started to tremble because the whole thing was so savage. I thought if the men could tie up and kill a pig like that, then they could easily do the same thing to me. By now I was terrified and wanted to run away, while at the same time I was rooted to the ground unable to say or do anything. And to make it worse I was supposed to be helping them. Once the pig was stabbed, it put up a ferocious fight and screamed so loudly it could be heard all over the parish. By now the blood was pouring out in fits and starts as the pig really went wild. It almost broke free when one of the ropes binding it legs came undone. Tom left the bucket beneath the gushing blood and told me to hold on to it; while he helped my father to hold down the pig as it was in its final death throes. It was kicking savagely which meant the blood was gushing out and splattering all over me. Soon the pig was dead and Tom went into the house with the bucket of blood so that Mrs O'Brien and Colleen could start making the pudding. They did this by boiling some onions, spices, herbs and oatmeal with added salt and pepper which they then added to the blood while it was still warm. Tom came back out and slowly poured the boiling water over the hessian sacks my father had thrown on the pig. The sacks were used to absorb the boiling water, thus tenderising the flesh making it easier to remove the bristle. When they started shaving the pig, I could see they were much more relaxed. They were laughing and joking and saying it was hard to beat, a-bit-of-hairy-bacon; that it was a pity to shave it off at all.

When they'd finished, they pulled the cart over to the open turf shed and hung the pig upside down over the doorway so that Tom Farrell could start butchering it. First he had to remove the intestines and clean out the large ones to make the puddings. As the pig had been left starving for two days, there was very little in the intestines. Tom turned them inside out, using a thin rod which he pushed through the skins before pulling it back out again; thus turning them inside out, It was my job to run into the house with them while Tom began butchering the pig, throwing each piece of meat he cut into the galvanized bath beside him. While all this was going on, Colleen and my mother were washing and salting the skins. Using a small funnel, they filled the skins with the black pudding mix and tied two pieces of twine about every twelve inches. They snipped off each length and put them into a large skillet to simmer slowly for ten minutes. To stop them splitting, they pricked the pudding every now and again with a needle and when they were cooked they removed what were now steaming coils of black pudding and hung them on the handle of the sweeping brush which they'd tied across the back of two chairs, so the puddings could set overnight. I was thrilled to see so many rings of black pudding which looked the very same as what was hanging in the shops. It was wonderful to think we were going to have black pudding whenever we wanted, particularly on Sunday morning.

By three o'clock, most of the grisly work had been done. Tom Farrell and my father brought the bath into the back kitchen. They packed and salted the two sides of bacon which had been cut into handy little pieces, into one of two tea chests. In the second tea chest, they packed, gammon, pork, bacon ribs, shoulder joints and other choice pieces, like the liver, heart and crubeens.*

And we had the pig's head, which my mother boiled for hours and hours

---

* Crubeens *(pigs' feet)*

that evening. When it was well cooked, the meat fell away and my mother added more onions, herbs and spices and poured it like soup into a large bowl where it set like jelly. It was then called brawn and looked like corn beef except that it tasted much nicer. Every now and again my mother used to get a piece of brawn from a friend or neighbour when they killed a pig: now it was her turn to give a little something back.

Soon she was complaining that if she didn't stop giving the best of the pig away, she'd have nothing left. But I knew she didn't mean it because we still had enough bacon, ribs and pork to last us for months. Sometimes people in the village would come together in somebody's house to play cards for a pig's head. And the winner of three games of twenty five got the pig's head and everyone had a great time because they had had tea and cake and maybe if they were lucky, a bottle of stout. When a pig's head was being played for in the village, I usually went along with my father. He'd sit there quietly at the end of the table throwing his cards, watching the rest of them arguing about everything from someone reneging and spoiling the game to farming and things in general.

Despite the thrill of playing for a pig's head I much preferred going to John Tarmey's during the winter. There, the men blathered away all night and had much more fun talking about everything from Hitler and *Mein Kampf* to the best looking women in the parish and what became of them. Tom Farrell was always there to give his penny halfpenny worth and I liked listening to him.

He enjoyed telling stories; and the more outrageous the better. He was also good at performing tricks. He used to love taking the silver foil wrapping out of empty cigarette boxes to stuff into his top pocket. Then while relaxing in John Tarmey's, he'd take out the silver foil and peel the white tissue off the back of it and chew it in his mouth for a few seconds while he carefully moulded the silver foil into the shape of an egg cup. Then he'd squeeze the wet tissue into the egg cup and in the twinkle of an eye he'd throw the egg cup straight up, never for one moment taking his eye off you. When I'd look up I'd see where the silver cup had miraculously stuck to the ceiling, like a mini prized trophy. And when I'd go visiting John Tarmey's house again the egg cup would still be stuck to the ceiling.

I used to think it was magic. John Tarmey's ceiling was full of silver eggs cups and he never ever complained when Tom decided to launch another cup into space while everyone else sat around the fire, laughing and talking.

As well as that John had a lovely collie dog called Shep that could do all kinds of tricks. John was old and feeble and always sat crouched in over the fire, with Shep by his side. But the minute we'd arrive, the dog would make room for us by ambling up to the back door where he'd lie quietly until asked to perform some task. John was always moaning about the price of cattle, the cold weather and the way the land commission had divided up the land; once owned by the landed gentry. Staring into the dwindling fire he'd call Shep and the dog would come running, eager to obey. All John had to do was tell the dog to bring down a sod of turf for the fire and Shep would run up to the basket, pick up a sod of turf and land it down at his master's feet. John would tell Shep to go for another sod and another, until there was enough turf down, to keep the fire going for another while.

Sometimes John would hold the fire tongs straight out, about two foot off the ground and as the dog approached, John would say, up; and Shep would jump straight over the tongs with the turf still in his mouth, drop it on the hearth and jump back out again. John Tarmey used to say that, that dog was better to him than a wife: and a lot less trouble.

'If I had a wife living here with me John Paschal, I'd have to do all the jumping; and my life would be a complete misery. Besides, I'd have to give her money every week just to keep her quiet and then she'd be off gallivanting around the town on her new bicycle, buying fancy hats and coats and the devil knows what: and I'd be left here at home shivering in my britches in case everything wasn't right for her. It's all right for you young fella, sittin' there laughing your head off and you not having a care in the world, but wait until you grow up, and you go over to England and you start drinking and going to some-a-them fancy clubs, where the women start throwing themselves at you. It'll be a different story then, I can tell you. They'll be up there on some big stage in London kicking their heels in the air, showing all their finery and everything and they'll want you to buy them a drink for all the trouble they went to: but that my dear man will soon take the smile off your face and you'll be singing a different tune. You'll come home here then on your summer holidays driving a big car, with the wind blowing in your hair, your tie flying over your left shoulder and people will think you're a millionaire because you look so handsome and prosperous and they'll want to hang on to your coat tails because they know you'll treat them all to a free pint-a-porter. Then they'll turn around and start talking about you behind your back because they think you're a bit of an eejit, who likes showing off and everything. But beware young man… it's all a show. I hope when you go away you'll be different. And remember one thing; keep your head on your shoulders. I'd hate to see you ending up in the gutter like half the Irish who go to England every year. England's no place for the faint hearted; let me tell you that. All John Bull ever wanted from an Irishman was for him to be strong in the arm and thick in the head.'

When John had finished his rambling, Tom Farrell would look at me with a smirk and say,

'Now John'een, haven't you heard it all? I'll bet you never heard the likes of that before? And the strange thing about it is, every word he's after saying is the gospel truth.'

And when I still wouldn't respond, he'd add mischievously, as he lit his pipe again by striking a match off the arse of his trousers, 'Ask your father when you go home and he'll soon tell you whether 'tis true or not?'

Again Tom would settle down in the corner, his back to the wall, puffing away contentedly while I'd watch each ringlet swirl its way higher and higher, clouding over the silver egg cups that adorned the smoke stained ceiling.

Most of the time, I didn't know what the men were talking about, but I knew my father would explain it all to me, if I asked him. He knew everything.

More often than not, my father would sit quietly by the fire, listening to everyone and to Tom in particular.

'...I remember, I used to work with our John in London; and one evening the fog was so bad it took us all our time to get home. And when I got home I started getting the dinner ready and I went out to the shop for a head of cabbage and dammy but I got lost on the way back, the fog was that bad. I was going around for about two hours trying to find the street where I lived. And the next bloody thing didn't I bump into a signpost. On me solemn oath I had to climb up on the signpost to see where I was going.'

'Liverpool, I suppose?' quipped John Tarmey, and everybody laughed. They laughed even more when my father said,

'I'd say, Tom 'twas the drink, it had you confused.'

Tom had another extraordinary gift; and that was to predict the weather. Himself and my father would always leave the rambling house around midnight and walk to the top of our new road where they'd part company. But last thing before they'd say good night, Tom would look up to study the winter sky.

'I'm thinking Ned, we'll have snow before morning.'

'Aaaah, I doubt it: 'tis too cold!'

'All right! Wait till you see!'

Sure enough when I'd get out of bed in the morning, there would be snow on the ground.

* * * *

On Monday morning, I told my friends in school how we had killed a pig. I already knew that most of their parents had a killed a pig, so from that point of view we had a lot to talk about. I had a slice of brawn for my lunch which I shared with EJ Lyons and John Keaveney. After our lunch break, The Chicken said to us, in the middle of our English class,

'When you have finished your revision I want you to go over your spelling and let me not hear a sound until I come back,'

We watched him pull the door after him and walk off down the corridor and into the girls' school. We knew he was going down to visit his lady friend and were ecstatic knowing he wouldn't be back for ages. We could do whatever we liked. Eamon Finnegan wanted to tell a joke but EJ Lyons wouldn't listen. All he wanted to do was whistle and imitate birds. He was mad to show us how he could imitate a flock of wild geese. And to demonstrate it, he slowly went, 'Geek... Geek...Geek...Geek: with each rhythmic beat of his imaginary wings. We smiled in acknowledgment, showing our appreciation; but Eamon had to go and spoil it all by saying EJ was a right looking geek. EJ went off in a huff while the rest of us start playing whirl-e-gigs which we had made at home out of old cotton spools. We kept spinning them on the floor to see whose whirl-e-gig could stay spinning the longest. But we could never agree. After a while, EJ came back and stood up on the desk. He stuck two fingers into his mouth and gave three shrill blasts. The blasts were so loud John Keaveney and myself were convinced The Chicken would hear them. We begged EJ to stop or he'd get us all into trouble.

'Look lads, yeer only a shower of sissies. Yeer afraid of the teacher; yeer afraid of yeer mother: yeer even afraid of yeer own shadows.'

When he said that it sounded so funny we all laughed. While EJ continued to entertain us, John and I suddenly noticed The Chicken standing outside the door, his arms neatly folded, looking in at us. But before we had time to say or do anything, EJ again stuck his fingers into his mouth and gave another blast. The Chicken was still watching. Suddenly, EJ realised there was something wrong because the whole class fell silent and he slithered down into his seat like an eel under a rock. The Chicken came in and slammed the door behind him.

'So, Mr Lyons has been entertaining you, has he?'

No one said a word, but you could see The Chicken was very, very angry. He went straight to the blackboard and picked up the cane.

'Well, I'm going to entertain all of you now, for a while. Mr Lyons, would you kindly come up here where I can assure you, you'll be most welcome,' he said, flexing the cane. But EJ did not stir. Instead, he crouched down and wrapped his two hands around the iron stanchion supporting his desk and refused to budge.

With three quick strides, The Chicken was beside EJ where he grabbed him by the scruff of the neck and tried to drag him out of the seat, but EJ had wrapped himself around the leg of his desk like an octopus. When The Chicken tried to drag EJ out, he ended up dragging the desk with him. Several times he tried to free EJ's arms and legs but he'd no sooner undo one than EJ would wrap the other round the iron stanchion again. After a fierce struggle, The Chicken managed to prise EJ away from his desk. The Chicken was in such a temper he lifted EJ and carried him bodily to the front of the class, with rivulets of oily sweat running down his ruby red checks. After an almighty struggle, he forcibly held out EJ's hands and gave him three of the best on each. Seething with anger, he grabbed him by the collar and fired him out into the corridor, shouting, 'Stay out there you blackguard and whistle away to your heart's content. And when you've finished you can come back in.'

Before EJ had time to say anything, he slammed the door with such force we half expected the glass to shatter, but it didn't.

There wasn't the faintest sound in the room as The Chicken stood behind his desk and began polishing his glasses, vigorously, while we buried our heads in our copybooks. We knew how close we'd all come, to getting a good flogging. And with a great sigh of relief, we resumed our English lesson where we'd left off, earlier. We'd only been studying a few minutes when we heard the call of the Blackbird outside the classroom door. We were so taken aback we could not listen to The Chicken as he rambled on. We were too engrossed in EJ's interpretation of a hill farmer and his dog rounding up his flock. EJ had taken us by surprise and was entertaining us to a wide variety of calls, culminating in the farmer's frantic efforts to get the sheep dog to separate his flock. The Chicken was asking us our spelling, but we couldn't answer, there was so much going on in our heads. What was The Chicken going to do now? What was EJ going to do next? We wanted the show to go on. It was like nothing we had ever witnessed before. Taking a deep breath The Chicken retreated and went behind his desk where he took out his white handkerchief. He sat down and began polishing his glasses, again. He started by fogging them up before wiping them meticulously while carefully considering his next move. He was trying hard not to show his discomfort but we could see he was near the end of his tether. For a minute or so, he made believe he was sorting out some books while we sat mesmerized, listening to EJ whistling contentedly, outside the door. It was now one song bird after another. Unable to withstand it any longer The Chicken jumped up and went out. He grabbed EJ and dragged him into the room. With his open palms he gave EJ two resounding slaps either side of the face.

'What exactly do you think you are doing… whistling like that? What?

'Well Sir,' says EJ, standing there defiantly, his cheeks blood red, 'you told me to whistle away to me heart's content and now you're asking, why I'm doing it.'

'Go and sit down! You stupid amadawn and let me not hear another sound out of you,' ranted The Chicken as he pushed EJ violently towards his seat. We all felt like clapping EJ on the back, but we knew he shouldn't have been whistling and jig-acting the way he was. Despite that we still liked him. We thought perhaps he should be on stage in the Parochial Hall or in a travelling road show because no one in the world could whistle like our EJ. He was the talk of the class, the talk of the school; and was certainly going to be the subject of my conversation when I went home from school.

Chapter Nineteen

I couldn't wait to tell my mother all about EJ, but as I approached our house I saw a tinker woman coming down the street trying frantically to get away from Mickey Billy's geese. I managed to get in the front door of our house before her. She had been to our house several times and usually had a baby close to her breast. She was still wearing the same gold hooped earrings she always wore and her weather beaten face was as wrinkled as ever. She normally came begging once a month and always asked for a fistful of tea, a grain'een-a-sugar, a cupful of flour, an egg or two, and a few copper'eens.

She'd generally take anything you'd give her but most of the time she'd haunt my mother for a sup'een-a-fresh-milk – for the bobby as she called the baby. To get rid of her, my mother would pour a fresh dash of milk into a special sweet can the woman carried wherever she went. As well as milk my mother would give her some flour, a few eggs, a grain'een-a-sugar and a fistful of tea. I was mystified as to where the tinker woman managed to put it all. She was always clad in an array of plaid shawls of every shape and hue. When my mother had finished looking after her, the woman would throw one half of the main shawl around herself and the bobby and all you could see of her were, her well worn shoes and greasy hair plaits hanging down her back, with two red ribbons. The tinker woman's last ritual, as always, as she was about to go away from the front door, was to extend a dirty hand and plead for more.

'Please Missus, and the blessin' of God on you. I hope and pray that you'll be lucky… I'll say three Hail Marys for you and the little boy if you'll just give me a few copper'eens as my husband is very sick and has to go to the doctor.'

'Ah Look! Is it what you think I'm a simpleton? You told me that auld story before. Didn't I see your husband down the town, there the other day and he as drunk as a stick,' retorted my mother.

'Ah that wasn't my husband at all. It must have been some other one; cross me heart and hope to die. My husband wouldn't touch a drop-a-drink if he was paid. He suffers from tuberculosis and 'tis the grace of God that he's alive at all; for he suffers terrible from convulsions.'

'Troth then it was him. I'd recognise your husband Paddy Mongan anywhere. He's the same man who promised he'd come back and clean the chimney for me. But faith he never came, because I was soft enough to pay him when he was stuck for a few bob. And I've been left waiting' here for him, like an auld bess. So you can tell him from me, that I'll redden his backside if he darkens my door again. I think now, I've given you enough, for today. I never refused you in my life: and yet you want more,' said my mother turning her back on the woman, but the tinker woman came a little further into the kitchen.

'Indeed then, you did not Missus, because you're a decent woman and all belonging to you were decent, which is why I'm pleading for a few copper'eens. Please Missus: you're my only hope. I'll say a special novena for yourself and your good husband and that fine son you have there with you.'

'Well, if you and your friends said half the amounts of novenas you're supposed to say, then I must be guaranteed a place in heaven. But remember… this is the last time I'm giving you anything. You know you have me damned, night, noon and morning,' said my mother, as she went up to the room to get her purse. When she came down she handed the woman three pennies and the woman bowed her head and said,

'May the Good Lord look down on you Missus; and may you never be short of anything. For 'tis a wonderful thing, the likes of you with a family of your own to rear, to give to the poor and to help save the likes of me and my children from the sweeping tide of starvation. I'll say three Our Fathers and three Hail Mary's in thanks giving and may the Grace of God be always with you.' Then adopting a business like tone she said, 'Tell me is the good woman next door, still around? I couldn't get near her on account of the geese.'

'Troth then she'd around, alright. And I wish to the Lord God almighty I had a few geese meself: and I mightn't be damned half as much.'

The woman bowed her head and wrapped the shawl tightly around her shoulders once more. She walked back up the street where Mickey Billy's geese came running out, forcing her to dodge this way and that to avoid them.

Mickey Billy's house was next to ours since Margaret Collins moved out to the head of the road. Their geese attacked everyone going in and out of the village. I hated it when I had to go past because they'd attack me too. Most of the time, however, I'd sprint barefoot past the house before they had time to attack me. But if I was coming from the well with a bucket of water, the gander would run out and try to bite me on the leg; his long outstretched neck hissing fiercely, while the rest of the flock rushed to his aid, cackling their support. By now I'd learned to carry a stick; and if the gander came near me, then I'd beat him off.

For a long time, I thought that there was nothing in the world as bad as Mickey Billy's geese: that was until Snowy came home from England and bought three wild horses. And because my father and Snowy shared the same boggy fields we crossed when visiting each other, it changed everything. Now I couldn't go up across without the horses running after me. To make it worse I had to bring the cows home from the boggy fields every evening for milking. And the minute the horses saw me rounding up the cattle, they'd come charging towards me.

In desperation, I used to sneak along by the ditch hoping the horses wouldn't see me but it was no use. They'd come charging down the boggy fields and wouldn't stop until they were almost on top of me. I'd be convinced they were going to kill me but at the very last second they'd swerve violently, throwing their hind legs into the air as if to say, get out of our way or we'll kill you. The cattle too were afraid of them and would frantically flee down the field ahead of them in an effort to get away. Once the horses started running, I'd be stuck to the ground, unable to move, until they slid to a halt before me. Ever so slowly I'd back away, towards the narrow gate as the horses stood staring at me with their curious reflective eyes, seemingly mystified by my presence. For a moment they'd watch me retreat; then come after me again and I'd scream for mercy and run for my life, half slamming the narrow gate behind me. They'd slide to a halt only because the rickety gate was too narrow for them to go through. Then they'd turn round and start buck lashing all over the field because they'd been deprived of their one chance of escape. Eventually the cattle would make their way towards me and I'd open the little gate and let them out one by one. Closing the gate after me, I'd make my way home shaking like a leaf.

I told my father about the horses chasing me but he didn't seem to think it was serious.

'Ah take no notice of them! They won't hurt you! Sure our horse never went near you?'

'I know she didn't, that's because she's not like them.'

But I wasn't impressed. How could I take no notice, I thought, when I might be killed? It was all right for big people because they knew how to mind themselves. I began to have horrible nightmares about cattle and horses chasing me across the boggy fields. Worst of all was the image of Collins's black bull as he sought to gore me to death with his long powerful horns tossing me round the field. Later he'd be joined by the three wild horses, all of them hell bent on killing me. One of the horses would stand on its hind legs and smash its front hooves down on me back as I fled out the narrow gate, knocking me to the ground. Then the horses would begin stomping the ground with their front hooves in a fiercely determined manner and I'd wake up screaming and my father would come down into the room and tell me it was all right, 'Ah! 'Twas only a dream you were having. Sure Snowy's horses wouldn't go next or near you. Go back to sleep now a grá and you'll be alright.'

Eventually I overcame my fear of the horses, but the black bull was the one animal I could never get out of my system. He was ever present in my dreams and attempted to gore me to death so many times I lost count. And that's what made me change my mind about wanting to be a matador in sunny

Spain. After all I had been through, I knew I'd never become a matador; not even if I was asked by the King of Spain himself: because, nobody, nobody in their right mind would want to become a matador, if the bulls over there were anything like what we had here in Ireland. Everything was fine until Snowy went and bought those horses and I started dreaming, I thought

* * * *

I was filling the turf basket with two buckets of turf when Mrs O'Brien, said,

'Would you ever run up to the well, like a good lad and bring me down a bucket of water. And when you have that done I want you to run down to Nora Keeffe's with a drop of buttermilk.'

I could hardly believe what I was hearing. Bringing a can of Buttermilk up to Nan Little's, shop or down to Nora Keeffe's house, was one of my favourite tasks. Every week I'd be sent down to the priest's house with a can of buttermilk for Nora. I loved it because Mrs O'Keeffe – as we called her – would always put something nice into the sweet can as a thank you gift for Mrs O'Brien.

Running up to the well, I couldn't help but recall all the lies I'd told my mother and all the bars and sweets and oranges I'd scoffed on my way home from the priest's house. I was a little concerned that sooner or later I was going to get caught.

I could never wait to see what was in the can, so the very minute I'd turn the corner, I'd take off the lid. There were usually two bars of chocolate, two oranges and maybe two apples in the can. Straight away, I'd slap the lid back on to avoid any temptation and I'd start walking on briskly. But I'd only ever manage to go five or six paces before I'd be tempted to have another look. Every single week I'd go through the same ritual: open the can, look in, slap the lid back on and walk a bit before deciding which of the goodies I was going to eat. I had to be extremely careful in case Mrs O'Brien suspected anything. She could nearly always tell what was going to be in the can. Despite that, I'd chance eating a chocolate bar and I'd hide the wrapper under a tree, in case she saw it on her way home from Mass. If she did, she'd know I had robbed the chocolate and I'd be in serious trouble. The chocolate bars were so enticing I'd have no hesitation devouring the second one, but it was too dangerous. Mrs O'Brien knew Mrs O'Keeffe was stone mad for chocolate; and that she had an ass load of chocolate bars in her house.

Now that I was back from the well, it was time for me to go on my weekly errand. Mrs O'Brien had the can of buttermilk ready and waiting. I set off out the door happy in the knowledge I'd be munching something nice on the way home.

Mrs O'Keeffe was her usual self as she handed me back the sweet can with a warm friendly smile.

'…and tell Mrs O'Brien I said thanks. Bye, bye.'

As soon as I turned the corner I stopped and looked into the can. Sure enough there were two oranges, an apple and a bar of chocolate. Now I was faced with one of the hardest decisions of my life. I slapped the lid back on and tried as I always did not to give in to temptation, but I knew it was a desperate struggle. I couldn't possibly resist an orange. I walked on a bit having decided I couldn't dare touch the chocolate, much and all as I'd like to. The main problem was; what was going to be my second choice? The first choice was easy. But one should plan ahead, I thought. I had no qualms at all about attacking the orange: it was so big and juicy looking. Besides, there would still be an orange, a bar of chocolate and an apple left; and the can wouldn't look so empty. I stood on the road to peel the orange. I kept a sharp look out in case anybody saw me. Someone from the village could easily come round the corner on a bicycle and I'd be caught, red-handed. I ate the orange like a savage; with the juice squishing all over my face, but I didn't care. I hid the peel under a bush and cleaned my hands on the grass because I could smell the orange juice off them. I ran my sleeve across my mouth to make sure there was no trace. Walking on towards the lake, I had an overwhelming desire to eat the chocolate. I stopped again and lifted the lid. I took out the bar and carefully examined the wrapper. I studied the image of the two pints of milk being poured into the making of it, which read *Cadbury's* milk chocolate. I pushed the foil wrapped bar out of its sleeve and took a peek at the milk chocolate inside. I held it to my nose to get a whiff of the chocolate aroma. It was exquisite. But after an agonizing delay, I decided it was too dangerous and pushed the foil wrapped bar back into its sleeve. Then I thought about eating the apple but that would only have left two items out of four in the can. I carefully considered the second orange. Again, that would have left only two out of four, so I slapped the lid back on again before it was too late. I knew exactly what would happen the minute I got home. Every lie I had ever told, about what Mrs O'Keeffe had given me had worked a treat; so I didn't want to risk it now.

I met my mother as I turned in the street. She was sweeping out the front hall.

'Well, how did you get on? Was there anybody there?'

'I think there was somebody there, but I couldn't be sure. I rang the bell but there was no answer. Then, as I was leaving the can by the door, like you told me, I thought I heard something; like someone closing a press door. I rang the door bell again and this time Mrs O'Keefe opened the door and I gave her the can.'

'Was there anybody there do you think or did you see any sign of Fr Keaveney?'

'I thought I heard someone talking before Mrs O'Keefe opened the door, but I couldn't be sure. It might have been the radio.'

'Did she give you anything or do you know?'

'She put something into the can because it's heavy, but I don't know what it is. She gave me a bar of chocolate for myself and said I was a great boy. She told me to say thanks to you.'

As soon as I left the can on the table my mother took off the lid, while I stood watching, nervously.

'Is that all she gave you? Are you sure you didn't take anything out?'

'No I didn't. I didn't even know what was in the can until you opened it now. But I ate the chocolate bar she gave me because I thought it was alright. It was only a small bar and not half as nice looking as that one there. She said she was sorry she hadn't more fruit to give you,' I added, trying hard to throw my mother off the scent.

'I hope you're not telling me lies? You know you can catch a thief, you can catch a mouse, but you can't catch a liar. But mark my words... I'll find out sooner or later whether you're telling the truth or not.'

She took the apple, the orange and the bar of chocolate and put them into a fruit bowl in the bottom half of the dresser. Once again I had won the battle of wits, or so I thought.

'Sure she shouldn't be giving us anything at all and we having loads of buttermilk. I must tell her not to give you anything anymore. It would be cheaper for her to buy milk. I'll stick on a pot of water so you can wash yourself down in the room. You know you have to be speck and span for the Stations in the morning. I better iron your soutane and surplice. What time did you say you had to be at Fr Keaveney's?'

'Mrs Patterson said to be there at a quarter past nine. Mass is at ten o'clock.'

'Well, make sure you're up in good time. And when you go to the Station house make sure you speak when you're spoken to. And if anyone gives you anything, make sure you say thanks; and put whatever you get into your pocket and don't lose it.'

I couldn't wait to go to my first Station house. I'd never been in a house where they said Mass and people come from all over the village. I was a bit worried because if Mrs O'Brien or Fr. Keaveney knew I was a thief, who stole chocolate bars and oranges I'd never have been chosen as an altar boy. I was delighted when I passed my examination and had finally become an altar boy. I was even more delighted when it was my turn to serve at the Stations. Each week an altar boy was chosen by Mrs Patterson to accompany the Parish priest on his rounds. For three weeks during the Spring and Autumn, each village in the parish took it in turns to host the Stations. If Mass was said in one house in the Spring, then the house next door would be expected to host the next Stations in Autumn; and so on until Mass had been said in every house in the village. If for any reason a person was unable to host the Stations, then they'd notify the Parish Priest and he'd ask the villagers to decide amongst themselves which house was going to host it. Most people welcomed the coming of the Stations as it gave them an excuse to run a lick of paint over the house and to have their homes blessed. But some people couldn't be bothered their backsides with the Stations or with painting the house. It was too much trouble they said.

There was a severe frost on the ground as I ran down excitedly to Fr Keaveney's house. Mrs O'Brien made sure that I was properly dressed with my hair combed and my shoes polished. And because I hadn't had time to get my hair cut she put a dollop of brylcream in my hair to keep it in place. She had ironed my soutane and surplice and neatly folded them into the small brown suitcase which I brought with me. When I reached Fr Keaveney's house, he was already out in the street ready to start the car. I stood there shivering as he took the starting handle out of the boot and inserted it beneath the engine. After several attempts, the car spluttered into life. We sat into the car and in no time we were winding our way out the country. Fr Keaveney was a jolly man who looked just like a lolly-pop. He was very easy going and started every conversation by saying, 'Well now do you see, it's like this....' Everyone liked Fr Keaveney. I was delighted to be sitting in front with him, even thought we hardly said a word. I could not believe how magical it was as we wound our way through the sand hills to Clomahara which was a neat little village on the outskirts of the parish. We pulled up outside Dan Hussey's house and Fr Keaveney took his gleaming brass buckled suitcase out of the car and handed me my little case, which seemed so insignificant.

Dan's was a beautiful white washed cottage with a thick layer of golden thatch. It had three dainty red painted windows with tied back lace curtains and geraniums. Outside the near gable wall were two buckets of water with a thin layer of ice on them. And though it was still early, people were cycling down little boreens and laneways, on their way to the Stations while others came on foot.

Dan Hussey was a big powerful rose cheeked man who came out to welcome us. And as I followed the priest into the house, I could see the kitchen was already crowded. People parted to either side like the red sea to let us pass safely through. There was a small table in the kitchen laid out as an altar with candles – which I knew I'd have to light – a crucifix and some flowers. There was a roaring fire with a few elderly women sitting round it. After a few friendly words, Fr Keaveney said if anybody wanted to go to confession he'd hear them in one of the rooms. Only two elderly ladies went into the room. When he came back he began taking the sacred vessels he needed to say Mass out of his suitcase: the Chalice, the Communion plate or Paten, the Ciborium which held the Sacred Hosts, the Purificator, the Pall, the Finger Bowl and the all important Mass Bell which I would have to ring three times during the blessing of the Eucharist. When Fr. Keaveney began to put on his stole and chasuble, I too opened my suitcase to put on my Soutane and surplice. When

Dan was happy all the neighbours were present he nodded to Fr. Keaveney. The priest began by asking Dan for salt so he could purify the water and bless it; thereby turning it into Holy Water. As he was about to start, he stuck out his ample chest and said,

'Well now do you see it's like this; it's not every day that I get to say Mass in such beautiful surroundings. First of all I'd like to thank the Hussey family for inviting me here to say Mass. I would also like to welcome you, the many friends, neighbours and colleagues of the Hussey family who are joining them in the celebration of Mass here this morning. And if anybody would like me to visit the sick, the housebound, the lame or the infirm, then I shall be happy to do so. Now let us kneel and pray and thank God for giving us the pleasure of taking part in this ceremony, In the name of the father and of the Sun and of the Holy Ghost....'

I knelt nervously beside Fr Keaveney, the Mass bell at my finger tip as people still tried to squeeze into the already crowded kitchen. One of the things I had to do during Mass was to hold the Communion plate beneath a communicant's chin as he or she knelt down to receive Holy Communion. If the Communion wafer fell from the priest's fingers or the receiver's tongue, the altar boy was expected to catch it on his plate, so the Sacred Host which was the Body of Christ would not touch the ground. It was deemed a sacrilege if the Sacred Host was allowed touch the ground whilst being distributed. Thankfully, nobody had ever let it fall whilst I was serving Mass in the church. But on one occasion, while I was serving, the Communion wafer fell from an old woman's tongue. Fortunately I was alert and caught it on my plate. On that occasion, the priest calmly picked it up again and placed it back on the woman's tongue. There were times when I found it almost impossible not to laugh as I watched certain individuals stick out their tongues. When they opened their mouths they reminded me of hungry looking scaltháns* opening their beaks to receive a worm from the mother.

The only difference between scaltháns* and people receiving Holy Communion, was the size of their tongue and their facial expressions. If a very religious woman, living in the town, was receiving Holy Communion, she'd kneel with her hands neatly joined and her head slightly inclined, like Our Blessed Lady. And as she was about to receive Holy Communion she'd close her eyes, open her mouth and put out her small pink tongue. But some old ladies would deem it an offence to put out their tongue. When that happened, the priest sometimes found it hard to place the Communion wafer on their tongues because their mouths were so small and his hand was so big. In desperation, he'd give the Communion wafer a bit of a nudge to make sure he got it into the mouth. It was a bit like posting a letter; getting it in properly was the all important thing. Other times I'd have to stifle a fit of the giggles

---

* Scaltháns (*young birds in a nest*)

as certain individuals knelt piously before me. The man in question, I might have seen at the last pig fair in Williamstown where he'd spent the evening roaming the town cursing and swearing and threatening to kill all before him. And here he was now, a walking Saint – ready to be canonised. And I'd have to stand there at the altar rail and hold the Communion plate beneath his ample chin and try not to think about the awful language I'd heard rolling off his filthy tongue while the priest momentarily paused as he struggled to separate the layered Communion wafers tightly packed in his chalice. Very often I'd be smirking away quietly to myself as I studied the various individual expressions, guaranteed to make a mouse hunter laugh.

I'd study a farmer's bushy eyebrows. I watch his mouth open like a hippopotamus and his thick grotesque tongue dart our like a viper, sometimes reaching right down to his chin. Having received the Sacred Host his tongue would just as quickly dart back in again. Occasionally a delicate looking man would be kneeling beside him; all meek and mild and saintly looking. But when he'd open his mouth to put out his tongue his eyebrows would shoot so high and his chin drop so low you'd swear he was going to vomit. But the ones I got a greatest kick out of were my friends in school.

If it was a girl I knew I'd smile politely, hoping desperately to make eye contact just to let her know it was me. But if it was John Keaveney or EJ Lyons, I'd raise the Communion plate to tickle their chin just to see if I could make them laugh, but they never did. But if it was Fatso Fannon or some other scholar I didn't like, I'd make sure to hold the sharp edge of the plate to their throat just to let them know I was in charge and that I had power over them.

In the Station house, I couldn't allow such wayward thoughts to enter my head for one solitary moment. What really bothered me now, was, how was I going to go around the room and hold the Communion plate when there wasn't room to put your hand in your pocket? Besides I had to watch the priest's every move and respond in Latin at various times. I had to make the sign of the Cross and bow when the priest did so during the Gospel.

I had to be ready to make a special sign of the Cross on my forehead, lips and breast with the front of my thump while reciting, *Glória, tíbi, Dómine.* I had to be ready to ring the bell at the appropriate times as Fr Keaveney genuflected before the Sacred Host; and again as he held it aloft before the congregation and they knelt; their heads bowed, muttering aloud, *Mea culpa, Mea culpa, Mea maxa, Mea culpa,* whilst striking their breasts three times. Then raising their heads they continued to finger their rosary beads whilst whispering their prayers devoutly.

When it was time for the priest to give out Holy Communion, I didn't know whether to walk in front of him or go behind him, the room was so crowded. It seemed to me there wasn't room to do anything. Sensing I was looking for inspiration, Fr. Keaveney whispered, 'You stay here John, I'll manage.' I knelt down again beside the altar, my cheeks on fire, not knowing whether I had made a hames of the Stations or not. When I looked up again and saw the trouble Fr Keaveney was having working his way through the congregation I realized there wasn't room for one person to get around never mind two. Still, I lowered my head and prayed fervently that no one would let their Communion wafer fall; or else I'd be in fierce trouble.

When Mass was over, there was a great sigh of relief from everyone including myself. Some of the Mass goers went straight home because they had things to do. But close friends and relatives of the family stayed on, each of them asking my name and how old I was. Soon they began to go around with tea and sandwiches and sweet cake. The Hussey family brought Fr Keaveney and I into what looked like a parlour where they had a special table set for the two of us. I could not believe a place at the table had been set for me, directly opposite the priest. It was a small round table covered with a decorative linen table cloth, trimmed with lace. On the table were the daintiest china cups and saucers I'd ever seen. The cups and plates and saucers had pictures of blue birds with yellow breasts like I'd often seen in our garden. And when I thought there was no one looking. I turned over the cup. Underneath, in dark blue was written the words, *Mason's iron stoned china.*

In a corner of the room was a china cabinet with floral decorated glass doors and in the other corner was a gramophone with the lid up which showed a picture of a loud speaker with a dog sitting up listening to the music. On the walls were large photographs that looked like Dan Hussey's father and mother and there was a large picture of a man with a moustache wearing a military uniform.

Pretty soon we were tucking into eggs, rashers, sausages and black pudding with lots of brown and white soda bread. When we had finished, two ladies whom I didn't know brought us beautiful crusted apple tart and cream topped with two giant strawberries. They insisted we have it, together with another cup of tea.

'Well do you see it's like this,' said Fr Keaveney as he spread the white napkin across his lap again, 'it wouldn't be nice to refuse such a beautiful desert after all the effort you put into making it.'

'It was I that made that, Father,' quipped big Dan as he stood in the doorway, smiling, his big rosy cheeks swelling with the humour of it all as the ladies started laughing.

'Well do you see, I always knew you were a dab hand with the accordion; and not a bad hand at football: but I never knew you could bake an apple tart,' smiled Fr Keaveney. For a long time the fun and laughter continued as Fr Keaveney and I finished our deserts.

When it was time to go, the Hussey family escorted the two of us out to the street and thanked us for such a beautiful service. Then I saw Big Dan hand an envelope to Fr Keaveney and before I knew what was happening, a woman planted a half-crown in my fist, saying, 'There you are now a grá, something for yourself. Put it in your pocket and don't lose it. And when you go into the town buy yourself an ice cream.'

I was ecstatic. All my dreams had come true. I was now a fully fledged altar boy who could serve a High Mass, a Low Mass or a Station Mass. As well as that I had one other accolade under my belt that no other pupil in school had: I was able to ring the bell for a funeral, though not everyone in the parish would agree. My next big challenge I thought was to serve Mass at a wedding. Hopefully I wouldn't have too long to wait.

On our way out of the village, Fr Keaveney stopped off at two houses to attend the sick and the lame while I waited in the car. The minute I arrived home, I give the half-crown to my mother and told her all about the Stations. She was very pleased and said she'd put it the Post Office for me. I knew that would be the last I'd ever see of it but I didn't care. I had no use for all that kind of money. Half-a-crown was a lot for someone like me to get: what could I do with it? I wouldn't dream of spending money like that on ice cream or sweets. I wanted my mother to have it as I knew it would make her happy. If I found a penny or a threepenny bit on the road which I often did, I'd buy sweets with it and not tell anyone except my friends in school. But if anybody gave me sixpence, a shilling or two shilling for myself I always told my mother and gave it to her in case she'd hear it. Besides, money was very scarce and hard to come by in our house, so every penny counted. The only money coming into our house from one end of the year to the other was from whatever my father got for the pigs or cattle at the fair; and whatever my mother got for her eggs. Now that winter was closing in fast there would be no eggs worth talking of, until spring.

Having served Mass one morning and then gone on to school, I came home in the afternoon to a surprise announcement from my mother.

'When you have finished changing your clothes, I want you to give your new shoes a good polishing because I'm thinking I might bring you with me, to Galway tomorrow.' Before I had time to get over the shock, she added, 'And when you have that done, I'd like you to run up to Colleen's and see if Snowy can cut your hair before he goes back to England. You have a head on you like Sweeney the tinker. But before you go, you might run up to the well and bring down two buckets of water and you won't have to be doing it when you come home.

'How are we going to Galway?' I asked

'Ah musha how do you think, but on the bus? Colleen is coming with us.'

I couldn't believe I was going to Galway for the first time in my life. The only thing I knew about Galway was that a bus stopped in Williamstown every morning on its way to the city. When it stopped in Williamstown, the driver usually got out and opened the boot and accepted boxes of day old chicks from Dom Blythe, who was a poultry breeder. Once or twice, my father had travelled to Galway on the bus and brought his bicycle with him. On that occasion he passed the bicycle up to the driver, who'd climbed up the ladder attached to the back of the bus. Sometimes there were as many as half a dozen bicycles perched on top of the bus as it set off for Galway. It was the only way to get round the city my father said.

I got up early the next morning to make sure I had all the jobs done. I had to milk the cows, feed the calves and then drive them up to the boggy field as my father was working for the County Council, drawing stones from the quarry with the horse and cart.

Shortly after half nine, Colleen arrived on her bicycle which she propped beneath my bedroom window. When the three of us were ready, we walked into the town and stood waiting in the square for the quater past ten bus to Galway.

It was a wonderful feeling to be sitting on a bus for the first time as we drove through Dunmore and Tuam. We arrived in Galway around half past eleven and crossed over the Fair Green in Eyre Square and down into Shop Street. Mrs O'Brien said we should have a cup of tea before we started looking round. We went into Lynch's café which was upstairs. We sat at a small table beside one of the windows that afforded us a view of Shop Street. But I was more interested in the suits of armour and pikes that adorned the walls. I read the historical plates attached to each item which said they had come from the Spanish Armada; ships that were wrecked off the West coast of Ireland in 1588.

There was a party of American tourists with gaudy looking pants covering their enormous backsides seated at the next table. An elderly waiter circled their table like a bumble-bee, trying to please them. He was laying down cups and saucers and napkins for them. Then one of the tourists – a big man with a gigantic backside who'd been studying the menu – said with an American twang,

'…I can't understand why you haven't got it. In America, we've got everything.'

But the bald headed waiter smiled and said, 'Sir, you haven't got Ireland: that's why you're here.'

The American who seemed to be in a pensive mood, suddenly laughed aloud, as did everyone else at his table,

'Gee, I guess you're right.'

In response to Colleen's inquiry, another waiter brought a trolley laden with refreshments to our table. I couldn't get over the wonderful choice of cakes and scones and tarts and cream pies and strawberry flans and everything. Colleen winked at me when she saw me eyeing up the strawberry flan. She told Mrs O'Brien not to worry about the price; that she'd pay for it and that we should go for the strawberry flan.

I could hardly believe I was sitting in a restaurant in Galway. It was the most incredible feeling I'd ever had. While I was studying the American tourists, I noticed Mrs O'Brien and Colleen were whispering. I didn't like that because I was on my own and had no one to talk to. I got the impression they didn't want me to hear what they were saying. From what I could gather it was something to do with nuns and babies. I couldn't understand why they were whispering. It made me feel as if I was in the way; that I wasn't wanted. And because of that I asked Mrs O'Brien if I could go and look at the suits of armour on the wall.

'Stay right where you are. I don't want you wandering round the place like some sort of a Glickin*.'

I sat there patiently and waited for the strawberry flan and tea to arrive. When we had finished we came down stairs and out onto Shop Street and began looking in the shop windows. Many of the windows had winter woollies on display, some with sparkling scenes of snow which reminded me Christmas was only a few weeks away. We went into two big shops called Moons, and Anthony Ryan's where Mrs O'Brien and Colleen bought curtains and wallpaper. We went into another shop where Mrs O'Brien bought a black coat as well as a few other things.

She asked the attendant if she could leave the bags in the shop for an hour or so as she didn't want to be traipsing around with them all day. The attendant said it was no problem; and put the parcels under the counter for her.

We crossed over the fair green once more and turned up College Road. On a hill in front of us, on the left hand side, was a huge gable end type building, that didn't have any windows. High up on the wall was a huge life size image of Mary Magdalene in mosaic: while over her head in curvature were the words, Magdalene Laundry: founded 1897. Mrs O'Brien went into the glass fronted office and spoke to a girl who was working there while we stood outside. The girl gave her directions and we continued walking up the hill until we came to a small mahogany door that was set in a high stone wall. Mrs O'Brien and Colleen stood hesitantly outside the door for a moment.

'Sure this must be it. Why don't you ring the bell and find out,' said Mrs O'Brien turning to Colleen.

Colleen pushed the brass coloured button that was set in the stone wall beside the door and waited. I wondered why there should be a bell in the wall when clearly it wasn't a house. I knew it wasn't a house because there were no windows or roof or chimneys or anything. Yet the wall had two doors; a small mahogany door like what you'd see in a fancy house; and a big galvanized steel door that a horse and cart could drive through. After a while we could hear someone unlocking the door inside. A small pale faced nun opened the door slightly and peered out at us.

---

* Glickin (know all)

'Can I help you?' she asked, still peering at us.

I'd like to see Bridie Rodgers. She asked me to bring her son in to see her. He's here with me now.'

'Who shall I say is calling?'

'Mrs O'Brien. And this is my daughter Colleen.'

'One moment,' the nun said and slammed the door in our face. We stood waiting for ages. Then the door opened again and a much older looking nun appeared.

Like the nun who'd answered the door earlier, her face was firmly encased in a tight fitting snow white veil beneath a long flowing black habit with loose fitting black sleeves. As soon as she opened the door, the nun pushed her two hands into the deep folds of her sleeves as if she were perished. She had a softly spoken voice and said something to Mrs O'Brien who was the nearest to her. She introduced herself and shook hands with us. Then she started talking about Bridie: about rules and regulations. And in a whispered conversation she said something about having to write to the Bishop and to the Reverent Mother requesting a meeting. Glancing in my direction she smiled and said,

'Isn't he a fine boy? He looks just like Bridie. He has the same features and everything.'

I hated it when people started talking about me like that. I turned my head away for a minute and concentrated on the red double-decker bus that was going down College road. As I hung around trying to look inconspicuous, I could see what appeared to be beautiful laid out gardens behind the nun. Over her shoulder I could see part of a huge stone building that looked as big as any of the shops in the city and I wondered why it was hidden behind a high stone wall with a door that was closed all the time. And when I stretched my neck and looked a bit further I could see nuns digging in another part of the garden where there were statues and things. When Colleen and Mrs O'Brien were ready to say good bye the nun said,

'I'm sorry… you've had to come such a long way.' Then she shook hands with the three of us, bowed her head slightly and said, '...and may God bless you.'

As we turned and made our way back down the hill towards Eyre Square, Mrs O'Brien seemed very angry and started giving out to Colleen about the nuns and having to write to the Bishop and the Reverend Mother; after all she'd done for them. I thought maybe it was something to do with the nuns that called to our house. Every other week two or three nuns would come to our house looking for money to help save the black babies of South Africa. One day, two nuns called to our house and collected money for the black babies and the very next day three more landed looking for money to help build the new cathedral in Galway. I thought maybe that was why Mrs O'Brien was so vexed. Hardly a week went by that someone didn't call to our house looking for money. Once a month Jim Burke the insurance man, called. Other times a lone tinker woman or a group of tinkers would call to our house looking for food and money. Four times a year every house in the parish had to give money to the parish priest who then read the names off the altar; stating how much each one had paid. These collections were called dues: Christmas dues; Easter dues; summer dues and the oats money which was collected during the harvest. The summer dues were often referred to by the farmers as the hungry dues because that collection took place in July when the farmers hadn't yet reaped the benefits of their crops. What annoyed an awful lot of parishioners was having the size of their contribution read out off the altar. Standing at the altar, the priest would start off with the biggest contributors in the parish which were the business people of the town. He'd shout their names out loud and clear so everyone could hear them. 'Harry Ryan, twenty pounds; Eddie Geraghty, twenty pounds; Tommy Glynn, twenty pounds; Brody McHugh, ten pounds,' and so on.

Working on a sliding scale, he'd list every household in the parish until he'd reached the smallest contributions which were bottom of the list. You could tell by the sound of the priest's voice that he didn't think much of them as he flew through the last few names in a barely audible voice.

'Lakeland South: Paddy Smyth, one shilling; Annie Tobin, one shilling; Margaret Collins, one shilling; Edward O'Brien, sixpence; Noel McGuire, sixpence; Mark Tarmey, three pence; Patsy Ganly, nothing.'

Patsy, on that particular occasion, was standing at the back of the church. Suddenly he raised his hand and shouted, 'Here! Here you are Father!'

When he'd finish reading, the priest would always give a sigh of relief, and say, 'And that concludes the harvest collection, which as you can see is way down on last year.'

Of all the priests to serve in our parish, Fr Keaveney turned out to be the most popular. And one of the reasons was, that he put an end to the public disclosure of his parishioners donations, saying,

'Well do you see, it's like this... it's not for me to equate the rich and the poor. Because, my dear people, there will always be those who have; and those who have not.'

A few days after my visit to Galway, I sat down to answer Bridie's letter.

My mother glowered at me and said, 'Maybe you should stop writing to that lady?'

Perplexed I looked at my mother.

'Why should I stop writing?'

'Ah... why do you think? From what I can see, the nuns don't want you going next or near her. That's why!'

What my mother was saying didn't make any sense to me, so I said nothing for fear of saying the wrong thing. And when I didn't respond, she added,

'It's hard times when you're turned away from the door: and they won't let you in to see your own mother?'

By now I was really confused. Mrs O'Brien was my mother. And Bridie was my mother – if I was to go by her letters, so what did it all mean?

'What mother?' I queried, glumly

'Ah, what mother me backside?' said Mrs O'Brien angrily, as she continued sewing the hem of a skirt, 'Bridie above in Galway! I tried to get you in the other day to see her – surely to God you know that – but they wouldn't even let us inside the front door: that's what I'm on about!'

I sat at the table, more confused than ever; the fountain pen still in my hand. I thought it better not to say anything because I knew Mrs O'Brien would get cross if I asked too many questions. For a long time she sat by the fire, saying nothing, then she added, 'Troth it will be a long time before I'll bother my backside with the likes of them again. You can write all you like, but I'm finished writing, anyway.'

I finished the letter and the following day she checked it over after I came home from school. She gave it her approval by bringing two pennies down from her room. She left the two coins on the table for me to post it, without saying a single word which was not like her.

There was no more said about Bridie and life continued as normal until I came home one day and sensed a distinct air of sadness in my mother's voice I'd not witnessed before. And as I sat eating my bacon and cabbage she sat pensively by the fire as if she were in a world of her own.

'You know your father didn't go to work today. He had to go to Castlerea… to get some tablets.'

She herself was always taking tablets for her heartburn, so I thought it might be something to do with that. Then she added, 'When you've finished your dinner, would you ever bring me down two buckets from the well. And if you have time then before you go up for the cows, you might clean out the pig's cabin because it wasn't cleaned out at all yesterday.'

I raced up to the well as fast as I could. The Well was almost full so it was easy to team the water without having to use the rope. Later when I had finished all the jobs, I sat at the table doing my homework. Again I thought I sensed an air of gloom but I couldn't be sure. I looked across at my mother who was sitting quietly looking into the fire as if in deep thought. But when I looked at her a second time I noticed her dabbing her eyes with a handkerchief. She was crying. All of a sudden, an overwhelming sense of sadness came over me because I'd never seen my mother crying before. I thought she was the strongest person in the whole world but to see her crying there beside the fire, when she should have been knitting away, was a hammer blow like I'd never felt before. After a minute or so she stopped crying, pulled herself together and said,

'You know … Daddy isn't well. He had to go to the doctor today and he told him he'd have to go into the hospital. And if that happens I don't know how I'm going to manage. It's the grace of God that I have you here to help me. If he goes into hospital, I'll have to hire a car to go up and see him. And to make matters worse there's no knowing how long they'll keep him. The doctor said he might have to have an operation.'

Her head sagged when she mentioned an operation and she started crying again and I wished with all my heart I was out in the garden doing something because now I too was ready to start crying. I sat there in silence not knowing what to say or do. I turned my face away because I didn't like what she was saying.

'…And here I am at this hour-a-me-life with nothing but pain and suffering to look forward to. It's all right for you, a grá, you're young and starting out, while I'm at the latter end of me days with nothing to show for it: and nothing to look forward to. It's been the same thing here, day in and day out, seven days a week for the last thirty two years: thirty two years in this God forsaken place with never a day off in all that time.'

I tried to put what my mother was saying out of my head but it wouldn't go. I hated it when she started talking about how hard her life had been. Instead, I began to recall some of the things Tommy the postman used to say to my mother. There wasn't a week went by that he didn't have a story about some man or woman that was in hospital. He'd throw himself down in the corner and say that such and such a one was bad in hospital And I often wondered why he'd never say such and such a one was good. Hospitals were places where people were supposed to get better, I thought. But instead of saying someone was getting better, Tommy would hop off his bicycle a few days later to tell my mother the man was dead; that he'd passed away during the night and him only a young man in his prime. Tuberculosis and cancer was such a scourge. Wasn't half the country dying from it? And hadn't the man's father died from TB: and all belonging to him? So, was it any wonder, the poor man died?

I sat silently at the table using the sleeve of my jumper to clean my nose. It was such a shock to be told that your father wasn't well and that he'd have to go into hospital. And though I never knew that my mother had planned to bring me up to see Bridie for Christmas it didn't matter anymore. I didn't care whether I saw her or not. In a way I thought it was the daftest thing ever: going up to Galway to see my mother Bridie, when the whole world knew Mrs O'Brien was my mother? Why else would I be living with her? As far as I was concerned, I couldn't possibly have two mothers. But if by chance my mother was right and Bridie in Galway was my mother too, then why hadn't I got two fathers as well? And if I had two fathers and one of them died, that would be great because I'd still have one left, I thought

With all that was going on in my head, I didn't know what to think. I sat at the table trying to will up the courage to finish my lessons. I had to do my Arithmetic, Geography, and History. I knew if I didn't do my lessons properly the teacher would kill me. But it was so hard to concentrate. Instead I sat at the table thinking, that instead of going up to Galway to see Bridie for Christmas, I'd now have to go up to the hospital to see my father. And the thought of seeing my father lying in hospital, made me want to cry like I had never cried before.

Chapter Twenty

I went to school on Monday with nothing but the thought that Doctor Roland was arranging for an ambulance to bring my father to hospital. All day Saturday and Sunday my father sat by the fire most of the time, saying very little. He looked old and feeble and hardly ate anything at all. But he still took out his pipe to have a smoke every now and again. The thing I disliked about him was the way his eyes appeared to have sunk in his head. Before, he looked bright eyed, especially after he'd washed and shaved himself. But now his grey stubbled features and white wrinkled forehead showed he was getting on in years. Going down by the lake with my friends Una and Sadie, Paddy Keegan and Tony Clancy, I knew I'd have to hurry home from school to help my mother do all the jobs

From day to day we never knew what subjects we'd be doing in school. We simply had to be ready for anything. Sometimes when we'd think we were going to have an easy subject like Geography or Catechism, The Chicken would unexpectedly say; will you take out your History books? So it was a great relief when the first thing he said on Monday morning was,

'Will you please take out your Geography books?'

I liked Geography and could reel off most of the major rivers, towns and cities in Ireland, as well as many of the towns' major industries.

It was in the afternoon when The Chicken, surprisingly said, 'Now, who'd like to start off by describing, the 1798 rebellion, that I sensed I was in trouble.

The minute he opened his mouth I realized I'd skipped most of my homework including History because of what had happened at home. It was too late now I thought. And if I was asked to read I didn't know in the name of God what I was going to do.

'Mr Rodgers, would you like to come up here and tell us about the, 1798 Rebellion and Declaration of the United Irishmen.'

I didn't mind reading at all, but I hated the way The Chicken made us go up in front of the class to read, instead of letting us stand beside our desks, where it was much easier. John Keaveney and I usually sat together. And if I came across a word I didn't know and Keaveney knew it, he'd whisper it. And if he had to read I'd do the same. I thought I was good at reading but when you had to stand on your own in front of the class it was more difficult, because you knew everybody was waiting for you to make an ass of yourself.

When my name was called, I ambled up to the front of the class and began reading *The Declaration of the United Irishmen*. I read the first paragraph alright but it was a bit of a struggle because I hadn't read a single word at home like I was supposed to. I could sense The Chicken was beginning to lose his patience. He shouted at me several times.

'Will you go on? It's like trying to drive a bloody donkey.'

The minute he said that, I lifted my head, half expecting to get a clatter across the lug. And when I looked at the page again I wasn't sure what line I was on. I ploughed on pretending I knew what I was talking about.

'Reformed!' exclaimed The Chicken. I stopped reading and looked to him for guidance 'Re-formed! Re-formed! Read it again, stupid.'

I read it again, the same as I'd done the first time in the hope that I'd never be asked to read again in front of the class. I had long since learned, that if you were no good at reading, you'd never be asked to go up in front of the class. Fatso Fannon was never asked, because everyone knew he was a jennet. Martin Newell was never asked because he couldn't pronounce his words properly. When he should be saying, ask, he'd say axe; and when he should say, three; he'd say free.

For my feeble efforts, The Chicken gave me a clatter across the lug and shouted at me,

'What did I just say? What am I after telling you?'

I looked at him, but I didn't say anything. He reached for the cane and waved it right in front of my nose as he again asked, 'What did I say?'

After a great deal of hesitation I answered, 'read it again, stupid,' on purpose, so as to really annoy him.

Striking the table with the cane, he shouted,

'Lord give me patience; patience; patience! I said, read it again. Only this time read it properly or I'll warp this stick across your backside.'

'...With a parliament thus 'formed, everything is...' I began

Using the end of the cane as a guide, he lifted my left hand upwards and said, angrily, 'Put up your hand; higher where I can see it.'

I held up my hand and he gave me a fierce wallop before repeating the exercise with my other hand. I let the book fall on the floor because my fingers felt as if they were ready to drop off.

'Let's start again: and this time I want no mistakes,' he shouted. And though I was in agony I began to inwardly revel in his discomfort. If EJ Lyons could stand up to him, then so could I.

'...With a parliament thus 'formed....'

Straight away The Chicken started rapping the side of me head with his knuckles threatening to kill me. He grabbed the top of my head and held it back so that I had a job to focus. 'Say the word, re-formed,' he bellowed into my ear.

I didn't feel like saying, re-formed, but I said it anyway to shut him up.

'So; we're beginning to learn! Are we? Now, let's continue!'

'...With a parliament thus 'formed everything is easy...' I said; just to show, it was anything but easy.

Turning round, he gave his desk an unmerciful wallop with the cane sending one half of the stick flying onto the air. I knew the devil was stuck in me, I didn't care and I didn't want to give in. And now that the stick was broke I knew he could no longer wallop me. Turning back, he roared,

'You'll not leave this classroom today, tomorrow or any other day until you get the word, reformed, into your thick skull. Have I made myself clear?'

'Yes... Sir,' I mumbled half heartedly as the tears welled up in my eyes despite my best efforts to curtail them. I knew that I should have said the word reformed, right the first time, but how was I to know that The Chicken would get so cross with me. Mrs Patterson was never like that, and I couldn't understand why he had to get cross with me. I always did my lessons, not like Fatso Fannon who never did a thing in his life.

'Well then, start again,' he boomed as he took a handkerchief from his pocket and began to mop his brow.

'...With a parliament thus 'formed...'.

With two quick strides he was by the fireplace where he seized the sweeping brush and turning round he swung the handle across my back; *Wallop*, almost knocking me to the ground.

'This is your last chance. I know you're more than capable. But you're simply trying my patience,' he bellowed, picking up his glasses which had fallen off, such was his assault on me.

Thankfully, I was saved when the three o'clock bell sounded. School was finished for the day or so I thought. But The Chicken ignored the clock and said I'd have to stay until I learned to read properly. With the handle of the brush he pointed to the top of the page and asked me to continue, so I started again for what seemed like the twentieth time. Now that it had gone three o'clock I knew the whole class would blame me if they weren't let out. So I decided to read it properly, though I was barely able to hold the book: my self esteem had taken such a battering. But then I thought it would be terrible to read it properly after all the agony I'd been through. If I read the sentence correctly now, he'd wallop us every single day in an effort to get something into our thick skulls. I stood there trembling, while he waited for me.

'...With a parliament thus 'formed, everything...''

'*Wallop! Wallop*! went the brush across my back as he roared 'Get out of my sight! Out of my sight! All of you!' and threw the sweeping brush back up against the fireplace.

There was such a rush for the door I was momentarily pinned against the jamb as we made our way out. Once out in the corridor EJ, shouted, 'Fair play to you Johnny, I knew you wouldn't let us down.' And as I ran down the corridor, I could feel my shoulders aching from the walloping I got. I knew it was my own fault and I was sorry for having been so bold, but what could I do. I realized it would be a lot worse if he wrote home and told my mother about me: then I'd get a trashing far worse than anything The Chicken could ever give me.

I made up my mind there and then to be on good behaviour for the rest of the week.

As soon as I arrived home from school, my mother told me how the ambulance had whipped my father off to hospital. She wasn't the better of it yet, she said. I worked hard all evening to make sure I got all the jobs done before it got dark. Despite that, I had to light the storm lamp and hang it up in the stable so I could feed and milk the cows.

A couple of hours later shortly before I was due to go to bed I was at the table looking at a photograph of the Galway team in *The Connaught Tribune*. I was trying to identify as many of the players as possible. For no particular reason, my mother came down from her room and stood looking over my shoulder. And because she was always giving out to me about playing football when I could be doing something useful – as she liked to say herself – I turned the page quickly so she wouldn't know what I was looking at.

'Jesus, Mary and Joseph what's that on your neck?'

I jumped off the chair fearing some horrible creepy crawly was about to attack me: a spider, a lizard or a black jack.

'Will you stand still a minute?'

I stood still, waiting for her to remove whatever creepy crawly was on my neck. Instead she rolled down the collar of my shirt, gasping; 'What... in God's name happened to you?'

'What's wrong?' I asked nervously, feeling I contracted some horrible disease like ring worm or that I hadn't washed myself properly, like I was supposed to.

'It's your neck! Jesus Mary and Joseph! Who did that to you?'

'Did what?'

'Ah! What me backside! Did somebody hit you with a stick or something?'

I thought about telling a lie, but I knew I couldn't; which was just as well, as she made me take off my Jumper and shirt so she could have a properly look at me.

'What in the name of God happened to you?' she gasped. 'Did you fall or did somebody wallop you?'

I knew straight away I was in trouble. I'd have to tell the truth: the whole truth and nothing but the truth or else I'd get another walloping. And one walloping was enough as far as I was concerned. If I told the truth about how I wasn't able to read properly, I'd get a walloping anyway for not having done my homework. So no matter what, I was in for it.

'Mr Feathers hit me, because I wasn't able to read,' I said.

'And did he hit you across the shoulders?'

'He did.'

'And was it today?'

'It was,' I cried, because Mr Feathers would probably write a letter, telling her how bold I was.

'And what did he hit you with?'

'He slapped me with the cane and when that broke he hit me with the brush.'

'You mean he hit you with the sweeping brush?'

'Yes!'

'Are you sure it was because you weren't able to read; that it wasn't for something else? I'll bet my last shilling you did something wrong?' suggested my mother, incredulously, as the dimple on her chin began to twitch, signifying her rising anger.

'Noooh, I didn't,' I pleaded; shocked that she wouldn't accept my explanation.

'Tell the truth and shame the devil, because remember... sooner or later I'll find out?' she said, standing, staring at me; hands on her hips, her grey plaited hair hanging down round her shoulders.

She wasn't happy until I gave her a blow by blow account of everything that happened: her florin sized dimple getting more erratic, with each revelation.

'Well, I'll tell you one thing, I'll give that fella something to think about when I see him tomorrow,' she said, giving my shoulder a thorough examination. She helped put my shirt and jumper back on, sighing wearily, as she sat down by the fire again,

'Do you know something I'm not worth thru pence.* I'll never be the better of this day, and poor Ned above in the hospital.'

I sat at the table trying not to look, but I knew she was crying again. And as she wiped away the tears she said, 'Would you like some bread and milk or would you prefer a-mug-tea with bread and jam?'

'A mug of tea, with bread and jam, please!'

I sat at the table with my bread and jam, wondered would I be let go to school at all the following day. And what if my mother came into the school? What was she going to say to Mr Feathers? And what would my friends think? But worst of all, what would Mr Feathers say to my mother when he told her I wasn't able to read, properly? She'd probably give me an almighty walloping the minute I got home.

I went to bed but I couldn't sleep: wondering what was going to happen. My shoulder ached as I twisted and turned, despite me denying to my mother that it wasn't sore at all.

---

* Thru pence *(three pence).*

I thought perhaps, I should run away; because no matter what way I looked at it, I was to blame. But when I thought about what my mother had said, 'I'll give that fella something to think about when I see him tomorrow,' I began to feel that maybe it wasn't all my fault: that maybe I should wait and see. Running away from home sounded easy. But where would I go? Where would I sleep? And if I did run away, I could never ever come back home again because my mother would kill me, stone dead.

* * * *

There was a loud knock on the classroom door. The place fell silent as heads rose and eyes swivelled to where I caught a brief glimpse of my mother's head scarved face outside the door. Every drop of blood drained from my body as Mr Feathers dragged himself slowly out of his chair and went to the door. I was mortified to think my mother was outside, waiting to give my teacher something to think about. When Mr Feathers opened the door, he stepped outside and half pulled the door after him. For a moment everybody listened.

'Mr Feathers, I understand you're the school principal.'

'Yes, how can I help?'

'I'm Mrs O'Brien – John Paschal's mother – and I have a serious complaint to make…' she began, before the door closed fully behind Mr Feathers, drowning out whatever it was she was saying.

Amid the background of raised voices, my friends in class turned to look at me, some poking me in the ribs with their rulers to ask a multitude of questions,

'Is that your mother?' 'She's mentioned your name?' 'Is she minding you?'

I was so upset, I hissed, 'Will ye shut up; I don't know who she is! I didn't see anybody,' I said, feeling embarrassed.

The first one to react was Fatso Fannon.

'Sure, Rodgers has no mother, isn't he a pauper.'

Everyone laughed except EJ Lyons and John Keaveney. I wanted so badly to box Fannon in the mouth, but I knew I'd be in trouble if I did. If any one left a finger on Fatso he went running to the teacher. And to everyone's surprise they got a going over instead of Fatso. The classroom fell silent again as the heated exchanges outside the door grew louder.

'…If you must know, Mrs O'Brien, he's a very obstinate child. Not only that but he's backward and unwilling to…learn…anything.'

'Excuse me! Excuse me!' shouted Mrs O'Brien. 'He may be backward and unwilling but that doesn't give you the right to treat him like an animal. How dare you raise your hand to any son of mine! If he needs chastising, I'm the one that will do it. And well able I am. He's under my care and protection and nobody has any authority to raise a hand over him, except me. And another thing, if it happens again I'll come down and I'll warp this ash plant across your backside in front of the whole class. You can count yourself lucky because this is the first complaint I've ever had. And I hope it'll be the last. Out in the jungle you should be taming animals. It would be more in your line, than … than…trying to teach children with a sweeping brush. I've had no trouble in the wide earthly world with him until you came along. As a matter of fact Mrs Patterson used to say he was one of the brightest pupils in her class. And that's not saying much for you. So you can put that in your pipe and smoke it. That's all I have to say now. Never ever, let me see a mark on that fella' again or you'll be in big trouble.'

After that barrage, I wanted to bury my head as some of the scholars started asking me a whole lot of questions.

'Mrs O'Brien, is she your Grandmother? Why are you living with your Granny? Who's Mrs O'Brien?'

Before I had time to explain anything, Mr Feathers came back into the classroom, quietly closing the door behind him. He looked badly shaken. He went straight to his desk and fidgeted nervously with his books for a few moments. Then he sat down and started calling out our names while filling in the roll book.

He never looked at me for the rest of the day and I felt a great sense of pride that Mrs O'Brien had put The Chicken in his box, and that maybe he'd never slap me again. John Keaveney said, Mrs O'Brien would make a great sergeant major. I laughed at the thought that she'd look a bit like the blue drummer boy that was on the drum my father had brought me from the fair in Ballinlough.

When I came home from school Mrs O'Brien was eager to quiz me.

'Well, did Mr Feathers say anything to you?'

'No. He didn't slap anybody at all today.'

'Now look here, me buckoo, you'd better shape up and behave yourself in school. I have more things to be doing than going down to Mr Feathers to speak on your behalf. If you did what you were told in the first place, I wouldn't have had to give him an earful. You have no excuse for not doing your homework. You have the light and you can stay up all night doing your lesson if you want to.'

Listening to her, I could feel my ears burning. I knew it was a small price to pay for my pigheadedness. From that moment on I resolved to do my utmost, at home and in school.

* * * *

On Saturday morning, I went on the bus went to see my father in hospital, along with Colleen and my mother. He was on the third floor of the Regional Hospital, in St Michael's ward. The first thing to strike me was the smell of ether and the shock of seeing people on stretchers and wheelchairs and crutches: and that was before I went into the ward at all. When I went into the ward, I was taken aback by the amount of beds in what was a gigantic room; fourteen in all. Amongst them was a young boy around about my own age. He was sitting up, his head swathed in bandages, while surrounded by doctors and nurses in immaculate white uniforms.

My father was lying in bed, half asleep when I first saw him. He was very pale and drawn looking. And without his teeth, his sunken shrivelled features looked awful. His teeth were left on a locker beside his bed, along with a large bottle of Lucozade and an empty glass. Hanging on the bedrail were two get well cards; and on the wall, over his bed, the name Dr Courtney.

He shook hands with us and said, 'Ye behaved well to come up.'

Colleen and my mother gave him another bottle of Lucozade, a packet of biscuits and a half a quarter of tobacco. They sat either side of him, talking, while I causally made my way over to the window where I could view the whole city. After a while, I noticed the young boy who appeared to have only one eye looking at me. I went and said Hello. He told me he was from Connemara and that he had tripped and banged his head on the steel oar bracket of a boat, while playing. He'd cracked his cheekbone and lost the sight of his right eye and the doctors didn't know if he'd ever get it back.

After about an hour, we said goodbye to my father. On the way out, Colleen and my mother had a word with the doctors. They were waiting on results. Everything depended on the results, they said. He might have to have an operation and he might not. They were still carrying out tests. On our way down from the third floor we went to see some friends of Mrs O'Brien's in St. Bridget's ward before making our way back into the city.

A few days later my father went under an operation. He was very ill and Mrs O'Brien had to hire Harry Ryan to go up and see him while I stayed at home to look after the house. I'd already told my friends in school how he was in hospital. They were very understanding. Hardly a day went by that someone in the yard didn't run up to tell me how their father had gone in to see him, because their father and my father were friends. It was nice to be told people were going in especially to see him. Everyone in Williamstown it seemed liked my father. But Fatso Fannon spoilt everything when he came running up to me in the school yard, after my father had the operation

'Heh! I hear your auld fella's in hospital. What's wrong with him?'

I was surprised Fatso should even ask. He never struck me as the kind of fella who cared about anyone.

'I don't know,' I answered reluctantly. 'Doctor Roland said he was very sick and that's why he sent him to hospital.'

I didn't know what else to say as my father's illness was never discussed in our house. Cancer and TB was a scourge as far as Tommy the postman was concerned. But Tommy had never said anything to my mother about his illness, other than to ask how he was.

'You know well what's wrong with him,' said Fatso, but you won't tell. I heard they had to cut off one of his balls.'

I looked at him, unable to say a single word. Instead, I turned and walked away. I wandered round the school yard in a daze. What Fatso had said was the vilest thing anyone had ever said to me in my entire life. And the pain I felt in my heart for my father that day, would not go away. I kept thinking how Snowy had cut our two Bonhams with a razor blade, while my father and I had forcibly held them. Did that mean the doctors did the same thing to my father? I was numbed by the whole idea. I wanted to talk to John Keaveney about it, but I couldn't. It was too private, too personal, too painful and too delicate a subject to contemplate for one solitary moment. Yet I could not banish the vile thought from my head. That night after I'd finished my lessons, I decided to ask my mother what was wrong with my father. 'What's wrong with Daddy? Why is he in Hospital? '

'Why are you asking?'

'Because…because…well… I just want to know.'

'Well, you know Doctor Roland sent him to hospital; don't you?'

'I do.'

'They said it might be… cancer. They decided to operate, in case he'd get any worse. Look! Why don't you go to bed now, like a good lad: you've to be up early in the morning to help me? Daddy will be alright… and home for Christmas, with the help of God,' she said, as tears filled her eyes. Pulling a handkerchief from her sleeve, she asked, 'Would you like me to put on some milk and bread for you?'

'No thanks,' I said, feeling there might be an element of truth in what Fatso had said. But I couldn't dare breathe a word of it to anyone. That was all she said about my father. I was still none the wiser. It was like every question I'd ever asked. There were no answers.

A week later, my father arrived home in an ambulance. He looked so weak and frail looking, I was afraid he might die. His appearance reminded me of the time he'd brought me with him to a corpse-house: and I had to stand with him, beside the coffin while we prayed. But all I could do was look at the grotesque features of the man in the coffin. Now, I thought my father looked like that and I didn't like it. He looked worse now than when I saw him in the hospital, I thought.

But then the day the school closed for the Christmas holidays, I came home to see my father pottering round the kitchen. Pretty soon he was in and out, doing odd little jobs and I knew he'd be alright. It was probably the nicest Christmas present I could have asked for, seeing him going in and out around the house. Yet, Christmas wasn't the same. From early on my mother had made it clear that there was to be no Santa.

'You're too old now for that sort-a-thing. I'm surprised at you: a growing lad like you. Santa's only for children. I'll bet Una's not expecting Santa; and she's younger than you,' she said, as she stoked up the fire beneath the Christmas pudding.

'I might get a parcel from Bridie?' I said, living in hope.

'I don't know whether you will or not! She mightn't have bothered sending you anything. She might have been expecting us to go in and see her for Christmas. Did you tell her Daddy was in hospital?'

'I did.'

'Well, in that case we'll have to wait and see. Maybe we'll arrange to see her in the New Year: that's if we're still alive.'

The thing I wanted more than anything else for Christmas was a pair of football boots and a pair of maroon and white socks. Now it began to dawn on me that I might not get anything at all. I sighed with deep resignation. I had been writing to Bridie for years; yet I had never laid eyes on her. And the more I thought about it the more confusing it got. She always signed her letters, from your mother Bridie. Somehow I felt, that had to be a lie. Mrs O'Brien was my mother because I was living with her for as long as I could remember: although somewhere at the back of my mind I had a vague recollection of having played with other children. But I could never ever remember living with Bridie: so how could she be my mother? And if by chance she was my mother too, it must be because they were twins, I thought.

For years I'd been told, at home and in school, that babies were found under a bush or head of cabbage. But this perception had begun to change rapidly. Everyone in our class knew that Nurse Finnegan and Nurse Geraghty secretly brought babies to people's houses in the middle of the night. Now I was struck by an absurd notion. If a woman wanted twins, did nurse Finnegan bring them to her? And if she did, where would she manage to get them? There were twin brothers in our school and they looked the same. They wore the same clothes, the same shoes, the same everything. As well as that they went everywhere together. That made me think Bridie and Mrs O'Brien must be twins. If they were, it would explain everything. But then why didn't they live together? To put me out of my misery I decided to ask John Keaveney.

'You know how babies are supposed to be found under a head of cabbage?'

'Yeah,' said John, questioningly, his eager eyes weighing me up.

'Then why is Fatso Fannon going round telling everyone that a nurse comes in the middle of the night and cuts the baby out of a woman's belly with a knife?'

'Yeah, he told me the same thing, but it's not true.'

'I know, but where do twins come from?

'I don't know. But I know where ordinary babies come from. Fatso told me the same story, but it's a lie. If what Fatso told me was true, the woman would bleed to death.'

'That's exactly what I thought,' I said, eager to show that we were on the same wavelength.

'When I told my brother Billy what Fatso had said, he laughed his head off. Billy knows everything about girls, but he wouldn't tell me anything unless I swore not to tell anyone else. He said that when a girl gets married she has to sleep with her husband for a year. And when they're in bed together the husband puts his willy into the girl the same as a bull does to a cow,' he whispered. 'The only difference is the man has to kiss the girl at the same time as he's putting his willy in. Then, after a year a baby will come to the woman in the bed. That's what he told me.'

'Kiss her?' I said, alarmed at the idea. 'God, I'd hate to have to do that. It's bad enough having to put your willy into them without having to kiss them as well. But how does the baby come to them after a year?' I asked, more perplexed than ever.

'That I don't know! I asked Billy that too, but he wouldn't tell me. So then I asked him, had he ever kissed a girl and he said, he had, lots of times and that it was brilliant. He reckoned it was nicer than drinking porter or smoking or anything like that. He said it made your heart go fast and sent a tingle through your body, like an electric shock. He said he tried kissing the last girl he met at the dance but she wouldn't let him. She kept telling him to slow down. He said she was stupid anyway because when he met her again a few weeks later, she said the same thing. Billy said, at the rate she was going on, it would take him seven years before he could ask her to marry him. And if she said no, then he'd have to start all over again. He's looking for a new girl now, so he can marry her: that way, he'll be able to kiss her every night.'

'Yuk. I wouldn't like to kiss a girl. I'd talk to her and everything but I wouldn't kiss her,' I said.

'Neither would I. But the funny thing Johnny is, when I told my oldest sister Philomena what Billy had said, she said he was making it up, to suit himself. She said what really happens is, when a boy meets a girl at a dance he has to show her how good he is at dancing and talking and everything. And if she likes him, she might meet him again at the next dance. After a few months she might let him kiss her. Then, after seven years if they still liked each other, they might get engaged and then get married. A year after that a baby will come to them in the bed. But there will be no baby unless he's a good kisser: and they have to kiss every night. When I told Philomena what Billy had said, about putting his willy into a girl, she got mad and called me an up-start. She said it had nothing at all to do with a man's willy: that it was all in Billy's head: that he'd be better off stirring his tea with it.'

When John Keaveney said that, the two of us laughed.

'But wait until you hear what I said to Philomena: I said his willy can't be in his head, it's in his trousers.'

Again the two of us laughed. But with a dubious expression he frowned, 'Now I don't know which of them to believe…I think my sister might be right. Remember the carnival? That must be why they have carnivals. Where else could you meet a girl to show her how good you were dancing or anything unless you met them at the dance?'

I agreed with everything John had told me. It was the most exciting news I'd heard in a long time. But the part that really interested me was the bit about having to put your willy into a girl every night for a year. The more I thought about that bit, the more convinced I became that it was true. After all, wasn't that how every living thing was created. The bull puts his willy – or rod – into a cow, while they were both standing up. The rooster did it while the hens were sitting on the ground. But the strangest of all were the ducks and the geese; they did it in the water, otherwise there would be no gosling or young ducks. So, it made perfect sense that a man had to put his willy into a girl, in bed, where no one could see them. The odd one out I thought was the jack ass. He was wicked altogether. He'd go through hell and earth to get his long black tool – as we called it in school – into a mare, even though she didn't want him to. One minute she'd be grazing away in a field and the next thing, a stray Jack ass going along the road would suddenly break into the field and go after her. She'd start running round the field, kicking her hind legs at him in an effort to get away. And if all else failed, she'd break out of the field and go running off down the road. But he'd follow her to the ends of the earth until he had her cornered somewhere. There he'd plunge his long black tool into her, sating his desire, before getting off her. Then he'd settle down for a few minutes before jumping up on her again and the funny thing about it was, this time the mare would stand there for him, ready and waiting. She's stand and let him do it as often as he wanted. And in no time at all the two of them would be palsy-walsy, grazing away on the side of the road.

Of course, I'd been witness to all this for as long as I could remember. But like my friends in school I never for one moment thought this reproductive process could apply to us humans. For years we'd been taught by Mrs Patterson and Mr Feathers that we'd been created by God, in his own likeness. Mankind was a class apart, from every living creature on this earth. We were human while every other living thing was inhuman, incapable of thinking for itself. When God created man, he gave him a brain with the power to think for himself. We were masters of all we surveyed; we were superior to every living thing. And it all started, the Catechism and the teachers said, when God took a rib from Adam's side and created Eve. But they never told us where it finished.

Thankfully, John and I were beginning to figure it out for ourselves.

After John Keaveney's extraordinary revelation, we updated each other, every minute, every hour, every day. We learnt that Nurse Geraghty and Nurse Finnegan helped to deliver the babies the same as my father and Tom Farrell had helped the cows to deliver calves. But what really knocked us for six was when John's brother Billy claimed that some girls had babies before they were married at all.

'That has to be a lie,' I said, as we discussed it during our lunch break.

'Why?' asked John, his bulging eyes probing the depths of my brain.

'To have a baby, a girl has to go to a dance, meet a boy and then she gets married. If she isn't married how can she have a baby when she hasn't got a husband to put his willy in?'

'Begod you're right! I never thought of that. You know something, Johnny, if you had brains you'd be dangerous,' he laughed, as we both ran across the school yard and started playing football.

The days leading up to Christmas we had lots of well wishers calling to our house, some to see how my father was. Though well on the mend, he was far from his old self. Mrs O'Brien treated everyone by giving them a bottle of stout or a glass of sherry. On Christmas Eve, Snowy brought Ned a bottle of Poitín which he said came from Connemara. Poitín was said to be a mountain dew that had a kick like a mule. But when I sniffed it I thought it smelt the same as the whiskey we had above in the room. Occasionally, my father heated a drop of Poitín in a saucepan for himself before going to bed.

Christmas Eve came round and when I still hadn't received a parcel from Bridie, I was very, very disappointed. It had never happened before. Why hadn't she sent me anything I wondered? Maybe it was because I hadn't gone up to see her, or else she hadn't received my letter. I just didn't know.

I couldn't wait for Christmas to be over and for Mrs O'Brien to make new arrangements for us to go to Galway, to see Bridie. It was the only thing I had to look forward to now: I'd been kept waiting long enough. I just couldn't wait to see this mysterious woman: the source of so many unanswered questions.

Chapter Twenty One

Meeting my mother for the first time
1959

It was my twelfth birthday. Bridie had sent me a pair of football boots, with maroon and white socks. And as I tried them on Mrs O'Brien said,

'I don't know in the name of God who you look like; 'Mongan' the chimney sweep or 'Sweeney' the pot mender. *Them boots,* are ten times too big for you: and as for *the socks,* they might come in handy when you're feeding the cattle during the winter. Why don't you take them off now like a good lad and put them away and try on the jumper, until I see what it's like.'

My heart sank the moment she criticized the boots and socks. I couldn't wait to try them out on the ball alley field. I knew if I was allowed to wear them I'd look like the big lads on the Williamstown team: that I'd be able to play better than anybody else; and with any bit of luck I'd be picked to play for Williamstown and someday maybe Galway. There was nothing in the world I wanted more than to play football for Galway. I wanted to be able to score goals and points like Sean Purcell and Frank Stockwell and Joe Young. If I could do that, then I knew I'd be picked to play in Croke Park and if that happened I might get a chance to go on a tour of America.

While I was examining the boots and socks down in the room, my mother shouted down to me,

'Come on, come on, smarten yourself up and don't be dilly-dallying down there. You know there are jobs to be done.'

I put the parcel away quickly because I knew I'd have to get all the jobs done if I was to have any chance of playing that evening.

But by the time I had finished everything and done all the jobs around the place, it was too late to go playing football. Not only that but Mrs O'Brien made me sit down and write to Bridie, to thank her for the parcel and then I had to do my homework. And because my father had gone visiting, there wasn't a sound in the house except the ticking of the clock as my mother sat by the fire knitting. Then, out of the blue, she said, 'Now that you're getting bigger your father is going to buy a donkey and cart so that you'll be able to work on your own. He's not getting any younger and I'm not getting any livelier. You should be well able to tackle up a donkey and cart and bring home the turf on your own.'

My father went to the fair in Castlerea where he bought a nice mare donkey. The donkey was already trained and it was easy to hitch her up to the cart whenever I had to go working. The first time I drove the donkey and cart, I had to go down to Harry Ryan's for a bag of flour and a bag of Indian meal. After that, I went working everywhere with her. The two of us got on fine and in no time at all I was racing the donkey and cart up and down to Johnston's, Gort Mór and Pairc Nuá, carrying barrels of water, stakes and wire as well as putting top dress out on the land.

In the meantime, I kept writing to Bridie in Galway and she kept asking me to go in and see her: even offering to pay Mrs O'Brien the bus fare. I could never make any promises to Bridie as nothing had been said in our house since our Christmas visit had been cancelled. Instead I had to continuously fob her off with lame excuses.

Then as I was writing a letter to her, for the umpteenth time, Mrs O'Brien said,

'I was thinking, one of these days I might hire a hackney and bring you up to Galway to see your mother. You know she never stops asking. And it would be an ease to get it over and done with.'

I loved the idea of going to Galway again, especially in a hackney to see my mother Bridie for the first time.

'Will we be coming home from Galway again or will we be staying there?'

'Arrah musha God help you! Is it what you think we'd be able to stay in a hotel and we not having two pennies to rub together? You can thank your lucky stars I'm bringing you up at all. It's just that I'm fed up listening to her asking, and I'm tired making excuses. I'm trying to arrange it at the moment. But there's no knowing whether the nuns will let us in or not. They said, if I wrote to the Reverend Mother and the Bishop and put in a request, they'd consider it. I did that before but sure I had to cancel it on account of your father being sick. Then again, there's no knowing whether they'll let us in or not, after they turned us away the last time.'

I finished writing the letter and then asked,

'Is it all right if I bring my football boots down to the field near the lake?'

She looked at me for a moment before giving her answer.

'Oh dear oh dear: I suppose it is. But don't stay too long. You know it'll be dark shortly.'

I went down to my room, grabbed my new boots and socks and walked out the door, as lackadaisically as I could in order not to arouse suspicion.

Once out the door, I shot down the road as fast as I could. I knew I wasn't supposed to go down the town but I kept running anyway. I could hear my school friends shouting in the ball alley field which meant there was a game on. I knew they'd have two teams picked, and that none of them might want me. But if I was lucky, one team might be a man short and that team would kill just to get me on their side. I jumped over the ditch and shouted at the lads. Matthew Deane looked over and screamed 'We want Rodgers! We want Rodgers!'

All of a sudden, the game stopped and the players started arguing about which team I should play with. But the team with six lads had no argument at all because Matthew Deane's team only had five. I threw myself down and put on my socks and pulled on my new football boots. I wrapped the laces around the soles of the boots like I'd seen the big lads doing and I ran out onto the field as if I was floating on air.

After about half an hour's play and much arguing, both sides agreed it was a draw. I turned and rushed home without changing my boots because it was almost pitch dark. But I didn't care. I was so happy to have tried out my new boots and to have scored three points. I knew then it was only a matter of time before I'd be picked to play for Williamstown.

* * * *

My mother and father were having strong words down in the kitchen as I lay in bed. I sat up listening. My mother seemed very angry. She was talking about bringing me up to Galway to see Bridie and was telling my father she needed to buy me a new suit before bringing me anywhere. But my father said,

'Isn't the suit'een he has; plenty good enough? And where's the point in going to all that expense when the nuns mightn't even let ye in?'

I knew then my mother was planning in earnest to bring me up to see Bridie. For the hundredth time I lay in bed trying to figure it all out. I recalled my last visit to Galway and how they had rung the door bell and how an elderly nun answered the door and how Colleen and my mother had stood whispering and talking for ages and how the nun had said she was sorry.

But what did it all mean? Why didn't the nun let us in to see Bridie? Maybe she wasn't at home, I thought. Yet I knew in my heart that Bridie's very existence was somehow shrouded in secrecy.

Two weeks later, after I had got my first full length suit, Harry Ryan's hackney pulled into the street.

'Will you be all right on your own do you think?' asked my mother as she looked at my father, who was slow enough getting up from the table.

'Ah, I'll be alright. Let ye go if ye're going,' he replied gruffly, following us out to where Harry held the door of the car open. Mrs O'Brien went round to the front and sat in beside Harry while I hopped into the back. On the way, we stopped off at Colleen's house to pick her up; then we hit the road for Galway.

'I hope Ned will be all right… on his own?' remarked Mrs O'Brien, as we settled down. I thought he looked pale yesterday. What did you think?'

'I thought he was alright. He's probably a bit tired, said Colleen.

'I know. But he's still not himself. I'd be afraid anything would happen to him while we're gone,' replied Mrs O'Brien thoughtfully.

'Mammy, he'll be alright! Stop worrying about him,' replied Colleen. 'Snowy said he'd call in to see him, on his way home from the town.'

'Hmm, the town!' grumbled my mother.

It was the first time I'd worn a full length trousers. They felt weird and prickly and uncomfortable around my legs. It was like having a coarse blanket wrapped around you all the time and I didn't like it. But the feeling of sitting in Harry Ryan's new car was something else. There was a lovely fragrance off the brown leather upholstery, like when I'd polish the chairs at home on Saturday mornings.

When I first sat into the car, I thought it was a marvellous feeling as we bumped our way out through the village. I thought it was better than the spin I'd had in Fr Keaveney's car. But, it was nothing compared to the feeling as we drove along the main road. The dashboard was gleaming as I watched the red needle on the speedometer climb higher and higher. Soon we were doing fifty. I would never have known we were moving at all except that the stone walls and fields kept flying by the window.

In Tuam we had to slow down, because there were a lot of scholars walking across the road towards the Cathedral. Some of the boys wore maroon and white jerseys as they carried their football boots slung over their shoulders. We sat looking out as the last of them crossed safely under the supervision of the teachers and then we started to drive on again.

'John, do you remember when you were in the Home… in Tuam?' asked my mother looking back at me.

I was completely baffled. The question seemed to have bounced off the top of her head and made no sense at all to me, so I ignored it, fearing I must have misheard what she said. When I didn't reply she added questioningly, 'Surely to God you remember the cathedral? You would have gone to Mass in the cathedral.'

I still didn't respond because I didn't know what's she was talking about. Colleen who was sitting next to me, said,

'John, do you not remember where you were born?'

I shook my head. No. I didn't like it when people said strange things and I didn't know what they were talking about.

'You were born in Tuam: not a stone's throw from the cathedral. Did you not know that? Do you not remember being in the children's Home? Mammy and I came up here one day and picked you out; and two lovely nuns brought you to Lakeland. Do you not remember?'

'Again I shook my head. No. My mind was in turmoil. I couldn't remember anything. To me, home was a very strange word. I thought home was where I lived with my mother Mrs O'Brien. But there seemed to be another home in Galway called the Magdalene Home where Bridie lived. Now Mrs O'Brien wanted to know if I could remember being in the Home in Tuam.

When I didn't say anything Mrs O'Brien turned to ask,

'John, are you alright? You're awfully quiet. You haven't said a word since you got up this morning and that's not like you.'

'I'm alright,' I answered, greatly embarrassed. I could feel my two ears burning with the shame of it all.

I knew I was a boarded out boy like some of the other scholars in school. But if Colleen and Mrs O'Brien came to Tuam to pick me out: what was I doing there in the first place? I had long suspected Bridie was my real mother because we shared the same name but that didn't necessarily mean that she was.

'Ah sure, he probably doesn't remember a thing,' said Colleen. Maybe it's just as well. I'm sure it wasn't the nicest place in the world.' And turning to look at me again, she added, 'you must have found it strange when you came to Lakeland, having to leave all your friends behind?'

Again I looked at her, my mouth half open. I wanted to ask what she meant, but with Mrs O'Brien and Harry Ryan listening, I couldn't ask. And though I often considered asking Colleen why I had two mothers, I could never pick up the courage, because with Snowy gone and she farming and trying to look after four children she always seemed too busy.

Soon we were admiring scores of nomadic travellers in beautiful horse drawn caravans making their way clip clop, clip clop along the side of the road, towards the city. As well as that I could see scores of men working in fields while horse and donkey carts rumbled up and down country lanes and by-roads with little jags of hay and straw.

When we arrived in Eyre Square, we pulled up outside the Odean Hotel. Mrs O'Brien made arrangements for Harry to collect us outside the same hotel at four o'clock'

'I could have asked him to drop us off outside the Magdalene but I didn't want him to know where we were going. Though he'd soon put two and two together, I'm sure' said Mrs O'Brien as she watched the hackney car make its way around the Fair Green. 'What time is it, I wonder, I never thought to ask him?'

'According to that clock across the way it's only half past eleven. Maybe we'll have a look around the shops first?' suggested Colleen.

After a brief look around the shops, we made our way back across Eyre

Square and began walking down College Road. It took us about five minutes to reach the long wall that had the two doors in it. Again Colleen pressed the door bell while I waited anxiously to see what would happen. While we were waiting, I glanced across at the row of neat red bricked houses. On a corner of the end house nearest to me was the name Magdalene Terrace on a decorative green name plate. Suddenly I heard the mahogany door beside us being unlocked on the inside and a small angelic looking nun peered out at us; and in a barely audible voice said,

'How can I help you?'

'We've come to see Bridie Rodgers. She's expecting us,' said Colleen.

'Who shall I say is calling?'

'Mrs O'Brien.'

'Do you have an appointment?'

'Yes we have. The Rev Mother, Sr Antonia is expecting us,' piped up Mrs O'Brien, lest she be fobbed off again.

'Oh... yes... she's expecting you,' said the young nun after a momentary pause. She opened the door fully and beckoned us in, making sure to bolt the door behind us.

As we followed her through the oak door, the first thing I noticed were numerous little gardens with floral beds and footpaths zigzagging their way right round an elaborate three story building in front of us. To the right of the building were two winding paths one of which led up a steep incline to a grotto of the Blessed Virgin. And immediately behind that again were what appeared to be two graveyards: one with numerous small, white painted crosses: the other with black painted crosses. As soon as we entered the front door of the main building, the young nun asked us to wait in the hall.

The wooden floor was dark stained and highly polished; and hanging on the left was a large picture of Our Lord. Underneath the picture was a small half moon, pie crusted table, with a bowl of fresh flowers. Either side of the table were two spoon backed chairs with red upholstered seats. And hanging directly over the chairs were two small wooden crucifixes. On the right hand side were two doors, amid a number of religious pictures right down the hall. The door nearest us had a small glass window that looked like an office: the second one further down was a mahogany panelled door. After waiting a while, the young nun came back accompanied by the Rev. Mother. She introduced us to the Rev. Mother, Sr. Antonia who was a stout elderly figure with large purple hands. After welcoming us, the Rev. Mother invited us into the parlour which was the second door on the right. When we went into the room I was immediately struck by the grandeur and splendour of the surroundings. A large round mahogany table stood in the centre of the highly polished wooden floor. And in the centre of the table was a huge bowl of apples, oranges, pears and bananas. All around the walls were numerous religious pictures and a large blood stained crucifix. On the marbled fire place were numerous little religious statues and wooden carvings. When I saw the mountain of fruit on the table it made me hungry. I wanted to reach out and grab an orange an apple and a banana. The fruit reminded me of a Jesuit priest who'd come to our school, asking us to seriously consider joining the Jesuit Order so that we could help bring the faith to South Africa. In South Africa, there was no need for money, he said. The country was like a great hanging basket with an abundance of fruit everywhere. The biggest problem they had in South Africa, was, what to do with it? While at the same time the people were starved of religious faith and belief. And if you were a non-believer in South Africa, then there was no hope at all for you.

While I waited along with Colleen and Mrs O'Brien, thinking over what the Jesuit priest had said, several nuns gathered in the hall and crowded round the doorway. Then a woman appeared in their midst and came into the room. The woman was introduced to Mrs O'Brien and Colleen and without waiting to be formally introduced to me she came towards me with outstretched arms, crying out,

'Paschal dear, how are you?'

I was totally lost for words. And though Mrs O'Brien had warned me to be on my best behaviour and to speak when spoken to I was unable to grasp what was happening. How could I speak when a woman I'd never seen before was hugging me and squeezing the life blood from my body, while everyone was staring at me? It was the most embarrassing moment of my life. No one had ever grabbed me and kissed me like that before. It was like a violation of my personal being. Holding me at arms length, Bridie looked at me proudly and exclaimed, 'Paschal, you look wonderful! You're so tall! And you look so smart in your new suit and everything. Aren't you going to speak to me? I'm your mother.'

I didn't know what to say. In a way I felt shocked and disappointed. Bridie was the complete opposite of what I had expected. Undoubtedly she was tall and thin with black curly hair that was as sleek and as shiny as a raven's wing, but it was her complexion that took my breath away. She was so frail and ghost like she frightened me. I had expected her to be like… well…like Colleen, maybe. But in truth I didn't know what to expect. She wasn't anything like what she looked like in the photographs, I thought.

When I didn't reply, Bridie again asked, 'Aren't you going to speak to me?'

But what could I say to a woman I'd never seen before. The whole episode was so embarrassing I wanted to die. And for the first time I regretted not having run away from home when this mother thing first reared its ugly head. Instead, I stood rooted to the ground and shook my head,

'No.'

'Aren't you going to say Hello to your own mother? Paschal! Paschal! I'm your mother,' pleaded Bridie again.

But I still said nothing. I dropped my head to avoid the prying eyes. Everybody was looking at me as if I had done something wrong. Again I mumbled,

'No.'

All I wanted was to scoot out the door. And if it hadn't been so crowded with nuns peering in over each other's shoulder I would certainly have made a run for it.

'Won't you say Hello to Bridie,' urged Mrs O'Brien, in a tone of voice that suggested I'd better speak up or face the consequences.

'I stood staring at Mrs O'Brien for a moment and could clearly see the disgust etched on her face, so I looked at Bridie, still holding my hand; and in a barely audible voice, I said,

'Hello.'

'Aw!' exclaimed the nuns in unison.

'Of course he can talk? If he's anything like you Bridie, he'll talk for Ireland. Who knows, he might grow up to be a priest?' suggested the Rev. Mother, warmly.

For some reason everyone laughed.

'Imagine! We'd have our very own, Fr Paschal,' added one of the nuns

'Lord wouldn't it be wonderful?' said Mrs O'Brien, proudly. 'If that ever happened, I think I'd die happy.'

'Shall we leave them for a while?' suggested the Rev. Mother, turning to the nuns.

Once everyone was out of the room and the door closed, Bridie put me sitting at the table and sat down beside me. And in a soft gentle tone of voice she told me how much she had missed me: that it was the greatest day of her life. But I wasn't really listening. It was all too much for me. It wasn't until she put her arm round my shoulder and brought me on a tour of the picturesque grounds that I began to see her as she was, for the first time. She wore a long sleeved cream coloured silk blouse, a three quarter length, navy pleated skirt and a pair of black patent shoes. But that could not hide the fact that she was extremely pale.

While walking the picturesque grounds, I could see nothing but little groups of women, here there and everywhere. They were all dressed in immaculate white gowns and caps and looked like nurses. Some were standing, watching, from a distance: some were walking in twos, threes, and fours along the main footpath that ran round the entire grounds. One of the main paths led directly to a small Church where Bridie made me join her for a moment in thanksgiving before coming back out again to kneel at the grotto of the Blessed Virgin which was the main feature in the garden. Growing hither and thither amongst the rocks surrounding the grotto were clumps of purple flowers bordered by delicate looking red and white daisies. And over hanging the Blessed Virgin like some giant umbrella, was a huge sycamore tree.

From the rear of the main building was a path leading to the two graveyards which were set on high ground close to the boundary wall. The two graveyards were enclosed within knee high, cast iron railings. The small white painted crosses carried the names of deceased penitents; but I did not know what the word meant: while all the black painted crosses carried the names of deceased nuns.

Seeing so many graves sent a shiver down my spine. I thought perhaps the Magdalene Home must be some kind of a hospital; and the word 'sanatorium' sprang to mind, though I didn't know what that word meant either. I had often heard Tommy the post telling Mrs O'Brien that such and such a one was in the sanatorium and I was convinced that this was such a place: though at the back of my mind was the notion that Bridie had told me she was working in a laundry. Was this one and the same place I wondered? Maybe the Magdalene Home was a sanatorium. After all, Bridie was so thin and frail looking, she must be ill, I thought. And yet she had such a soothing temperament, it had a calming effect on me. On closer inspection, I saw she had beautiful brown eyes with extraordinarily high cheek bones that gave her a mediterranean appearance. But nothing could disguise the fact that her extremely high forehead and taut sallow complexion gave her a ghostly appearance.

All over the picturesque grounds women in white gowns tended the gardens, planting flowers and bulbs. Bridie did not speak to them but gave them a cursory nod. She didn't have time to talk to them, she said. She wanted to bring me back to meet her friends before they all went back in to work. On our way, Bridie took out a small leather purse and gave me the gift of a brand new one pound note. I had never had so much money in all my life. I was overcome with happiness. I realized then she was the same person who'd been writing to me and sending me parcels for years and years.

And when she suddenly put her arm around me and gave me a gentle hug, I was less frightened by her appearance, though I still couldn't grasp what the whole Bridie episode was about.

As we walked towards the back of the main building again, I could see scores of women, standing gawking. Some of them came forward to meet us. They were laughing and jostling each other excitedly as they began to give me, penny bars, bags of sweets and chocolate bars. Bridie introduced me to her friends Julie and Noreen, and Josephine and Lilly and a whole lot of other girls. Julie told Bridie I was the spitting image of her which seemed to make her very happy. But before I knew what was happening Bridie was approached by two of the nuns and told the visit was over. It was time for us to go they said. The nuns escorted the two of us into the main building and down the corridor to the parlour once more. There, we were treated to tea and cake and biscuits, while the Rev Mother continued her conversation with Mrs O'Brien and Colleen outside the door. While they were talking, Bridie who was sitting beside me gave me a hug and said, 'Paschal I want you to know I'll be thinking of you and praying for you every day.'

As soon as we'd finished our tea, the Rev. Mother stuck her head in and said,

'Bridie dear, I'm afraid time is up: they have to go home now.'

Outside the parlour door, Bridie, hugged me once more and said,

'Paschal love, thanks for keeping in touch and for coming in to see me. I don't know what I'd do if it wasn't for your letters. Won't you promise to keep writing? And some day please God, I'll make it all up to you?'

I promised I'd keep writing, whilst one of the nuns then led Bridie back down the corridor where she stood and waved, tearfully, one last time. On reaching the main exit the Rev. Mother and one of her assistants unlocked the small mahogany door and let us out onto the street. And with a cheery wave they said good bye, then slammed the door and bolted it behind us.

Walking down the hill towards Eyre Square Mrs O'Brien said to Colleen,

'Well…that was something! We better say nothing now because magunnagh is listening. We may as well go down to Shop Street and do a bit of shopping. We might get a hackney later to bring us to the hospital, to see Delia Tully.'

I knew straight away the word magunnagh was a reference to me. It made me feel uncomfortable. It meant they couldn't say anything about Bridie in my presence in case I'd take offence or convey it back to Bridie.

'Yeah, that's a good idea!' said Colleen, as the three of us walked back down the hill towards the city centre. 'I'd like to get a few things for the kids. And if we have time, I'd like to go to an electrical shop, to see a television.'

Mrs O'Brien stopped in her tracks and looked at Colleen as if appalled by the idea.

'A television? Well Jesus, Mary and Joseph, what do you want to look at a television for? Is it what you're thinking about buying one?'

'No, No,' replied Colleen, slipping her hand into Mrs O'Brien arm to coax her along. 'I'd just like to see what they look like. Máirtín was telling me they have one where he's staying in Manchester. I'd love to see what one looks like.'

'Troth 'tis far from televisions and radios and bathrooms you were reared. It would be more in your line to finish painting the house.'

'Oh come on, come on, forget about it! Forget I opened my mouth! We'll go into Anthony Ryan's and see has he any bargains,' said Colleen, sighing in exasperation as I tagged along taking in all the sights. And though the three of us went from one place to another I could not drive Bridie's parting out of my head. Why was she crying? Why couldn't she simply have come home with us, to Williamstown, I wondered? Why?

Chapter Twenty Two

On our way home I made my mind up I'd ask Mrs O'Brien about Bridie. At least I now knew what Bridie looked like, but I wanted to learn more.

The following day she was setting the table while my father was gone to the forge to shoe the horse. I was churning the butter – or making the churn for her as she liked to call it – in the middle of the kitchen. Now was as good a time as any to ask about Bridie I thought, before my father came home and we had to go turning hay. As well as that, she was in good humour. That was important I thought, before I opened my mouth. After I'd finished churning, I brought in a bucket of turf, while she was draining and salting the butter. With a great deal of trepidation I finally broached the subject

'Mammy, if Bridie in Galway is my mother, why can't she come down here and live with us?'

Stopping to take a deep breath, Mrs O'Brien hesitated for a moment before turning to look at me.

'Aaaah! Why do you think? We've hardly enough room in the house for ourselves: never mind Bridie! Even if we had, I don't think we'd stick it long under the one roof.'

I hadn't thought about that. But encouraged by the fact that she was prepared to talk about her at all, I replied,

'But couldn't she live in some other house… maybe Colleen's? Her house is a lot bigger than ours?

'I don't know whether she could or not! Besides, it's a long story. You're too young a grá to understand anything like that. When you're older, maybe sixteen or so, you'll understand better.'

I felt dumbstruck. This was not the answer I was expecting. I was annoyed that I'd have to wait until I was finished school and maybe working in Galway before I'd know anything. When Mrs O'Brien saw I wasn't impressed, she asked,

'Why are you asking?'

I thought about that for a moment, shrugged my shoulders as I held the turf bucket and said, 'Because, because… I'd like to know. I'll be too old to ask when I'm sixteen. I might be… gone to America or Galway and I still won't know.'

The shock on Mrs O'Brien's face was unbelievable. She left down the butter spades and rested her hands on her broad hips as the dimple on her chin began to quiver.

'Well Glory be to God Almighty, I've heard it all now. Soon enough you'll know: and when you do, I hope you'll be man enough to deal with it. What in the name of God put that question into your head: that's what I'd like to know? Besides, what would you be doing in America; and plenty-a-work here for the likes of you – if only you'd do it? Is it what you think you can go swanning* off to Galway or America like that, with no money in your pocket or no job to go to: is it?

Again I hadn't thought about that.

'I dunno,' I answered, humbly.

'*I dunno*,' she replied sarcastically. 'Lord but you were always a great one for questions. Well I'll give you a few answers fair and square; the rest you'll have to figure out for yourself. The first thing you have to learn, me bucko, is that you can't go anywhere without a trade; not even up to Galway – or around Williamstown for that matter. No one in the world wants you if you haven't got a trade. There are too many latchicos** around Williamstown as it is; and I don't want you growing up to be another. Even if you stayed at home and worked the land, it would be a nice thing to have a trade: in case things didn't work out. Why do you think Bridie is living and working above in Galway? Why? I'll tell you why. It's because she has no qualifications and nobody wants her: that's why. And unless you pull yourself together and learn all you can, nobody will want you either. Have you got that now, have you?' she asked, glowering at me.

'I have,' I muttered, sorry that I'd opened my mouth.

Then, changing to a more conciliatory tone she added, 'Why don't you finish bringing in the turf now, like a good lad. And when you have that done you might bring me down two buckets of water from the well; and be ready to go to Johnston's when Daddy comes home.'

I could have cried when she mentioned the land. I just didn't want to stay at home and work the land. I had seen Snowy and numerous other spalpeens*** home on holidays with their new suits and well oiled hair; driving motor bikes and gleaming cars. All I wanted was to be like them. I didn't want to be turning hay below in Johnston's and cleaning out the pigs' cabin for the rest of my life. All I wanted was to play football and to be a famous cyclist. Nevertheless, I thought about what Mrs O'Brien had said. I had often heard her using the word latchico* and already knew it meant a good for nothing so and so, or layabout. And I didn't want to be a layabout, above all ease.

I went out the front door, the bucket in my hand, but with an ache in my heart. I was still none the wiser as far as Bridie was concerned. I still knew

* Swanning *(wandering off)*.
** Latchico *(layabout)*.
*** Spalpeens *(holidaymakers home from England)*.

nothing. Bridie's existence was somehow shrouded in secrecy. I got a horrid feeling that I was in essence the son of a bitch and that my existence had something and everything to do with the words pauper and bastard. I knew that a pauper was a person who had nothing: and that a bastard was a bad person. But however hard I tried I couldn't understand how those words could apply to me.

I hung around the house waiting for my father to come home. When I saw him, he was walking with his head down as if he were a thousand miles away. As soon as he let the horse into the field and came into the house, I had an uneasy feeling something was wrong as I watched him sit by the fire as if to warm himself.

Looking at me he said. 'Maybe you'll go down and start turning the hay on your own. Somehow or other… I'm not in great form. I was thinking maybe I'd go as far as the doctor before I go down to Johnston's

'Jesus, Mary and Joseph, is it coming at you again?' asked Mrs O'Brien, anxiously as she came in from the back kitchen. 'I knew you weren't well this morning when you got up and I told you not to go to the forge, to leave it for another day. But no; you had to go. And now you're not able to wag. Is it your stomach that's at you or is it that you're not feeling well?'

'Ah…I'm a bit out of sorts, that's all,' answered my father, without any great enthusiasm. And for the second time in my life, I began to feel as though my world was falling apart. If anything should happen to my father I didn't know what I'd do. 'Can't John go down… and make a start. I'll join him later,' he added, looking at my mother for approval.

'Well faith then, you'll do no such thing! You'll go straight up to bed. John would you ever run down to Dr Roland and tell him Daddy isn't well. Tell him I sent you down. And if he's out on a sick call, leave a message with whoever is in the dispensary, for him to call up as soon as he can. Hop on the bike now like a good lad, and don't be long.'

The following day my father was back in hospital. Dr Roland had come out to the house and arranged for an ambulance. Mrs O'Brien and I had to turn the hay on our own two or three times that week before it was ready for tramping. Tom Farrell came to help us when it was ready. It took the three of us the whole day to turn it all into cocks; row after row after row of hay-cocks up and down the big field. It was the hardest week's work I'd done in my entire life.

I was now old enough to take responsibility for a lot of the things that had to be done around the place. I spent a lot of time on my own in the bog trying to save the turf. Sometimes Colleen and Sadie and Una joined me while Mrs O'Brien looked after things at home. The following Saturday herself and Colleen went up to Galway on the bus to see my father. He was much better, they said.

After four weeks he was discharged; and was advised to give up smoking altogether and to take a long rest.

'Bedamn but, 'tis great to see you home,' said Tommy the post as he sat in the corner opposite my father while Mrs O'Brien put on the kettle.

'Well…people can say what they like about the hospital – it's all right if you're sick I suppose – but if you're middlin' at all, you're better off at home,' said my father thoughtfully, as he held his hands out to the glowing embers.

'Of course you are: and why wouldn't you? You can't beat your own fireside. And aren't you the lucky man that has Kate and John here to look after you,' said Tommy, reflectively. And then in a more pensive mood he added, 'Sure the Lord have Mercy on the dead, I do often think, if poor Sylvester was still alive, he might be as big as John there now – maybe bigger: and I wouldn't have to be killing myself working when I'd go home in the evening.'

'Well… there's that in it I suppose,' acknowledged my father.

'Yes, but how long will we have John with us? He's thirteen now and he'll be soon going to the Tech in Castlerea or Dunmore: and we won't see him at all then,' said Mrs O'Brien. 'By the time he's home it'll be too late for him to do anything, except his homework. Still… he might learn a trade or something.'

'Aaaaah! Bad cess to them teachers and their homework: closing down, them Technical schools would want! Closing down! What good are they? My eldest girl spent two years cycling up and down to Castlerea and she still had to go to Dublin for a job. What harm but she's not a bit happy. All she wants is to go to America. But if I had my way, I'd keep her at home altogether. But of course herself wouldn't hear of it,' said Tommy, as he sat back contentedly, smoking his cigarette.

'Well, John better stay at home here when he's finished school: for I'm damned if I'm rearing him to let him off to Dublin… or Galway for that matter. It's the least I can have at the latter end of me days: someone to look after me and comfort me in me auld age,' said Mrs O'Brien, wistfully.

'Certainly, certainly; and that's the way I'd look at it, Kate.' acknowledged Tommy. 'But sure these young ones; they don't know what they want. I see Geraldine – our second eldest – and she too is mad to be off.'

'Ah' sighed my father wearily, 'no one know what'll happen. John could end up in England or America – like them all. Who knows?'

'Tell me, young fella; what would you like to do?' asked Tommy, looking at me as I tried putting a few tacks into the soles of Mrs O'Brien's old shoes.

I was going to tell him how I wanted to become a cyclist in the Tour De France and to play football for Galway, but I knew Mrs O'Brien wouldn't like to hear that, so I simply said,

'I don't know…I might take up carpentry,' I added quickly, knowing this would please my mother.

'Well there is plenty of carpentry work around here, for you,' retorted Mrs O'Brien, giving me one of her looks. Then turning to Tommy she added,

'It would be great if he took it up. Can you imagine having a carpenter in the house? He could put glass doors on that auld dresser for a start... and I wouldn't be killed dusting and cleaning it every day. They're always looking for carpenters, they tell me,' she added, as she began pouring out the tea.

'I'll tell you what's wrong with young people, today! They're too bloody lazy. That's what's wrong! They won't get out-a-bed in the morning. But if they were over in London or New York, they'd get out,' said a disgruntled Tommy, flicking the ash of the end of his cigarette, the imprint of the postman's hat clearly visible around his thinning bald head and wrinkled forehead

'Believe me they would,' endorsed my father, as Mrs O'Brien handed Tommy a mug of tea and a two thick slices of currant cake which she'd made earlier.

'Well the blessin' of God on you Misses,' said Tommy taking a last puff of his cigarettes before stubbing out the butt on the edge of the hob so he could smoke it later.

Working in the bog all day and doing odd jobs around the house when I came home was something I didn't mind. Saving hay was a different matter. It was such heart breaking work I detested every minute of it. Over the years, I had helped turn the hay so many times only to see it come wet the following day. Then my mother and father and I would spend days going through the same old rig-ma-roll, twisting and turning and shaking it out until such time as it was bone dry and fit for tramping. Saving the hay always took place during my school holidays and I often cursed my luck for being home from school. If only I could attend school all year I wouldn't have to work so hard, I thought. I loved books and would read them day and night if I could get my hands on them. The thing I liked about books was that they transported me to distant lands I'd never known before. I could be the captain of a ship that sailed the seven seas: I could be a policeman who rescued a pretty girl from drowning: I could be a thief who pulls on a mask to rob a bank. In a word I could be any one. But above all I could be a hero. The way I wanted to be a hero when Mr Feathers gave us a composition to write, entitled, 'A day in the bog.'

If anybody knew anything about the bog I did, I thought. From that point of view I made up my mind I'd write a good composition. It was such an easy task I pushed it to the back of my mind knowing I could write it, last thing in the evening, after I'd all the jobs done.

As soon as I came home I cleaned out the stables, I brought in the turf, I went to the well and I milked the cows. I had just finished milking when Colleen unexpectedly came running down across with an urgent request.

Standing in the kitchen facing me, breathless, her dark curly hair glorifying her rosy complexion she gasped,

'John, would you ever do me a favour! Would you be able to cycle up as far as Dunmore? I want you to deliver a letter to Mr Nestor, the Welfare

Officer. You know Mr Nestor don't you?'

'I do.'

'I know it's getting late. He called to the house today but I missed him. I wanted to register the children so I could get the children's allowance; otherwise I'll have to wait until next year. I have the form filled out and everything, but it has to be in by tomorrow. I thought I'd be home in time from the bog, but I missed him.'

'Whose bike will I go on?'

'Well you're not bringing mine,' said Mrs O'Brien, laying down the law, as she stood up for a moment, the back of her skirt raised, warming her backside by the fire, while she assessed the seriousness of the situation. 'You can bring Daddy's bike if you like but you're not bringing mine, because you'll make kettle binders of it.'

'Look,' said Colleen trying to avoid any disagreement, why don't you run up across? You can bring Máirtín's bike. It's brand new and better than Daddy's.'

'OK! What'll I do when I get to Dunmore?'

'You know how far it is, now, don't you? It's a good spin, nine or ten miles!' she said, stressing the seriousness of the undertaking. Now, as you're going into the town you'll come on a fairly steep hill. You'll know it when you get there because there's a school on the right hand side; you can't miss it. As you go down the hill into the town, you'll see a row of five or six red bricked houses, on your left. Mr Nestor's is the first house… I think. When you get there, knock, and make sure it's the right house and give him this letter or leave it with whoever is there. If there's no one there, put the letter under the door: or if there's a letterbox drop it in. Will you be able to do that do you think?'

'Yeah, I will.'

'Call to my house on your way home so I'll know you're got back safe and sound. I'll have something ready for you by the time you get back. And you can bring Máirtín's bike home with you, because it'll be too dark to run down across.'

'I will,' I replied confidently, though I'd never cycled more than five miles before. I was very keen to try out my cycling skills; even though it was getting late. I folded Colleen's letter and slipped it into my inside pocket.

'The flash lamp is left on the hob beside the fire. Make sure to put it on the bike before you leave. I'd be grateful if you could do that for me because there's no one else I could ask.'

I grabbed my cap and set off out the door as Colleen began to tell her mother how she'd bought a new television. And I began to wonder had she finally got round to seeing one in Galway; and what it might be like to look at.

I ran up across and was met by Una, and Sadie and Kevin and the baby.

They told me they had a new television locked above in their sitting room. It was like a radio only bigger, they said. Their mother had promised them they could look at it later, if they were good. Nearly everyone in school had said their uncle or auntie in either Dublin or Galway had a television in their house. But I thought it was all lies because none of Mrs O'Brien's relatives in England or America had ever said anything about having a television; and neither did Bridie in Galway, and she should know.

I found the flash lamp on the hob beside the fire and checked to see if it was working properly. It was: though the battery wasn't great. I slotted the flash lamp onto the front of the bike and set off on my errand of mercy. By the time I reached Dunmore, I was lathered in sweat. I knocked on the first red bricked house going down the hill and handed the letter to a startled Mr Nestor, as he stood at the door in his slippers. He was a little man with a small tight mouth, a mop of snow white hair and inquisitive looking eyes. I told him my story. Taking the letter from me, he disappeared into a back room and came back out a minute later with his spectacles on, the opened letter in his hand.

'Did you cycle up from Williamstown?'

'I did, Sir.'

'Why couldn't Mrs Fox have come up herself?'

I wasn't expecting this so I said the first thing that came into my head. 'She couldn't come herself because she had to mind the children.'

'And where was she when I called today? The children were there on their own…with no one to mind them.'

'The…the baby was sick and she had to bring him to the doctor,' I lied, as a cold sweat began to break out on my forehead.

'Oh! Well thanks for bringing me the form. Tell Mrs Fox, not to worry. I'll look after this, for her.'

I grabbed hold of the bicycle beneath the window, while Mr Nestor stuck his head inquisitively out the door and said, 'Will you not be afraid cycling home in the dark?'

'Arrah… I'll be alright,' I said, as I turned the bicycle and set off cycling helter-skelter back to Williamstown. I was very anxious to see the television, to find out if what the girls had said was true. Nobody in Williamstown – that I knew of – had a television and I couldn't understand how Colleen could have one.

I'd travelled quite a few miles when I began to think I might be on the wrong road. Somehow or other I thought the houses and trees looked different, more eerie and ghost-like in the ever darkening gloom. I slowed down and stopped in the middle of the road. All I could hear and see were dogs howling in distant farm yards and house lights twinkling way down in what looked like a valley to my right. From what I could gather I was perched on a hill. Yet I hadn't felt under pressure cycling, so it was hard to figure out how I'd come to be so high up; and on the wrong road; if it was the wrong road? Suddenly I was faced with an awful dilemma. Was I imagining it: or was I on the wrong road? And if I was, should I turn back? The thought of turning back and cycling miles to get on the right road again horrified me. I could not recall having veered off to the left or right and yet I instinctively felt I was on the wrong road. I decided to carry on. It was the safest bet, I thought. After cycling on, I came to a crossroads where the ever fading flashlight finally went out on me. I could just about make out a road sign pointing to the left. It said, Williamstown five miles. I was greatly relieved to find out this road would lead me home, while at the same time I was shattered to realize I still had another five miles to go. And to make things worse it looked as if it was going to rain, So, I put my head down and began cycling as fast as I could. But trying to chart the road ahead in the absence of a light was a nightmare. I could see the dark outline of trees and hedges ahead of me as I sped along. Once or twice I was stricken with fear as I clearly saw the ghostly outline of an elderly person on the road in front of me. Thankfully it turned out to be no more than a bush or gate post. And when I saw a flashlight moving erratically on the road it was a relief to know there were other human beings on the road, besides me.

Shortly after that, I recognised Woodlawn graveyard. I knew then I was only a mile from Colleen's house. And I stepped on the pedal in earnest in the knowledge that I had completed the journey to and from Dunmore in record time. Suddenly I collided with something frighteningly hairy that catapulted me over its body and into a heap of briars. I ended up on top of my head inches from a roadside drain. I could hear something racing off down the road and recognised it as a braying donkey. I realized then I'd cycled straight between a donkey's hind legs as it grazed along the side of the road, and it had kicked me into the air. It was the most incredible fright I'd ever had and I realized how close I'd come to ending up in a drain.

When I reached Colleen's house, I told her all about my nightmare journey. She was delighted that I'd managed to deliver the letter safely. Straight away she set about mending my cuts and bruises: much to the amusement of Una and Sadie. When she'd finished, the girls dragged me up to the sitting room to show me their new television. I stood in bewilderment watching a smaller version of a cinema screen on what looked like a big grey box in a corner of the room. The television was left up on the china cabinet. On top of it was an aerial that for all the world looked like two knitting needles, standing straight up, but with one of them at an acute angle.

The picture was black and white, with grey lines, which every now and again faded away completely only to come back again, crystal clear. Colleen called me down into the kitchen and made me sit down at the table where she gave me a good feed of ham and cheese.

'Why don't you stay with us a while'een now and watch the Everglades. The man who brought me the television said it was the best programme. It's on every week. It's about a lawman, who goes after robbers in a speedboat and puts them all in jail. It will be over at nine and you can go then. I've another flash lamp and I'll give it to you going home,' said Colleen. 'Don't let on to Mammy that you were watching television at all.'

'Can John stay and watch television with us?' asked Una, as Sadie and Kevin came excitedly into the kitchen. When Sadie saw me hesitating she pleaded, 'Ah please; stay and watch it with us.'

'Arrah do! What harm will it do you? Don't you deserve it after that long journey?' urged Colleen.

I was mad to stay and watch it but I knew Mrs O'Brien would be expecting me home any minute. If I wasn't home soon she'd be giving out, I thought. But the temptation was too great. It was a golden opportunity to sit and watch television for the first time; so I relented. I settled down to watch the Everglades while Colleen tried to improve the picture by adjusting the twin aerials sitting on top of the television which she called rabbits ears, because you could point them in any direction. But no matter how much she twiddled with them she could not improve the picture. Very often she made it worse, and we had to shout and tell her when to stop fiddling; the picture was perfect. It was wonderful to be sitting in the comfort of a couch, in a sitting room watching an episode of the Everglades. I'd been to the Parochial Hall to see a film a few times but nothing could compare with Lincoln Veil and the Everglades. I liked Lincoln. He was a good man who kept going until he'd rounded-up all the robbers and put them in jail.

Cycling home from Colleen's I couldn't make up my mind which excited me more, seeing Lincoln for the first time or the thought that I'd cycled to and from Dunmore in record time. Once again I had retained the race leader's yellow jersey, in the Tour de France and I was extremely happy.

But it was a different story when I went back to school on Monday. I had barely sat down when The Chicken clapped his hands in eager anticipation and said,

'Now, who'd like to start off this morning by reading their composition, 'A day in the bog.'

The minute he opened his mouth I knew I was trouble, because I had forgotten all about the composition. I should have done it either Friday or Saturday evening instead of practising my football skills. While I was considering what sort of punishment awaited me, Frank McGee began waving excitedly. He was eager to read out his composition while the rest of us slowly rummaged through our school bags. I opened my copybook and stared down at the blank page as Frank stood up. I was in a state of panic because I didn't know what excuse I was going to give. I knew I'd have to make up some excuse for not having written anything. It had been three whole days since the teacher had asked us to write it. I had to come up with something – and quick

– otherwise The Chicken would belt the living daylights out of me. I was sitting in the fourth row, trying to keep one eye on the teacher and one eye on my copybook. I was afraid I'd be asked to read, next.

When Frank finished reading he sat down, while The Chicken mused in silence; slowly pacing the floor. He kept polishing his glasses until he could almost see himself in them.

'Not bad! But you might have told us what kind of a turf slean* your father was using. Was it a breast slean or a down slean?'

'Well…' replied Frank, standing up, 'he started cutting with the down slean; and when the turf bank got too deep, he began cutting with the breast slean – it was easier to throw the turf out on the swarth than up on the high bank,' he added cautiously.

'Ah! Now I know, because you've just told me. Why didn't you say that in your composition?' asked The Chicken.

'I didn't think, Sir.'

'You didn't think! How often have I heard that before?'

While The Chicken was pacing back and forth; reflecting on what he'd heard, I began to scribble a few words; but I didn't have time. I was afraid I'd get caught in the act.

The Chicken stopped pacing for a moment, looked at Frank and said, 'Very well!'

Frank sat down, a smug expression on his face. He had acquitted himself well.

'John Keaveney, what can you tell us, about your day in the bog?'

When I heard John's name being called I breathed a sigh of relief. It was close. Very close. John was sitting beside me which meant I was unlikely to be asked. Those who hadn't been asked to read would simply hand up their copies for correction, later. So there was still a possibility I might have time to write something.

But what could I do when I was such an eejit, I thought? All I ever did was day dream about being famous. I wanted to play football for Galway: I wanted to be a matador in sunny Spain, while at the same time I wanted to be a cyclist in the Tour De France. If I went to Spain and became a matador, I knew more people would cheer for me if I killed a bull than would ever cheer for me if I scored a goal for Williamstown or Galway. But I also knew that I could no longer face a bull, because I was afraid of them: they would simply gore me to death. The only option open to me now, was to become a cyclist or a footballer.

John Keaveney was still reading. And every line he read made my heart ache. I knew I could have written the exact same thing, only better. Painfully I sat listening, '…then, when we had finished our tea, we started tossing the turf

---

* Slean *(a spade like implement for cutting turf)*

again and stayed at it all evening until we had it finished. Daddy said he was glad to see the end of it. Then we gathered up our things and came home.'

The Chicken was standing his hands behind his back, facing us. He didn't seem too impressed, so he asked John,

'What kind was of a day was it?'

John, who was still standing, looked at him querulously '…It…it was fine, sir.'

'I know it was fine. If it was raining you wouldn't be in the bog would you?'

'No Sir.

'What I want to know is, was it warm or overcast? Was there a clear blue sky? What were people wearing? I was looking for something that might paint a picture for me without necessarily having to spell it out. For instance if you saw a man with a straw hat and a white sleeveless shirt cycling into town, what would that tell you?'

I put my hand up to show that I knew the answer. I knew from past experience that if a pupil looked eager and showed an interest in his subject, the teacher was unlikely ask him to read: concentrating instead on the dunces – as he liked to call them.

The Chicken studied the hands waving frantically.

'Yes?' queried The Chicken, looking straight at me.

I stood up and rested my hands on the desk to stop me from trembling. I knew at that precise moment I should have kept my mouth shut and not drawn attention to myself. And to make matters worse, everyone sitting in front of me turned round and started gawking.

'Well Sir, it tells you that the man is on holidays; that it's very warm: that he's wearing a straw hat to keep the sun off his head.'

'Correct! If it was just an ordinary day there would be no need to wear a straw hat: therefore the weather must have been very warm. As well as that he was wearing a white sleeveless shirt, which would suggest the man worked in an office or was indeed on holidays.'

Pausing to reflect on my analysis for a moment he unexpectedly said, 'And what can you tell us… about your day in the bog?'

I stood looking at the teacher for a moment. I didn't know what to say as I fumbled with my copybook on the desk trying to make up my mind whether to tell the teacher straight out that I'd forgotten to do my homework or to make up some excuse. Either way I knew I'd be slaughtered, so I decided to brazen it out. I picked up my copybook as if about to read something, but all I could see were two blank pages in front of me, with a few words scrawled under the title. I took a deep breath as I began to read.

A day in the Bog
'The day was wet, we couldn't go.'

I left down the copybook as everybody in my class looked at me for a moment before they burst out laughing. Even The Chicken smiled as EJ looked round and winked at me. When everyone had quietened down, The Chicken looked seriously at me and said,

'Is that it?'

'Yes Sir.'

I stood there trembling. I could feel myself choking on the lie. Again there was a hint of laughter, as The Chicken rocked back and forth on his heels, a serious expression on his face. 'The day was wet; we couldn't go. Ummh! Would you care to bring up your copybook, so I can see it?'

I went and handed him my copybook. I stood rooted to the ground while he leafed through my homework. With a look of resignation, he handed the copybook back to me and indicated I was to sit down as my friends started tittering again.

'Quiet! He barked. 'I don't know what you find so amusing. Perhaps you'd like to think again about what you've just heard.'

I had only just sat down, when the teacher said aloud, 'Mr Rodgers would you care to stand up and read it out again, so that some of our less enlightened friends, might hear it?'

I stood up and read it out once more, as a deathly silence fell across the room.

I could not believe what was happening. Why hadn't The Chicken belted the lard of me when he'd given me such a hard time before? When I'd finished The Chicken said,

'I asked all of you to write a simple composition entitled, 'A day in the bog.' I expected you to set the scene for me, to paint a picture which would encapsulate all of the activity that goes with having to spend a day in the bog. If I was lucky I might have heard someone describe the intensive labour involved in, cutting, spreading and rearing the turf. Mr Rodgers might have told us what it was like to try and make a fire in the bog and to boil a kettle. He might have told us something about the scented heather, the soaring lark; that sings all day amid the deep blue sky. And what did I get. Nothing! Absolutely nothing! Why?

Again there was a deathly silence. 'Have you lost your tongues?' asked the teacher, in a measured tone of voice. I'm asking, why Mr Rodgers hasn't told me one iota about his day in the bog?

This time, several hands were raised. The Chicken nodded toward EJ.

'Yes?'

'Well, Sir… he's after saying the day was wet, so he couldn't go.'

'Yes! Strange as it may seem, if I hadn't seen that one line written, with my own two eyes, I'd say our friend here had forgotten to do his homework. But who am I to argue; when he has the neck to stand up here and read out his composition, consisting of one solitary line. He could have told me face to face, that the day was wet, he couldn't go. But no, he chose to write it down and for that I should be eternally grateful: because it paints a very bleak picture indeed. If it were possible to transfer that image onto a canvass, it would be a master piece. Of that I have no doubt. If you think about it, his composition does two very strange things. On the one hand it tells you absolutely nothing: and on the other it tells you everything. The day was wet, we couldn't go. But let's not get too carried away.'

Looking me straight in the eye, The Chicken asked, nonchalantly,

'Have you by any chance, ever spent a day in the bog?

By now my head was spinning, I didn't know what to think. I felt The Chicken was waiting to spring a verbal trap. And unless I trod very carefully, I'd end up being verbally snared.

'I have…Sir.'

'Very well, then. I'd like you to write me… two pages; describing your day in the bog. And bring it into me tomorrow morning, because I can't wait to read it.'

Again there was laughter as everybody turned to look, while all I could do was mumble,

'Yes sir.'

Having sat down again I got the feeling Mrs O'Brien's visit to the school had been well worthwhile. Now I couldn't wait to tell her how well I was doing in school. But I couldn't dare tell her the true story. I decided I'd wait until I had the composition written; then I'd show it to her, detailing my own version of what had actually happened in school.

That evening, after she'd read my two page composition, she said,

'Take care you don't get a swelled head. I noticed there was no mention of the day you near fell into the bog hole and drowned; or how you made kittle-binders of me brand new bicycle?'

After that reminder, I knew my composition was only middlin'. She handed back the copybook, saying

'Look! Have you got your Soutane and Surplice ready for Mass in the morning? Bring it up out of the room until I see does it need ironing.'

* * * *

It was my turn to serve Mass every second Sunday as well as two or three mornings a week. On top of that I had to serve Mass during the missions. Every year, up to half a dozen Missionaries would come to our parish to preach and say Mass three or four times a day for two whole weeks. The first Mass was at seven o'clock in the morning, the second at eight and the third at seven in the evening with various religious services in between. During Mass, I had to sit on the altar steps, facing the congregation while the Chief Celebrant gave hair-raising sermons on the evils of drink and the wanton desires of the human flesh. Despite the threat of eternal damnation, arising from man's wicked desire to commit sins of lust, via thought, word and deed, I couldn't help but look at all the beautiful girls sitting in the front row. Some of the girls used to smile which made my heart beat faster at the thought of kissing the girl of my dreams, who happened to be sitting right there in the front row. She'd turn red and I'd feel awful embarrassed at the thought that she knew exactly what I was thinking and I'd have to turn my face away and pretend I wasn't interested in her at all, while the other altar boys, sat restlessly, either side of me

Very often when I'd come home from serving Mass I'd be sent straight down to Harry Ryan's, with a basket of eggs – while I still had my good clothes on. Later Mrs O'Brien would go into town herself to sort out the bills. She'd have to pay for all the bags of flour, bran, pig meal, Indian meal and Clarendo.* Only then would she know what money she had, which was the highlight of her week's shopping.

Not a single day went by that I didn't have some special job to do. I might have to paint the windows inside or outside. I might have to fix a latch on a window or press door that wouldn't close properly.

I might have to clip the wings on a few of the hens to stop them flying into the vegetable garden where they were uprooting everything.

And, though my father had fully recovered, a lot of the work was left to me. There were days when I had to bring a cow to the bull; stakes and barbwire to some distant field where the cattle had broken into our neighbour's land. And, once in a very pale moon I'd be sent cycling to Ballymoe, Castlerea or Ballinlough on an urgent message.

I really loved it when I had to cycle somewhere new as I'd sometimes see a girl I hadn't seen before. Another favourite trip of mine was going to confessions on Saturday evenings, where I'd see lots of girls cycling to Williamstown church to confess their sins. With two priests hearing confessions every Saturday evening, the middle section of the church would be full, the girls waiting to go into the confessional box on the left hand side, while the boys waited on the right. Most of the girls tended to go to confessions between seven and nine in the evening as opposed to confessions between two and four in the afternoon, which more often than not was frequented by elderly parishioners. Therefore, I did everything in my power to make sure I'd be in Williamstown around eight o'clock so that I'd meet some of the girls coming out while admiring those going in.

I so desperately wanted to say *Hello* to some of them but I never had the courage. Instead, I'd watch them as they turned their bicycles for home. As they did so they'd sometimes give me a warm smile, which made me even more anxious to see them again. I always smiled back before turning away as

* Clarendo *(animal feed)*.

if about to go into some shop: only to turn round at the last minute to find they too were looking round and I'd feel awfully embarrassed because the girl of my dreams had caught me looking at her; while all I'd wanted to do was to make a good impression.

And in an effort to meet some of the girls, my friends and I would cycle over to St Patrick's well every Sunday. We were supposed to be praying but we were only ever interested in chatting up the girls. And if the girl of my dreams happened to turn up on her bicycle – like she'd promised – I'd spend the entire afternoon circling her on my bicycle, captivated by the sound of her voice, the lilt of her laughter, the twinkle in her eye, the curl in her hair, but above all, to absorb the beauty of God's creation and to question my overwhelming desire to plant a luscious kiss on her beautiful rose tinted lips where I'd never planted a kiss before.

John Keaveney, EJ and I would do everything in our power to encourage the girl of our dreams to go behind a wall or better still, to hop up on the bar of our bicycle so we could cycle up the road to show them some mysterious object. What this mysterious object was, we ourselves never knew. It seems it had something to do with lust and everything to do with our imagination. But we never had much luck, however, because a friend or older sister would advise them to have nothing at all to do with us: and our wanton desires.

As time went on and we grew bolder we learned a few courtship tricks of our own, such as letting the air out of the girl's bicycle, which necessitated the lady in question having to hop up on the bar of our bicycle so we could escort her safely home; while a friend cycled behind and wheeled the supposedly punctured bicycle.

But come Monday morning it was business as usual. I'd be first up to make the fire and put on the kettle. Then I'd put out the ashes, empty the piss pot, milk the cows and drive them out into the fields for the day. By the time I'd all that done, Mrs O'Brien would be up, pottering round; ready to lambaste me if everything wasn't right, while Ned pulled on his wellingtons to go ambling about the place.

At night, after I'd finished my lessons, I'd sometimes have to write a letter on behalf of my mother or father. I'd write to the health board pleading for new teeth for my father and reading glasses for my mother, which they couldn't afford. Other times I'd have to write letters to the dole office explaining why my father Ned was no longer fit for work and why he couldn't take up the job that was being offered by the Board of works or Galway County Council.

As well as that I had to write to Bridie every week; to fill her in on everything that was going on round the place. In return she'd write back and I'd try to unravel the mystery of the blacked out passages which seemed to suggest she was almost illiterate. A lot of the time whole paragraphs as well as odd words here and there would be blacked out. Because of that I began to question my dubious relationship with her. But, as long as she was prepared to keep sending me parcels then I was prepared to keep writing to her. Often when I'd write a letter and show it to Mrs O'Brien, seeking her approval, she'd go off in a tangent of her own.

'I pray to the Lord God Almighty, that they keep that lady there. It would be a devil entirely if she were to come down here looking for you: and I after rearing you for the last ten years. But of course…you don't care. You'll do what suits you, anyway.'

I always felt uncomfortable when she began talking like that. It was as if I was to blame. By now, I'd learned to say nothing; no matter how much she castigated me. I tried hard to keep on the right side of her by offering to do some small job, like going to the well for another bucket of water so that I could get out of the house and not have to be listening to her. Despite that, she'd still have it in for me, in one form or another.

'…I suppose... if it saves you doing it in the morning… it'll be alright. And when you have that done you might hold the wool for me. I'll wind another ball, just to have it done, in case you're not here when I need you. Since Colleen got that cursed television, I never know when I'll see you.'

Again, this annoyed me. I only ever went up to watch Lincoln Veil and the Everglades on Wednesday nights from 8.30 to 9. Admittedly, it was the highlight of my week and I couldn't stop talking about him. He was a great law enforcement officer who'd stop at nothing to see justice was done.

On Sunday afternoons, if there was a match being played above in Croke Park, then I'd ask Mrs O'Brien and Colleen if I could go up to watch it on television. When the All Ireland football final was shown the whole parish seemed to converge on Colleen's house. The sitting room and kitchen would be packed with barely enough room to stand inside the front door. For those who couldn't get a view of the television in the sitting room Colleen would turn down the sound on the television and turn up the sound on the radio so that everybody could hear the match.

Snowy too was a football fanatic and would fly home unexpectedly from England just to watch the match in the comfort of his own home. At half-time, there would be a lot of good natured banter amongst the visitors who'd never seen a television set before. And as always they were ably abetted by Snowy who'd know how to rise them, to get the cráic going

'Isn't television a mighty thing all the same: how we can sit here and watch Down playing Offaly above in Croke Park in front of 90,000 people? We'll never see another invention like it: not in a hundred years?' said Snowy, trying to elicit some wry comment.

'Aaaah…,' sniffed Tom Farrell, as he stood lackadaisically against the back wall and pushed the cap to the back of his head, '…People said that when man invented the wheel: and look what Henry Ford did? He made a metal box, stuck an engine in the middle and put four wheels under it. And the man that invented the television or someone like him will make one that small, you'll be able to carry it round with you like a hand bag.'

'Ah Tom, Tom you're rimming it,' roared Snowy with laughter. Then a lone voice from the other side of the smoke filled room piped up,

'I think Tom... you'd want to pull that cap down over your eyes again; you seem to have water on the brain.'

Quick as a flash Tom retorted, 'And you'd want to keep your mouth shut or you'll get a broken jaw.'

Again there were howls of laughter, as the visitors revelled in Tom's verbal put down.

And not to be out done, Snowy added his own brand of humour by looking round the room as if searching for something,

'Where the hell I wonder... did I leave the first aid kit?'

When play resumed all you could hear was the voice of Mícheál O'hEithir, the match commentator as the two teams lined out to face each other, for the second half. I was heartbroken because Galway weren't in the final. Though they had won the all Ireland final two years earlier, I had never seen Galway playing. But I still knew every member of the Galway team, by name, where they played, what age they were, and what they did for a living. The majority of them were farmers but there was a solicitor, a bank clerk and two Guards on the team. My three favourite players were Sean Purcell, Frank Stockwell and Joe Young. And despite the fact they were not in the final they were still my heroes on a beautiful sunny day when Snowy should have been out cutting oats, while the weather was still fine.

'I'll tell you what I'll do,' said Snowy looking at Colleen, when everyone had gone home and we were all sitting round the table, having out tea, 'as soon as I've finished this drop-a-tay, I'll go down as far as the town and hire four of the best men in this parish so we can cut and tie all the oats tomorrow. I'll pick them up in the morning and be ready to start mowing around ten; the dew should be lifted by then. John, tell Ned to come up tomorrow afternoon, as soon as ever the two of ye come home from the fair. What's more, I'll have two men ready to help ye start stacking the oats as fast as we're cutting it. We'll have no more of this bollixology,* going around stooking. We'll stack every bit of oats as we're cutting it.'

'And can you do that? Will it not heat?' asked Colleen, alarmed.

'Can I do that? What do you mean can I do that? Of course I can do it! You said yourself the oats should have been cut a fortnight ago....?'

'Well I was trying to get it cut: but when you wrote and said you might be coming home, I decided to wait. Besides, I shouldn't have to be traipsing round the country looking for people to cut it: it's a man's job,' interrupted Colleen, moodily

---

* Bollixology (*messing*)

'A…very…wise…move; if I may say so. For once in your life, you did the right thing, honey. I'll go down now to Cunneelly's pub and I'll hire Pake Tarmey, Martin Tee, Pooky O'Brien and Mick Long; and some other two – if I can get them. Everything will work out grand. By tomorrow evening, with the help of God, not alone will we have the oats cut, but we'll have it stacked as well. That should open a few eyes around here,' said Snowy as he reached across the table for a bit of butter. 'We'll have no more of this auld codology, where it takes a man a week and a half to cut an acre of oats: and another two weeks to stack it. From now on, we'll do things in style,' he added, humorously with an air of devilment.'

'Lord but you're an awful simpleton. I heard you talking like that before,' said Colleen dismissively,'

'Do I detect a note of…what's that big word… sarcasm?' queried Snowy, derisively

'Look! I don't care if you get down on your two bended knees and cut it with a scissors; I just want the damn thing cut. You know, the weather's not promised good? We could have been at it today… and had some of it cut. But no! You had to sit around all day, entertaining your friends,' said Colleen with a look of disenchantment, as she began to feed the baby.

The following morning my father and I went to the cattle fair in Williamstown bright and early, knowing we'd have to spend the afternoon cutting the oats above in Snowy's big field. My father went to the fair because he wanted to buy two suck calves as we had a lot of milk and it was my job to help bring home the calves as soon as he bought them. Around eleven in the morning, I spotted Snowy going into Cunneelly's pub along with Martin Tee and Mick Long – who were said to be legendary mowers. Snowy appeared to be in great form and in no particular hurry to go home. By the time my father had traipsed up and down the town a few times, found what he wanted and had done the deal it was nearly one o'clock.

'Come into Cunneely's; and I'll treat you before we go home,' he said, turning to me.

I had often been in Cunneely's pub on fair days where my father would have a few bottles of stout while I'd have a mineral before going outside to hang around with my friends.

When we went into Cunneelly's pub it was a seething mass of humanity. Snowy was half way down the bar, in the midst of telling a funny story. The resulting laughter could be heard half way down the street. As soon as he spotted us he called us over and insisted on buying a round. You could clearly see that cutting oats was the last thing on his mind. A few minutes later Sergeant Boyle came into the pub in his uniform, as if on the lookout for a wanted man. Snowy and the Sergeant's eye balls met and they looked at each other for a fleeting moment. It was the first time they had come face to face since the case of the stolen hens.

'Well...,' said the Sergeant, forced to acknowledge his opponent's presence, while resuming his search for the wanted felon.

'What do you mean, well?' A well is where you'd get water; a pub is where you'd get a drink; and a whorehouse is where you'd get a bit of cur-is-teach,* but you won't get that here. So what will you have to drink, me auld sagosha**?'

'Ah bejeepers, Snowy I can't. Not in the line of duty. I'll be going home shortly for me dinner...,' said Sergeant Boyle, adjusting his hat.

'Well it never stopped you before. Have this one for old time's sake. It's the least I can do. Then you can eff off about your business,' said Snowy, jovially.

'Bejeepers I better not, I'm supposed to...'

'Aaaah have a drink, can't you, when the man's willin' to make it up with you!' said my father, as Martin Tee and Mick Long echoed his call, 'Ah yes, yes!' 'It wouldn't be right to refuse, after the man offerin' to treat... the head of our local constabulary.'

'Won't ye be long enough dead?' added my father, with a shake of his head.

'Well, that's as sure as you're there, Ned,' said Snowy, revelling in the Sergeant obvious discomfort.

'Well...' began the Sergeant hesitantly, '...in that case I'll have, a half one***'

'That's more like it,' said Martin Tee, his grizzled grey features masking his merry making.

'Chief,' called Snowy aloud, turning to the barman...

'Wait, wait! Hould your horses a minute...' intervened Mick long, with a comical shrug of his lean shoulders. '...can't you let *me* buy a round and the day that's in it?' 'Chief...!' he called aloud to Johnny Feeney the barman, '...would you ever decorate the mahogany again: and give this law abiding gentleman, here, in the military uniform, a decent, *half one,' he added with another shrug of the shoulders, like a prized fighter going into battle.

'Right you be!' said Johnny with a ready smile, as he skipped about behind the counter serving half a dozen customers at the same time.

The result was Snowy had a joyous round in the company of Sergeant Boyle, with a firm shaking of hands to seal their friendship, to let bygones be bygones. Then they all had another round with more laughter and gaiety and another one with added merriment and half a dozen more until I was sick and tired wandering in and out of the pub waiting for my father, to go home.

I was afraid to face home on my own because I knew I'd be asked where Daddy was; and why had I come home without him. In the end I had to go

---

* Cur-is-teach (*come in*)
** Sagosha (*friend*)
***   Half one (*a whiskey*)

home and tell Mrs O'Brien that Daddy was still in the pub and that the two calves we bought were in a stable at the back of Cunneely's pub, because I couldn't risk bringing them home on my own.

'Well God Blast you to hell, did you have to wait until this time of the day to come home and tell me? Did you?'

'I thought Daddy would come home when he finished his drink; but people kept treating him… and I didn't know what to do

'You didn't know what to do! But you knew enough to stay in the town all day listening to a-shower-a-drunkards. And you have the cheek to come home here, one hand longer than the other; leaving the calves below in the town after you. For all you know they could be stolen. Some farmer, you're going to make' shouted Mrs O'Brien as she made a swipe at me with the dish cloth. 'What am I supposed to do? What? And I sittin' here all day; waitin' for ye? For all ye knew, I could have been thrown here beside the fire, as dead as a door nail, and not one of ye would care. That's what I have to look forward to, after thirty four years of killing myself around this place,' she ranted, stamping her foot on the ground, her fists hanging menacingly as the dimple on her chin took on a life of its own. 'I thought ye were supposed to be coming home early to go cuttin' oats? Or is the drink more important?' she shouted, following me out the hall door as I tried to get away. 'Go down to that cursed town again as quick as your two legs will carry you and don't come home again without them calves, or I'll kill you,' she screamed, making another charge for me with the dishcloth.

I ran down to the pub as fast as I could. There was uproarious laughter in the bar as Snowy stood in the midst of the silent crowd imitating some local character. I couldn't face walking up to my father who was in a circle of friends to tell him what was wrong. So I turned and left. As I was leaving, I spotted Una coming out of Geraghty's drapery shop next door. She too was wondering where her father was and when I told her he was drinking with my father and explained my predicament she offered to help me bring the calves home.

It was sometime after midnight when my father and Snowy stumbled in the door. I was in bed but I heard the commotion outside the front door and Mrs O'Brien giving out as she helped steer my father into the house.

The following morning Mrs O'Brien was in a foul mood. When breakfast was over she turned to me and said, 'Will you run up across and see if Snowy is going cutting the oats today or not? And tell Colleen if they're cuttin', Daddy and yourself will be up later.'

I darted up across as fast as I could: taking great care to sneak along the ditch so the horses wouldn't see me. I'd just darted across the open bog into the next field when they spotted me and started whinnying excitedly. They broke into a fierce gallop, their tails in the air as they ran after me, but they were too late.

Already, I could feel a mist blowing against my face as the spell of fine weather threatened to come to an end. By the time I reached Colleen's a steady drizzle had begun to fall.

'Jesus, Mary and Joseph don't say it's raining?' said Colleen, seeing me. I told her what my mother had said. But I could see by the look of her that she was not impressed.

'Thanks for coming up. But if this Lúdraman*, here – pointing to Snowy who was sitting at the breakfast table lookin' out the window – 'did what he was supposed to do yesterday, instead of wasting his time below in the town drinking porter, we might have had some of it cut.'

'Do you honestly believe I wasted me time in the town yesterday?' asked Snowy, an air of bedevilment on his crimson features.

'Well of course I do! What was it, but a waste of precious time: when you should have been at home cutting oats and the sun cracking the stones: drinking with your so called friends: a gang who'd drink porter out of an auld piss pot if they could get it! If that's not a waste of time then I don't know what is?' snapped Colleen, as she noisily cleared the dishes off the table, while the children could be heard running wild upstairs.

'So, I spent a day in the town drinking porter, which you happen to think was a waste of precious time. Well I'll be damned. I'll tell you one thing, my pretty little woman, the amount of time I spent in the town yesterday is compared to the amount of time I'll be wasting away above in Woodlawn graveyard. And I know where I'd rather be,' said Snowy, derisively.

Suddenly, Colleen seized the bread knife and made a lunge for Snowy, 'I swear to Jesus, I'll gut you if you don't shut up and…,'

Quick as a flash Snowy grabbed her wrist in a vicelike grip, as he playfully pleaded for mercy.

'Jesus, Colleen go easy, go easy or you'll butcher me… with that thing!'

'And butchering you'd want, you bastard; you good for nothing simpleton,' shouted Colleen, as she fought like a tigress to break free of his grasp.

'Jack, did you hear what she called me? You're a witness. Tell Kate when you go home what Colleen's after calling me,' gasped Snowy as they continued to wrestle in the kitchen while I stood awkwardly in the doorway not knowing what to think; half afraid I'd be a witness to murder.

Tightened his grip on Colleen's wrist, she was forced to drop the knife with the point of the blade a hair's breath away from his exposed gut as the two girls came running down the stairs.

'You better go home John…,' gasped Colleen, as Snowy relaxed his grip and Colleen turned round and landed a hefty body blow followed by another. 'As you can see…there will be nothing…*thump*… done today…*thump*… because it's raining.'

---

* Lúdraman *(A bit of a fool).*

'Well I hope it rains for forty days and forty nights and that we all end up back in Noah's ark,' laughed Snowy, as I turned to go home. Closing the door after me I could hear them wrestling again as a breakfast mug crashed on the floor. Passing the front window I could see Colleen, and the children pummel their father as he again pleaded for mercy.

It was several days later: after the weather had picked up again, that Snowy finally cut the oats. Not only that, but he cut and tied and drew the entire crop into the haggard, all in one day. There was no such thing as stooking or stacking it out in the fields. Once again he was the talk of the parish; only this time for all the right reasons. People envied him for his modern farming methods.

After that momentous day's work, farming in Ireland was never ever to be the same again.

Chapter Twenty Three

1962

I came home from the bog late one Saturday afternoon, to find three strange women sitting at our kitchen table; stuffing themselves with ham and cheese and tomatoes and the devil knows what. It was such a shock to walk through the front door and see my parents pampering them and attending to their every need. I had expected the table to be set for me, after a hard day helping Colleen to rare the turf while Snowy was in England. It was an even bigger shock when one of the women stood up and said, excitedly 'Glory-be-to-God-Almighty; is this him?' as she unexpectedly reached out and gave me a hug. I stood there transfixed, not knowing what to say or do as the woman began talking excitedly to me, 'Paschal love, how are you? 'God, but I wouldn't know you; you're so tall!'

Seeing the shock on my face, she asked, 'Do you not know me? Paschal! I'm your mother, Bridie!'

'Yes,' I croaked, in my filthy garb, while she clasped me proudly to her bosom. I nearly died as everybody sat watching me being reunited with my mother Bridie for what was the second time in my life.

Of course I knew who she was. How could I forget? But it was the shock of seeing her there when I came home from the bog that caught me by surprise. Somehow I thought Bridie looked different now. She seemed older, greyer, and thinner. She was like a walking skeleton; so pale and fragile looking. The other two women remained seated, as they looked on admiringly. Turning round Bridie introduced me to her friends, whom I vaguely recognised after my visit to Galway.

'Paschal love, these are my two friends. Remember you met them in Galway: they gave you the sweets and the chocolate? This is Lilly – the quiet one...,' she laughed.

Lilly was a small blond woman with pearly white teeth. 'And this is Margaret. She's like meself, as mad as a hatter.' Margaret was dark haired, strong and robust looking. She had enormous hands and wore thick brown framed glasses. As I shook hands with them I got the impression that Margaret was jolly, she seemed to smile all the time while Lilly was dour and serious

291

looking.

I knew Bridie lived and worked in the Magdalene Home in Galway which to me was a commercial laundry. I knew this because every week a lorry with the words, Magdalene Laundry, College Road, Galway, called to one of the shops in Williamstown, where they provided a collection and delivery service. Other than that, I knew nothing at all about Bridie or the Magdalene Laundry, despite the fact I'd been writing to Bridie for years.

And here I was now, turned fifteen, seeing my mother Bridie, for only the second time in my life and I hated it. I particularly hated her calling me Paschal. Granted, I was christened John Paschal, but everybody in Williamstown called me John and that was what I wanted to be called.

I stood there not knowing what to do with myself as Bridie encouraged me to sit down beside her so that she could talk to me. And seeing the reluctance on my face, Mrs O'Brien said,

'Why don't you go out to the back kitchen and wash some of the muck off your face so Bridie can see you?'

That request nearly drove me out of the house altogether. I went out to the back kitchen to wash myself, vowing that I wasn't going to go back in. I just didn't want to see Bridie or anyone belonging to her in the house. All I wanted was my tea. I was starving.

I soon learnt, listening to their conversation that my mother Bridie and her two friends Lilly and Margaret, had escaped from the Magdalene Laundry. Escaped! The words set alarm bells ringing in my head. So, these three women, who were dining at our table, were criminals of some sort or another: and the mere thought that one of them was supposed to be my mother was horrifying. I stood quietly listening in the back kitchen trying to come to terms with the awfulness that Bridie was supposed to be my mother. The whole thing was one awful nightmare as far as I was concerned. All my life I'd referred to Mr and Mrs O'Brien as my mother and father. Yet somewhere at the back of my mind I knew I was different. I was boarded out, but what that had to do with either Bridie or Mrs O'Brien I did not know. I'd given up trying to find out because all I ever got was, children should be seen and not heard and all that auld rubbish.

As well as that I was sick writing letters, thanking Bridie for the letters and parcels she'd sent me. I had grown accustomed to receiving parcels addressed specifically to me and I accepted them without a care or a thought for the person that had sent them. But when my foster mother Mrs O'Brien brought me up to Galway to meet my mother Bridie for the first time something changed. I thought Bridie was the most wonderful person in the world and I would gladly have stayed with her that day had I been asked. But now that I was seeing her again I didn't like her.

Mrs O'Brien called out to me as I stood listening in the back kitchen.

'John, are you going to stay washing yourself all evening? If it took me that long to wash my face, I think I'd drown myself.'

I was mortified. I thought I would die there and then after that horrid remark because now everybody was laughing at me as I went back into the kitchen. I said nothing but stood there like a fool, as the three women sat lazily around the table having finished eating while Mr and Mrs O'Brien sat either side of the fire. There was no place for me to sit because we had a bag of crushed oats on one chair and a spare bag of flour on the other which stood either side of my bedroom door. Bridie, however, made room on her chair and pulled me down beside her.

My father meanwhile had decided to help the women escape by offering them money. He encouraged them to make a run for it, to go to England, while they had the chance. He told them there was a boat train leaving Castlerea later that evening. He said he'd hop on his bicycle and go into Williamstown and arrange a taxi for them.

An hour later, as the women boarded the taxi, Bridie hugged and kissed me and pleaded with me to keep writing to her: and to visit her if I ever went to England. 'I'll write and forward you my address, as soon as I find a place over there,' she said, kissing me tearfully, while I stood motionless, devoid of any emotional feeling.

I was relieved when the car drove down the road and around by the lake, on its way to the station. I knew then that we'd be safe should the Guards come to the house looking for three women who'd escaped from the Magdalene Laundry. I didn't know what terrible crime these women had committed but whatever it was I didn't want to be caught up in it. They must be bad women I thought, if they had to escape by climbing over the wall. For the first time, I came to the conclusion that the Magdalene Laundry must be some sort of a prison, for evil women. That the women within its boundary walls were forced to scrub and wash clothes for their sins the same as male prisoners in jail were forced to sew mail bags: that that was why there was a big wall around the Magdalene Laundry and why there were no windows and why the door was kept locked all the time. But I couldn't understand why Mr and Mrs O'Brien were helping them to escape: and I was too afraid to ask my mother or father what crime Bridie had committed because I knew the answer I'd get.

Days later, everything had returned to normal. When Bridie wrote to me from Northampton, I answered her and told her how well I was getting on at home and how I might be going to Secondary school, for a year, come September.

Sending me to school in Castlerea was a difficult decision for the O'Brien's. Every other evening they discussed it briefly around the fire before going to bed.

'...I don't care what you do. As far as I'm concerned he's long enough going to school. He'd learn just as much if we kept him at home, instead of buying more books and all that rubbish,' said my father, as I lay in bed listening to their conversation.

'Well I dunno either. I'd like him to stay at home too because I'm not able for the work anymore. But I think we should give him a chance to learn a bit more. After all, what's another year? He was showing great promise, when he finished here below: so a year in Castlerea might do him the world-a-good,' said Mrs O'Brien.

'Well… it's up to you,' replied my father, as he pushed back the chair from around the fire, a clear sign he was fed up talking about it. He went outside to check that everything was alright, as he usually did, before going to bed.

Mrs O'Brien took the decision to buy a bicycle for me and I started cycling to Castlerea, in September. EJ Lyons, John Keaveney and Eamon Finnegan started the same day. Every morning we used to meet at the head of the school road in Williamstown and cycle down to Castlerea together. By the time we reached Trien – which was halfway – there would be twenty to thirty boys and girls cycling together. I liked going to the Tech, where I learnt Mechanical Drawing, Woodwork, Rural Science, History, Geography as well as English. My favourite subjects were Woodwork and English.

By the time I'd cycled home, it was too late to do anything major around the house. On Saturdays I helped my father bring home turnips and potatoes with the horse and cart so that he wouldn't have to do all the heavy work on his own during the week. As the winter approached, we continued to bring home enough potatoes and vegetables from the fields to sustain us for the following week.

On Friday afternoons, I played football for the school team and on Sundays I played for the Williamstown under sixteens.

The school closed for two weeks during Christmas and I was glad of the time off as cycling nine miles to school every morning in the wind and rain was hard work, despite the company of some delectable females.

In the days leading up to Christmas, I had to help Tom Farrell, along with two other men, load sugar beet on to a big lorry which brought it straight to the factory. It was very heavy work as twenty tons of sugar beet had to be thrown up over an eight foot high crate with beet forks. When Tom's beet was loaded, he in turn had to help his two neighbours load theirs and I was instructed by my father to help them too.

Apart from helping Tom, who was a family friend, I was paid ten shillings a day for loading beet. My father was no longer able for heavy work but he did much of the lighter jobs around the house, while I was away.

Snowy came home from Manchester, as he always did for the festive season. And as usual he had a new mode of transport with him. This time he was driving a cream coloured Simca car. He brought Mrs O'Brien to first Mass on Christmas morning which made her very proud indeed.

On St Stephen's day, it started to freeze in earnest, as Snowy went back to Manchester. A week later when I started back to school it was still freezing, hard. Three weeks later Snowy came home again as all construction work in England had stopped he said, owing to the severe frost.

Tom Farrell sat beside the fire in our kitchen, his back to the chimney breast, puffing away on his pipe as he regaled my mother and father on the severity of the frost. I sat at the table doing my homework while cocking my ear every now and again.

'It's a long time since I saw the water frozen in the kitchen,' said my father.'

'Arrah what are you talking about, the eggs on the dresser were frozen when I got up this morning,' sniffed Tom, as he curled the corner of his upper lip to release a jet of smoke like a steam engine under pressure.

'Well, maybe,' acknowledged my father doubtfully, as he held his two hands out in an effort to keep them warm while my mother sat afacing the fire, an extra heavy cardigan about her shoulder as she began ripping the wool, off yet another old jumper.

'There's no maybe about it...' said Tom, emphatically, as he pulled the stem out of his pipe and cleared the blockage with one blast of his powerful lungs. '...I took three eggs off the dresser to scramble them for me breakfast and when I cracked them on the side of the saucepan they stayed in the shell: and when I looked at them, I saw they were frozen.'

I smiled to myself, thinking Tom's tale was of his own making, but as the heavy frost continued it wasn't too long before everything in the house was frozen; the eggs, the butter, the buckets of water, even the jugs of milk in the bottom half of the dresser, everything. So before I went to school in the morning, it was my job to go to the well to break the ice with a crow bar so I could bring down two buckets of water for Mrs O'Brien.

It froze continuously round the clock through January and February. And though the sun shone for a few hours each day, there was still a Siberian chill that would put a hump on your back, forcing you to turn up the collar of your coat, before sinking your hands deep into your pockets. The early morning frost was enough to turn your runny nose into icicles if you found yourself walking by naked hedgerows where twigs, leaves and branches snapped under the weight of little birds as they desperately sought worms, maggots and other tiny insects.

The village street, normally a quagmire of muck and sludge during the winter months was transformed into a living museum, with frozen foot prints everywhere. Every bird, animal and human foot print was preserved like something from a prehistoric age. The circular pieces of ice embedded in the various hoof prints added to the mystique and served to highlight the forces of nature. The frozen prints too were testimony to the age of every living thing from cows to calves: from songbirds to crows, from rabbits to foxes to dogs. In the early days, I only had to apply the merest touch of my toe for the icy to snap. The curved hoof prints resembled many of the stained glass windows in Williamstown church such was the intricate and exquisite design of each wafer thin piece. But as the heavy frost intensified, I could no longer break the hoof prints; not even by pounding them with the heel of my wellington boot. And each morning, after yet another night of heavy frost with the merest sprinkling of snow, I could chart and identify every animal as they went through the village. My favourite prints were of rabbits, followed by birds. There was something incredibly powerful about being able to track and identify every species of bird and animal that had crossed our garden during the night. Sometimes I'd track a rabbit that had passed right through the village; up past the well, where it had turned into a field only for the track to emerge again further up the road, where lo and behold I'd sometimes spot the rabbit as it made a desperate run for cover.

Soon, the cattle had to be kept in altogether as the freezing fog was slow to clear, yet quick to blot out the emerging sun. It was no longer safe to drive the cattle on the road, my father said. He was afraid they might fall and injure themselves. Without realizing it, the bags of potatoes we had in the shed soon dwindled away and we were forced to go down to the potato field with the pick and shovel to break open the pit of potatoes which was covered with clay to a depth of twelve inches. We soon found we had no use at all for the shovel. Instead, we had to prise away slabs of frozen soil with a pick and crowbar in an effort to get at the potatoes. It was like opening up a monolithic tomb as we prized four foot long slabs of soil out of the way. Underneath, the grass and rushes we found the potatoes were frozen too. And when we somehow peeled the grass and rushes away with our bare hands, we found the top layer of potatoes stuck to the grass, while most of what lay underneath was red rotten and no longer edible. My father almost cried when he saw the state of his hard won crop.

He stood up and gasped loudly trying to comprehend what lay before him. And though we had wrapped ourselves up well for the job in hand, it was our hands and feet that suffered most. It felt as if our toes and fingers would fall off. The pain in our finger tips was torturous as we tried to sort out the good potatoes from the bad in the stench riddled pit. Every few minutes we had to stop, to swing our hands vigorously round our shoulders, to jump up and down in a vain attempt to put some life back into our frozen limbs.

Incredibly, we made two trips to the potato field one day before a thickening band of freezing fog began to close in all around us. We were desperate to cart home all the potatoes we could before they were completely destroyed. We emptied each sack of half rotten potatoes onto the floor of the shed. We covered them with straw and canvas bags before going into the house to revive our drooping spirits with mugs of steaming hot cabbage soup followed by bacon, and cabbage.

Despite the severity of the frost, my friends and I cycled to school every single day. With our hands thrust in our pockets, we somehow guided our bicycles free wheel up hill and down dale. Once in school, we shivered in the cold classroom all day long while our English teacher and principal, Mr Mulvihill, stood with his back to the fire. In the woodwork room I learned how to make a tea pot stand; a towel holder and a three legged milking stool. Some days we were told not to go to school the following day, as the heating system had broken down and would have to be fixed, yet again.

Back home, the lake was the main source of recreational enjoyment as my friends and I spent evenings and weekends sliding, as the arctic like weather tightened its grip on the landscape; transforming the entire country into a Siberian wasteland. Even the wash stone – as it was called – on the edge of the lake was frozen over and hidden from view. The wash stone was a secluded spot where the villagers came once a year to shed their clothes and to wash away the yearly grime with a bar of carbolic soap. It was a place of great danger, with deep holes either side of the wash stone where I once slipped and might have drowned had it not been for the tall reeds which enabled me to pull myself clear.

On Sunday afternoons, my friends and I held competitions to see who could slide out the furthest. There was little or nothing between us: it all depended on how good a run we got at it. Every now and again we could hear echoing sounds and running cracks on the ice, as we danced and threw heavy rocks on the surface to see if we could break it, but we couldn't. Very cautiously each day, we ventured out further and further. We were careful not to go too far as our parents had warned us again and again. We could not actually see the ice as it was covered with a light dusting of snow that glinted in the brilliant sunlight as swans, ducks and geese circled the clear blue skies in an effort to find streams and gullies while we playfully threw snowballs at each other.

We were messing around on the lake one Sunday afternoon when Snowy drove up from the town in his new car and pulled up a short distance away. He got out of the car along with three men, one of whom was Sergeant Boyle. When the Sergeant saw us larking about he shouted,

'Hey lads, ye shouldn't be out that far; it's too dangerous. It's all right to play around the edge, but for God's sake keep away from the middle.'

We looked at each other panic stricken: unable to make up our minds whether to go or stay. One false move it seemed, could spell disaster.

As we nervously made our way back, Snowy shouted at me, 'Jack, you heard what the Sergeant said. I'm surprised at you: I thought you had more between your ears: going out on the flippin' lake like that: sure 'tis pure madness!'

I was shocked to hear Snowy giving out to me, like that. I was disgusted with myself for having been caught red handed. Now, he would probably tell Mrs O'Brien and I'd be in trouble, again. I said nothing as John Keaveney, EJ Lyons and Eamon Finnegan stood watching. We didn't know what to do with ourselves. But a few minutes later we were sliding and throwing stones on the ice while Snowy walked right out, testing the middle of the lake. After a few minutes, he made his way back to his comrades who stood around shivering, waiting for his analysis.

'There's an east wind out there boys, that would cut the balls clean off you! Come on! We'll go home in the name of God, and have a bit-a-dinner,' he said hopping in behind the wheel. Turning to us he said. 'Don't go out there lads, whatever ye do.'

We stood looking at each other, mesmerized, woollen caps over our ears to ward off the biting chill, as our every breath turned into white jets of fog. We watched the men get into the car and Snowy take off with a roar of laughter. Then, to our utter amazement, he swung the car violently to the right, over the sedge, towards us; and out onto the lake. The nearside front passenger window was partially down and we could hear Sergeant Boyle shouting excitedly,

'Snowy! Snowy, where the do you think you're going?'

But Snowy took no notice. He kept driving as Sergeant Boyle half opened the car door, pleading with him to stop. 'For Jesus sake, is it trying to kill us you are?'

All we could hear out of Snowy were howls of laughter as the two back seat passengers had terror clearly etched on their faces as the car sped along as if it were on a tar road. Then picking up speed Snowy drove faster and faster around the perimeter of the lake while slowly inching his way towards the centre where he put on the brakes and the car spun round and round as if it were a Dodgem car in an amusement arcade. Several times he spun the car around; and each time as it was about to stop, he'd reeve it up again, making the rear wheels spin erratically as they sought to grip the glass like surface before gradually picking up speed again to go whirring across the lake once more whilst Snowy's comrades pleaded for sanity.

'Aaaah Snowy, Snowy! In the name of Jesus, Stop! Stop, before we all end up in Hell!'

'Why would I stop? Why would I stop?' roared Snowy, 'If I do, we'll all end up dead!'

For about fifteen minutes Snowy treated us to a spectacle the likes of which we never saw before. When he was satisfied he had his three passengers in a state of acute anxiety, he drove out past us. Lowering the window he leaned out and shouted, 'Sergeant Boyle says 'tis ok to walk on the ice.' His infectious laughter as the car rocked and bumped its way over the sedge and out onto the road again made us realise Snowy was a man, a class apart. It was an audacious stunt designed to terrorise his passengers, and in particular Sergeant Boyle.

Word of Snowy's daring escapade spread through the parish like a dose of bad news. 'It was only the Grace of God, Missus that saved them all from drowning! Only the Grace of God!' said Tommy the post as he sat by the fire, while I finished whitewashing the inside of the back kitchen. 'And he with a new car and everything. How well he wasn't afraid he'd bloody drown?'

'Oh I don't know what to say Tommy! I don't know,' sighed Mrs O'Brien, as she put a few sods of turf on the fire. 'Anyway, thanks be to God the big freeze is near over; for now, anyway. But sure it will take weeks for the ground to thaw out and not a bit of ploughing or anything done. I was hoping we'd get the ploughing done before the Easter so John could help us sow the potatoes while he's off school; but no, we can't have that much pleasure. What harm but we'll have to buy seed potatoes and cabbage seed and everything; that's if there's any to be had. Lord, isn't it awful, to think that after all the hard work, we haven't a spud to our name?'

'I know I know! But isn't it happy for you, that has the likes of John to give you a hand. Did you ever see anything to grow like him? Tom Farrell was telling me he's a great worker altogether. He said it was no bother to him to load the beet. And that's bloody hard work let me tell you.'

'Oh he's able to work it alright…only thing is, you have to make him do it. He'll be sixteen now in May. It's all right if he doesn't get into bad company and start drinking… and going to dances and the devil knows what.'

I was keen to hear what Tommy would say about going to dances. I had no intention of going to a pub as I had seen enough unruly behaviour in the town to know drinking wasn't for me. On the other hand, I couldn't wait until my sixteenth birthday to go to a dance. But, I'd a while to wait yet.

'Bedamn but Kate, I wouldn't like to see him drinking, above all things; and as for going to a dance? Well, that's a different matter. But it's the pubs; that's what has the young people ruined: the bloody pubs!'

'Troth then, Tommy, I wouldn't like to see him going to a dance either. Sure they're nearly as bad as the pubs. They tell me, its two and sixpence to go into a dance now: that that's what it was on New Year's Eve.'

'It was then! It was then! Two and bloody sixpence!' agreed Tommy. 'And no talk at all about the cost of bringing the lady friend: that's another two and sixpence. Add in the price of a few fags and a bottle of orange and I'm telling you, Kate, you won't have much change out of a ten bob note.'

'Ah, stop it will you. Is it trying to upset me you are…?'

'No, no! I am not, just giving you the facts!'

'…Well I'm telling you Tommy, John will not be going anywhere, until he's eighteen, at least. He'll have to finish school and find himself a job first. When he's earning and able to stand on his own two feet he can go where he likes.'

Hearing those words, my heart sank like a stone. How was I ever going to meet a girl or get talking to one if I couldn't go to a dance? All my friends were planning to go to their first dance once they reached sixteen. If they were sixteen by the time Williamstown Carnival came round, they could go, their parents had told them: but if they weren't, they'd have to wait until Christmas or Easter.

I'd be sixteen in May, which meant I could go to the carnival dance if I was let. But if what Mrs O'Brien was after saying, was correct, then I couldn't go until I was eighteen and that was pure madness altogether.

'Ah, jobs how are you, Kate? Look I think I told you before about my eldest lady? She wasn't happy until she went to America.'

'You did: and it's a worry; but what can you do? I'd like John here to take up carpentry and maybe work at home. I'd hate to think I spent the last ten or eleven years rearing him: and him to go off without a care or a thought in the world, for those that reared him'

When I heard what Mrs O'Brien was coming out with, I switched off altogether because I didn't want to hear another word. I wanted to finish school, to get a job as quickly as I could: any job, just to have a few bob of my own. How else could I get money to go to a dance I asked myself? I wanted to meet a nice girl and I wanted to save up to buy a motor bike or a car. I didn't want to stay at home where I'd have to scrimp and save all my life, rearing and selling pigs, three or four times a year.

I was still day dreaming when Mrs O'Brien came into the back kitchen to check up on me.

'Well the blessing of God on you: you're nearly finished,' she said looking all around and admiring the snow white walls. 'That ceiling wasn't painted since I don't know when: and you know something, it needed doing badly. I never realised it was as dirty. When you have finished, I'll give you a hand to clean the place up and we can put things back the way they were.'

Mrs O'Brien always gave the house a bit of a spring cleaning around the Easter and it was my job to help her take all the cobwebs off the ceilings. I had to help her take the delf off the dresser so we could give it a good wash before varnishing it. I had to help her wash and paint the front windows and whitewash the back and front of the house as well as the hens' cabin and the outdoor lavatory. These were jobs I hated as it upset the routine of everyday life. I would much rather have gone to the well for ten buckets of water. My father never had to do anything like that around the house; and I envied him his freedom. He could go pottering in and out all day long and his tea would be ready for him whenever he felt like it.

The only time I could get away from the house was when I ran up across to Colleen's to watch Lincoln Veil and the Everglades. Any free time I had in the evening, I spent playing football in the ball alley field, opposite the new church

As far as I was concerned, summer and my sixteenth birthday couldn't come half quick enough. All I wanted was the freedom to express myself on the football field and to get on the Williamstown minor team. And should I be fortunate enough to be let go to a dance, that would surely help to impress the girls, I though.

Fast approaching my sixteenth birthday, it became my only thought, my one and only dream.

Chapter Twenty Four

Battle of wills
1963

After a late spring, summer had finally arrived and I'd finished my first full year in the Tech in Castlerea. Now that I was on holidays, once more I had to help save the annual crops. The O'Briens were unsure whether to send me back to school for another year or not. They'd make up their minds come September, they said.

I didn't care one way or the other and was prepared to do whatever they felt was best for me. The only downside was that I never had any money to do anything or go anywhere.

I'd been picked to play for Williamstown minor team, or at least to make up the numbers. That meant I got an opportunity to play football in Dunmore, Tuam, Kilconly and Caherlistrane. I worked extra hard round the house in the hope, I'd be let go to the opening night of Williamstown Carnival, which was now only a week away. On Saturday morning, I made up my mind I'd do all I could, then I'd ask Mrs O'Brien could I go to the dance; knowing it would be almost impossible for her to refuse.

That evening I sat at the table having finishing my tea, while Ned was still up in Colleen's. Mrs O'Brien was standing ironing our shirts for Sunday Mass. After a few false starts I managed to say, 'Mammy... is it alright if I ask you something?'

'Well... there's no harm in asking. What is it?'

'Can I please go to the carnival tomorrow night?'

She stopped ironing for a moment and looked at me as if I had two heads.

'Is it to go to the dance?'

'Yes?'

'Well glory be to God Almighty... I don't know what to say to you! You're on that bloody road, morning noon and night. If you're not asking to go to a football match, you're watching television or reading newspapers: and where you manage to get the money for them newspapers, I just don't know!'

Mrs O'Brien had such a hatred of me reading, I was forced to hide the *Evening Press* in the rafters of the stables. I was so addicted to sport I used to save up any penny I'd get so I could buy the *Evening Press* at least once a week. That way I could read about the Tour De France, the bull-run in Pamplona, and the Galway football team. I particularly liked reading Joe Sherlock's column, *In the Soup*. I liked Joe's analysis, especially where the Galway football team were concerned. And buying the *Evening Press*, whenever I could, was the only way I could keep up with what was going on around the country. It gave me great pleasure to spread the newspaper across the broad expanse of the cow's back – where I was supposed to milking and feeding them – knowing I would not be disturbed.

But if Mrs O'Brien found out I was actually spending money on newspapers, she'd kill me; which was why, when I was caught once or twice, I made out I'd found the papers lost in the town or that one of my friends had given them to me.

She was still standing beside the ironing board; the two of us staring at each other, eye ball to eyeball with not a single word being spoken. Her grey hair plaited and coiled on her head; with the forked tail of it sticking out beneath a brown hair net, like a viper, ready to strike.

These bouts of prolonged silence I'd come to regard as the silent treatment. They were specifically designed to wear me down, to ground me into submission. But when the blood rose in her cheeks and her furrowed dimple began to twitch erratically, I knew my chances were fading, fast.

'Look at you! I just don't know what to say. I never met anyone like you in all my life. I declare to God you'd wear the cross off an ass. Don't you realise you're far too young to be let go to a dance? It's bad enough having you out gallivanting around the town on swinging boats and the devil knows what, without having you traipsing up to that cursed marquee. Don't you know that?' 'Don't you?'

'I don't,' I mumbled.

'You don't…?' she queried, with a raging expression.

'And where are you going to get the money? Where?' she asked, glowering at me.

'I have the money I got from serving Mass… and the Stations. You said you'd put it in the Post Office… for me.'

'Well Jesus, Mary and Holy St Joseph…but that beats all ever I heard. Isn't that money long gone… or what sort of ass are you? How do you think, I cloth and feed you every week? Is it what you think the few things Bridie sends is enough to cover your backside? Is it?' she shouted at me angrily, before picking up the iron to slam it down on my father's shirt, with renewed vengeance.

'No,' I mumbled: shocked that all the sixpences and shillings and half crowns I'd given her over the years could have disappeared, without I ever spending as much as one solitary penny. As far as I was concerned, there should have been a neat little pile of coins stacked in the Post Office with my name on them: not to mention the lovely ten shilling note I got from Paddy Kirrane for serving Mass at his wedding. But it was all gone now, on clothes and things: and I hadn't as much to my name as would have bought me a thru penny ice cream. I had foolishly thought Mrs O'Brien bought everything for me out of her house keeping money, from the sale of eggs and turkeys and the like. Now I felt bad for having said anything at all about the money.

'*No*,' she mumbled sarcastically, imitating my response. 'Lord, isn't it great how you thought about that money! How you thought it was still there! No talk at all about how we're supposed to live? How do you think I pay Harry Ryan for flour and pig meal and tea and sugar and every other thing damn that comes into this house? How? And where do you think I got the money to put a new bicycle under your backside, so you could go to school in Castlerea? Where? And what about all the school books I had to buy? Is it what you think money falls down the chimney: is it?' she ranted, on and on.

'No I don't,' I replied angrily, looking her straight in the eye.

'Believe me you don't,' she answered, as she again slammed the heavy iron down on Ned's shirt. 'When I was your age there was little talk of dancing, let me tell you that. There were fourteen of us in the house and the only thing that bothered us was, when or where were we going to get the next bite to eat. And if we were lucky enough to have a-skep-a-praties, we'd sit on the floor with not as much as a knife or…or a plate between us. And as for butter…or a grain'een-a-salt… well Lord God Almighty, but we'd…we'd have killed for it. Now the whole bloody world is gone mad! People would go dancing, before they'd feed themselves.'

After that historical lecture, I was again subjected to another bout of the silent treatment. Then, as if suddenly struck by divine intervention she asked, 'Are any of your friends going?'

'John Keaveney and Eamon Finnegan said they were going. I don't know about E J Lyons.'

'EJ Lyons! EJ Lyons… Huh! Well…because it's the opening night and you worked hard all week, I'll let you go. But remember; you'll not be let go outside that door again until you're finished school. It would be a lot different if you were at home all the time and had a decent job. It's not as if I have money to be throwing around the place for dances and the devil knows what!'

Hearing her say the words, *because 'it's the opening night and you worked hard…'* almost made me cry with joy. My hard work had finally paid off. I was free to go to my first dance. The thought of paying my very own half crown in and setting foot inside the big white marquee where girls would be twirling round and round made me delirious with excitement. I wanted to run straight out the door and jump for joy.

After second Mass on Sunday, I arranged to meet my friends in the town where we'd spend an hour on the swinging boats and bumping cars before going up to the dance.

As always during the carnival, the amusements on the village square were a kaleidoscope of colour and flashing lights, to say nothing of the music. The swinging boats too swung ever upwards, creaking beneath the neon lights as the portrait like bumping cars sparked into life; bouncing erratically off each other, sending sparks raining across the wire meshed ceiling. Nearby, the incessant ping of rifle shots could be heard coming from the rifle range, where eager young men in peaked caps lined themselves up to take pot shots at the moving targets: to show how good they were. But the unclaimed prizes proved the crack shots were not all they had cracked up to be.

After two goes on the bumping cars and two goes on the swinging boats, John Keaveney, Eamon Finnegan and I decided it was time to make our way up to Glynn's field, where the big white marquee was situated. Ahead of us men and women were walking briskly towards the marquee from where a haunting melody rent the air.

> *Beautiful dreamer, wake unto me.*
> *Starlight and dewdrops are waiting for thee;*
> *Sounds of the rude world, heard in the day,*
> *Lulled by the moonlight have all passed away!*
> *Beautiful dreamer, queen of my song,*
> *List while I woo thee with soft melody;*
> *Gone are the cares of life's busy throng,*
> *Beautiful dreamer, awake unto me!*
> *Beautiful dreamer, awake unto me!*

There was a queue at the cash desk while we waited to go in. Sergeant Boyle and Guard Macmillan stood talking to two men beside the entrance, eyeing every one as they went into the dance.

Once inside, we could see the dance was in full swing, with Johnny Flynn's brass band entertaining the crowd. The sight of so many girls, in beautiful dresses nearly took my breath away. After every three numbers, the band stopped playing, while the MC announced a short interlude. Couples who'd been out dancing together parted company, as if they'd been ordered to do so: the girls going to the left to join their friends, while the men made their way to the right or back down to where my friends and myself were standing inside the door. During the break, a male steward came out of the Gents' cloakroom with a box of *Lux* flakes which he sprinkled on the maple floor to make it easier for dancing. When the music started up again, men rushed to the opposite side of the marquee in a frantic effort to seize the lady of their choice before she was whisked away by some other admirer. The girls too had their secret desires as they refused lots of invitations to dance whilst waiting for the man of their dreams to come along.

Neither my friends nor I dared to venture out onto the floor because we didn't know how to dance. To add to our torment, we didn't know what to say to a girl to entice them out to dance. Even if we knew what to say we weren't prepared to risk being turned down. Some fellas only had to nod their head in the general direction of the dance floor for a girl to come running towards them, while others went across and politely asked only to be turned down. Some men simply grabbed a girl and tried to force her out onto the floor. When the girl point blank refused to go with them, the offending males effed and blinded them whilst all I could do was stand and watch, achingly.

My friends and I spent the entire night admiring the girls from afar. And I got a major shock when a girl I'd never seem before suddenly approached and asked if I'd like to dance, saying it was a lady's choice. I was too embarrassed to say yes, as I had no idea what I was supposed to do once I was out on the floor.

When I said no, the girl tried to grab my hand and when I point blank refused to budge, she cocked her snoot and called me a 'Big head,' before storming off to ask some other fellow who was only too happy to oblige. My friends were having a great fun at my expense; though they too were adamant they wouldn't dance if asked. The last thing any of us wanted was to be laughed at for having stood on some girl's toes while out dancing. Every lame duck dancer in the parish was known by the girls and avoided like the plague. Still, it was heartbreaking having to stand around watching girls being waltzed sedately round the floor by men old enough to be their father. But it was nothing compared to the slow dances where our hearts bled at the sight of beautiful looking girls wrapping their arms lovingly around men's shoulders while gazing hypnotically into their eyes. By now we knew we'd only ourselves to blame. Sooner or later we'd have to learn to dance. And the only way to do that we surmised was to go dancing somewhere else: somewhere like, Castlerea, where no one would know us.

Planning to go to another dance so soon after my first was a major problem. I knew I'd have to wait until the time was right. But was the time ever right, I asked myself again and again over the summer months? I was at the mercy of Mrs O'Brien's good will. It would cost me half a crown to get into a dance; and I needed another two shilling to share a taxi with my friends. All told, I needed five shilling at least. And in an effort to achieve my goal I made sure to do certain difficult jobs around the place: jobs I knew, that would please Mrs O'Brien: like fixing the clothes line and cleaning the chimney. Every year she had paid Mongan, the chimney sweep two shillings to come and clean the chimney. But because he never came back after she'd paid him in advance to do the job, she was forever giving out about him, particularly when fist sized lumps of soot rained down the chimney onto pots and pans as she cooked our dinner. So I went down the road and cut a fine furze bush and tied a long rope to the end of it. I pulled it up onto the roof, while my father held the ladder. I dropped the rope down the chimney leaving the bush perched on top of the chimney while I went down into the house to pull it down. But the bush was too big and got stuck in the chimney. I sweated buckets trying to pull it down and if it hadn't been for my mother and father helping me I'd never have got it down. It was worse than pulling a calf. When we finally managed to drag the bush down the chimney it brought mountains of soot with it. As a result there was dust and dirt everywhere. Everything in the kitchen had to be washed again. Nevertheless, Mrs O'Brien was very pleased and said I was a God send around the place.

Because there didn't seem to be a favourable time when I could ask to go to another dance I decided one Sunday afternoon to chance it; knowing there was a dance in Castlerea that very night.

'I met John Keaveney after Mass and he asked if I'd go to Castlerea with him, tonight.'

'And what's bringing him to Castlerea? Isn't he going back to school for another year?' said Mrs O'Brien, finishing off her mug of tea beside the fire.

'He is. But his mother told him he could go… for helping with the work.'

'Aaaah…work me backside! What work did he do: except what we're all doing?'

When I didn't respond, I was once again, subjected to the silent treatment while she sat weighed me up.

'And is it to a dance he's going?'

'Yes. The Rhythm Stars are playing. Aiden Tracy – he's a good friend of mine in school – he plays with the band, himself and his two brothers.'

'Look here now! I thought I told you before, you're too young to go dancing; and you not even finished school. And another thing, your father thinks you should stay home from school now and I think he's right. You've enough schooling done now. It's well past time you pulled yourself together and found a job: something that'll bring in a few pounds and take the weight off our shoulders. But of course you won't: because you're too lazy. Look at Frank Collins, the way that fella used to work. Off on his bicycle every day of the week, painting, and making cribs and turf baskets for his mother; while all you ever do is play football and look for money to go dancing. And look at that Tracy lad; that friend of yours; that plays with the band: 'tisn't waltzing round the floor like a Lord you'll find him! Huh! Believe me it's not!'

When she mentioned Aiden Tracy, I knew I'd shot myself in the foot. There would be no dance for me on Sunday night or any other Sunday unless I found a job.

I was both relieved and disappointed I didn't have to go back to school. I made up my mind, there and then, to find a job: it was the only way out. With any bit of luck I'd soon get a job, have my own money and could go where I liked. Or so I thought.

Big farmers in the parish were noted for hiring men on a daily basis during the summer months. As a result I soon found myself working odd days, helping them with the harvest while at the same time I had to help harvest our own crop which was the smallest we'd had in years. I also had to help Colleen because Snowy was in England and Una was in boarding school, in Tuam.

Ned was so pleased with my efforts round the house he let me go to Croke Park to see Galway playing Dublin in the all-Ireland football final on the third Sunday in September. Galway were beaten, but the result was soon forgotten when I met a beautiful girl with big green eyes on my way home. My heart was all a flutter when she sat down next to me on the train. Soon, we were laughing and talking as the packed locomotive rumbled its way west. She said her name was Deirdre. She was a third year student in the Convent in Castlerea. I didn't recognize her, though I thought I knew all the good looking girls in Castlerea. Deirdre had a great sense of humour. She had long flowing black hair which she flicked over her shoulders every time she laughed.

As we neared Castlerea station, we could see the shade of night coming down. She was worried about cycling home in the dark. She didn't have a light on her bicycle, she said. When I asked her where she lived she said Cloonkeen, which to my delight was on the Williamstown road. As I had to cycle home the same road I offered to cycle with her. She seemed pleased but made it clear I could not go too close to her house, in case her parents saw me.

We were having such fun hopping on and off our bicycles at the foot of every hill we ended up walking most of the way. We got on so well together we somehow ended up giggling in a two-bay hayshed, along the side of the road. And it was there in the hay I had my first passionate kiss as we sought each other's lips, hungrily. I was in seventh heaven exploring her sensuous body when my senses were suddenly assailed by a vicious dog, barking, not more than six or eight feet below us. To add to the shock, a yard light came on behind what we thought was a tumble down shack. And though we clung like leeches to each other, our passion waned and died a thousand times.

We lay in silent agony for what seemed an eternity: or at least until such time as the dog stopped barking and the light went out again. Then we slithered quietly down the side of the hay and ran towards our bicycles as fast as we could, fearing we'd get our arses bitten by some man eating dog. That narrow escape took the wind out of my sails; and put an end to what was my first romantic interlude.

Every other day I applied for jobs I'd seen advertised in both the local and national newspapers. Jobs like, shop assistants, office clerks, factory operatives, where it said; 'No experience necessary, full training given.' I applied for at least a dozen jobs, only to receive one or two replies to say the posts had already been filled.

Then I saw an advertisement in the Irish Independent: it read, 'Bus conductors urgently required.'

I wrote off and applied to CIE, the State Bus Company, hoping I might get a job as a bus conductor in Galway. A week later I received an application form in the post and I set about filling it in. I noted that applicants had to be aged between 19 and 45 years of age, be fully fit and with no impaired vision. So, I upped my age to 19 – even though I was only sixteen and a half – and duly filled in the form. Ten days later, I received a reply informing me that as I was five foot eleven in height, I was ineligible. I was an inch over the regulation height they said. I felt aggrieved, as I'd added an inch to my height when filling out the application form, feeling it would enhance my prospects of getting the job. I could not recall seeing anything on the application form about height regulations. After mulling over the subject for a few days and being an avid fan of the Dear Sir or Madam show on the radio, I decided to write a letter, expressing my views, taking great care to lie about my age.

> Lakeland
> Williamstown
> Co Galway.

> 1ˢᵗ November 1963

Dear Sir or Madam,

As a nineteen year old, I recently had the misfortune to apply for a job as a bus conductor with CIE. The advertisement read, 'bus conductors urgently required,' which led me to believe I had a reasonable chance of getting a job. I informed CIE in my application, that I was of sound mind and in good physical health: that I'd passed my primary examination before going on to do a year in secondary school, where I came away with an intermediary certificate in both English and Woodwork. You can imagine my surprise, when my application was turned down on the grounds that I was an inch over the regulation height of five foot ten. What do these people expect me to do: put a stone on top of my head?

Foolishly, I thought, that as a young man of sound mind and body, they would be only too glad to employ somebody like me. Sadly, I was mistaken. Seemingly, it was just a dream of mine that I might find a worthwhile job in my own country. Instead, I'm left with no choice but to sail the seven seas in search of employment while CIE place advertisements in some far flung newspaper, seeking oriental stock of Chinese extraction to work as bus conductors in Dublin.

Your sincerely,
J P. Rodgers.

P.S. I'll send you a post card, when I reach Hong Kong.

I posted the letter, and to my surprise I listened to it being read out on RTÉ radio a week later. It was the talk of the parish and the fun was great while it lasted: but it didn't get me a job. The search continued. I applied for several more jobs with companies who advertised for workers in both Dublin and Galway. Each time a letter of rejection arrived, Mrs O'Brien would sit down and start crying, while I tried to busy myself about the house. And when I didn't say anything to help ease her concerns, she'd start giving out.

'Look at you! You don't even care. You think you'd go and find something useful to do around the place and not be depending on the likes of me for money for them cursed newspapers: papers you can't even find a job in!'

And because I wasn't in the mood to answer her or was bereft of ideas, she kept badgering me.

'Did you hear what I said?'

'Yes mother, I heard you the first time!'

'No you didn't. You don't take a blind bit of notice of anything I say. I might as well be talking to the wall. But believe me, you'll remember it yet; when it's too late: when you're on the side of the road, starving with the hunger.'

'Mother, I'm doing my best. I'm sick applying for jobs when people won't even bother answering my letters. I even wrote to Snowy!'

'You what!' she said, wheeling round as she was putting a few sods of turf on the fire.

'I wrote to Snowy.'

'And what makes you think he'll find you a job…and… and…he hardly able to find work for himself?'

'I don't…know. But If I can't find a job around here I'm going to England.'

'And where did you get his address?'

'Colleen gave it to me.'

'Well that's a bloody good one. The two of ye in cahoots, plotting and planning…'

'We weren't in cahoots! I just told her how desperate I was to find a job. And she said maybe I should write to Máirtín.'

'Oh Lord! But there's a pair of ye in it! Wait till I see her'

A week later I received a letter from Snowy. It was addressed to Jack Rodgers which was what he always called me.

Ancoats Inn
Ancoats street
Manchester

Jack

If you want work, come over now.

Máirtín.

That was it. There was no good bye; kiss me arse or anything like that. Why he had to keep calling me Jack I didn't know. Analysing the main body of the letter, I thought it was the shortest on record. Recalling the decorative letters, Mrs O'Brien used to get from uncle Paddy in New York, I was of the opinion there were more words on an American stamp. The American stamp had a picture of a golden eagle as its symbol, in an oval setting, with the words, *United States of America, In God we trust*, eight words. Snowy had set a new record, possibly the shortest letter ever written.

Despite the lack of details, I was really excited at the prospects of going over to England. When I showed the letter to my mother and father they were dumbfounded. They didn't know what to say or do as I hung around, awaiting their response

'Oh, I don't know what to say,' said my mother, sighing wearily in the corner. 'Isn't it great how you had to write to him? But of course that's you. You can't wait to be on the road. But troth you'll soon find out, life's not a bed of roses.'

That evening, I was again subjected to another bout of silent treatment. In desperation she turned to my father as he sat across from her, leaning in over the fire, the crooked stemmed pipe dangling from the corner of his mouth, '...And what do you think? Have you anything at all to say for yourself?'

'Well...,' sighed my father, pensively, as he removed the pipe and spat into the fire, the phlegm sizzling as it always did, on the glowing coals. '... I don't know what to say; rightly. If he was a year older I'd say go; but as it is, I think he's too young. I'd rather he had a bit more flesh on his bones.'

Listening to them, I was terrified I wouldn't be let go. I had seen what it was like to go to Dublin on the train and the freedom it gave me so I felt compelled to speak up.

'But Daddy I can't get a job around here. I can't get a job anywhere in Ireland. I've tried everywhere.'

After another bout of prolonged silence, he said, 'I dunno. It's up to yourself what you do. But if I was you, I'd wait another while. England's not all it's cracked up to be.'

'It's not up to him...' emphasized my mother, '...it's up to us. We're the ones feeding him and looking after him. And if he goes, where do you think he's going to get the money? Where...if we don't give it to him? One way or the other he's going to cost us money? We're damned if we do and we're damned if we don't.'

'I'll send home money to you every week; as soon as I start earning,' I said, trying desperately, to win the war of words.

'After thinking about it for a while my father finally said, 'Maybe you could give it a try... for a few weeks... and see how you get on. You could come home again in March, for the ploughing.'

'You know... that's a great idea...,' said my mother, slowly warming to the idea. 'Except that I'd be left here, pottering around on me own. And I'd have to start trudging up and down to that cursed well, again,' she added, resentfully.

'But it would only be for a few weeks. You won't feel until Christmas and I'd be coming home after that,' I said, eager to keep up the momentum that appeared in my favour.

'Well...,' cried my mother, resigning herself to the fact I might have to go away after all: the tears suddenly welling up in her eyes, '...if you have to go, you have to go. Only, I don't know in the name of God how I'll manage without you. And though you have me heart broke night noon and morning, I know I'll miss you.'

I turned my face away as she pulled a handkerchief from the sleeve of her jumper and dried her eyes. She was still rambling on while I was lost for words at the thought that after months of uncertainty I had at last found a job and would be leaving home in a matter of days: venturing out into a brave new world. In a week or two I'd be working in Manchester, earning good money and free to go to as many dances and pictures as I wanted. I'd be the first in my school year to have ventured abroad. For an hour before I went to bed, Mrs O'Brien lectured me on how to behave myself and warned me on the perils awaiting me if I didn't heed her advice.

The following morning she began to put a few things together for my going away, while Ned finished some fencing down in Johnston's. She began ironing a few shirts and then she picked up where she left off the night before.

'And don't forget to write every week. And I suppose you'd better write to Bridie and tell her you're going over: because I'm damned if I'm able anymore.'

After a momentary pause, she continued while I got the shoe-last and put a few more tacks on the soles of her shoes which were beginning to rise, again.

'Maybe if that job's any good and you manage to save a few pounds, you'll send it home: because God knows we could do with it. And whatever you do don't start drinking and squandering money on girls and the like. There will be any amount of primed lassies over there that'll leave you with a hole in your pocket if you're not careful: so I'm warning you, be careful. I don't mind you going to the pictures now and again but remember, keep your head on your shoulders.'

Suddenly she started crying again, as she handed me the ironed shirts to put into my suitcase.

'I don't know how I'll manage without you. I never thought I'd see the day when you'd be gone from me… and I'd be left on me own; with no one to do a hand's turn for me.' After a few minutes, during which the tears ran freely, she pulled a handkerchief out of her sleeve and put a stop to her sniffling. 'Maybe in God when you come home you'll join the Guards. At least you'd be at home where I could see you. If you did that one thing for me, I think I'd die happy. If you had a job like that, you'd be made up for life. But sure you won't: you won't do anything I say or listen to anyone.'

All morning I had to listen to her prattling on until it was time for her to go to the town to buy a sailing ticket. It was a relief to have the house to myself for an hour or so as I went about the place doing the usual jobs, bringing in bags of turf, buckets of water from the well, boiling potatoes for the pigs as well as cleaning out the stables and giving hay to the cattle. And in an effort to keep my mother on side, I brought in the eggs and washed them so she'd have less and less to do when she came home from the town.

When she returned, she handed me the ticket in an envelope with the travel arrangements clearly written out.

'Put that into the pocket of your suit and don't lose it.'

I was to catch the Sunday evening boat train from Castlerea to Dun Laoghaire: the ten o'clock sailing from Dun Laoghaire to Holyhead: the 1.45 am train from Holyhead to Manchester – changing at Crewe: arriving at Oxford Road station at 5.45 am Monday morning.

First thing Saturday morning, she sent me down to the Post Office, to send a telegram to Snowy, informing him of my arrival. All through the weekend I was delirious with excitement as I informed my friends of my imminent departure. On Sunday afternoon, I did the rounds of the parish saying good bye to friends and neighbours. I finished up with a visit to Nan's shop which was unbelievably quiet. Nan bade me sit down, to have a cup of tea while gently squeezing a pound note into my fist.

'A little something to help you on your way a grá'een,' she gasped, as tears came into her eyes. 'And may the Lord look after you and protect you always; wherever you go: because you were always a grand lad'een.' Turning to hide her tears, she stemmed the tide with the hem of her dirty apron before sticking the poker into the fire to extract a little warmth. Sitting on the ragged sofa I couldn't help but observe her fading beauty.

Her once blond ringlets – still bound into a hive of multicoloured hair curlers; together with the ringlets hanging either side of her rouge tinted cheeks – had turned decidedly grey. Her lifelong trade mark, her high heeled shoes, with their nimble yet firm step, had finally given way to a pair of fur-lined

American bootees, as she slowly shuffled in and out of her dwindling shop. Outwardly, she had lost much of her glitz and glamour; yet inwardly, her king sized heart was still paved with gold.

Back home, all I could do was count down the hours as I waited to go to the station. I was anxious to get away as soon as I could, now that I had the opportunity. I was fed up being told what to do and what not to do, but most of all I was fed up having no money. Without money I was hamstrung. I couldn't buy anything. I couldn't do anything, I couldn't go anywhere. It was all fine and proper during the day when I was busy working the fields but during the evenings or at weekends I couldn't venture outside the front door. And when I did, Mrs O'Brien wanted to know exactly where I was going and what time I'd be home. Ever since I'd been to the All Ireland Final in Dublin I'd a hankering to go dancing in Castlerea, hoping against hope, I might bump into Deirdre.

And though I'd earned a few bob, working a day here, a day there and had given it all to Mrs O'Brien, she would not hear of me going to a dance when I asked her; and certainly not to Castlerea.

'Is it to Castlerea? Well, you're not going; not while you're under the roof of this house. A right looking trick-of-the-loop you'd be, at your age, going into a dance hall. I know I let you go here below, but that was a once off: and 'twas the biggest mistake I ever made. You'd think now after all your cycling up and down to school, you'd be sick and tired of it. But no: you want to be on the road night noon and morning.'

It was times like these I resented the way I was being portrayed. It was as if I never ever got off the bloody road. Yet here I was about to go on the longest journey of my life and there wasn't a word about it.

All evening I tried to keep myself busy; doing little jobs in and out of the house in case Mrs O'Brien changed her mind. I had a dreadful fear something would go wrong: something to stop me catching the train. So, the scarcer I made myself, the better I thought. I topped up the two buckets of water in the back kitchen and went to the well one last time. I stood at the top of the village feeling a tinge of sadness that I was about to leave it all behind. So much had changed in the few short years I'd been there. The once compact village, with its neat row of thatched houses was but a shadow of its former self. The entire roof of Kilby's house had long since collapsed. The red door and neat little windows had lost their shape; and the front wall bulged out at an acute angle: though the naked chimney still stood proud and tall against a clear blue sky.

Tobin's old house was but a glorified outhouse, used to house young calves, while the thatched roof was slowly giving way to the elements. As well as that, Annie's new house – though neat and tidy – looked totally out of place, as it sat well back from the side of the road.

And to cap it all, Mickey Billy's house was on its last legs. It had been condemned by the Council. They were forced to provide temporary accommodation for them in the town while they sought a more suitable home elsewhere. It was something of a mystery how Mickey Billy and his wife could have survived in what was, a hovel, particularly during the big freeze.

Walking down past what used to be Collins' old house, I couldn't help but recall Frank kneeling, setting the cribs for his elusive songbirds. Gold finches it seemed were the order of the day. Not only had Frank's old house disappeared, but grass and weeds had crept in over the entire foundation, where the concrete floors used to be. Perhaps someday they'll be unearthed by an archaeologist. Now it was but a fading memory; a thing of the past; and would always be so. There was no longer anyone in the village capable of weaving a basket or making a birdcage. I regretted not having taken up the craft when the opportunity arose. Maybe it was because one of Frank's old bird cages still hung in our old shed, a firm reminder that I myself was lacking in creativity; or maybe it was because I could never bring myself to imprison a feathered friend within some cell-like structure.

Of the five thatched houses originally standing, ours was the only one to have stood the test of time; and it had a new slated roof. I couldn't help but wonder what would happen to it now as the O'Brien's grew older; and I went away. Would I come back in the spring, like I'd said; or was it all a figment of my imagination? It was a question I did not like; and dare not answer.

Mrs O'Brien was like a hen; waiting to lay an egg as she went in and out the front door; watching; waiting, for the hackney to arrive, with my small brown suitcase, ready and waiting. My father sat, leaning in over the fire, his outstretched hands seeking warmth as I myself stood by the window, watching: waiting. Harry Ryan's car I felt, might come in the new road instead of the old one which was now partially flooded. Suddenly, Mrs O'Brien came back in.

'Jesus he's coming up the road. Oh Lord God Almighty; what am I going to do, now that you're going?' she began to sob, as my father stood and momentarily turned his back to the fire, while I waited for the car to stop. As soon as it pulled up outside I picked up my suitcase and turned to Mrs O'Brien to say goodbye as she began to wail and cry openly. I took her hand firmly to say goodbye. I pecked her on the cheek like Bridie had done to me. It was the first emotional contact I'd ever had with her. I was unable to say a comforting word as my father followed me out to the waiting car and I turned to shake his hand. Harry Ryan took my suitcase and put it into the boot as I climbed aboard.

As the car pulled away I looked out of the rear window and waved to my mother and father as they both stood in the street, their hands raised. Immediately I felt an overpowering sense of shame that I was deserting them, when they needed me most: and after all they had done for me. They had brought me up as if I was their own flesh and blood. They had done everything they possibly could for me. No two people in this world could have done more. Yet here I was going away from them; not knowing when I'd see them again. And as the car approached the first bend I looked back once more and saw

Mrs O'Brien holding aloft a white handkerchief as they both stood waving. I too shed a tear. Their harsh existence I thought, was but a lifetime of eggshells and broken dreams.

It was the last time I'd ever see the two of them together. And all of twenty years before I'd come back home, again.

THE END